MENTAL HEALTH IN
MODERN SOCIETY

LONDON

GEOFFREY CUMBERLEGE

OXFORD UNIVERSITY PRESS

MENTAL HEALTH IN MODERN SOCIETY

THOMAS A. C. RENNIE, M.D.

Associate Professor of Psychiatry, Cornell University Medical College; Director, Division on Rehabilitation, National Committee for Mental Hygiene

AND

LUTHER E. WOODWARD, Ph.D.

Field Consultant, Division on Rehabilitation, National Committee for Mental Hygiene

NEW YORK
THE COMMONWEALTH FUND
1948

PUBLISHER'S NOTE

THE COMMONWEALTH FUND is glad to make this book available as a contribution to contemporary thought in the field of mental hygiene. The authors, who have had entire freedom of expression, are wholly responsible for all statements of fact and opinion.

PUBLISHED BY THE COMMONWEALTH FUND
41 EAST 57TH STREET, NEW YORK 22, N.Y.

———

PRINTED IN THE UNITED STATES OF AMERICA
BY E. L. HILDRETH & COMPANY, INC.

To E. C. R. B.

and

H. B. W.

PREFACE

Wɪᴛʜ the war's end came problems of peace. To some of these problems war itself brought an answer. This was particularly true in the field of medicine, which made discoveries between Pearl Harbor and V-J Day which would have required twenty years of normal peacetime living to test out and to make effective. Of psychiatry it can be said that it finally came of age, moving out of its professional isolation into the social area of prevention and of co-operation with other disciplines. The lessons that the war taught us need to be recorded, digested, and made permanent for the future. That is the task which Chapters I to IV of this book attempt.

War kills many millions of people. War maims many others. Thanks to sulfa drugs, penicillin, blood banks, and the skill of physicians and nurses, the lives of many are saved and their physical functions are restored to a degree heretofore unbelievable. With prompt and thorough medical care and the use of prosthetic and other mechanical aids, most of the wounded are restored to useful and essentially normal living. The restoration of physically handicapped individuals has come to be known as Rehabilitation. The same word applies to the restoration of those whose emotional and mental equilibrium has been disturbed. As defined by the National Council on Rehabilitation, "Rehabilitation is the restoration of the handicapped to the fullest physical, mental, social, vocational and economic usefulness of which they are capable."

Rehabilitation, then, requires psychiatric insight and knowledge as well as surgical and medical skill. Among the outstanding contributions of psychiatry to the treatment of the physically disabled, are the findings of Rusk, which indicate that convalescence is speeded up if attention is given to personality factors and that psychiatric principles can be applied with great benefit to the treatment of paraplegic and other neurologically determined disabilities and to the restoration of the maimed, the disfigured, the blind, and the crippled.

War warps the emotions and personalities of many who wage it and of many who watch. It does so in varying degrees, merely altering attitudes in some cases, and causing complete disorganization in others. War leaves a mark, slight or serious, on everyone, civilian and soldier alike. Many recover from war's effects spontaneously. Others need professional help to enable them to get back to zestful and abundant living.

War reveals facts which in normal times escape attention. The recent war brought to acute focus an awareness of the high incidence in this country of mental and emotional disorders, commonly grouped together with certain neurological diseases as neuropsychiatric disturbances. The number of men rejected prior to induction or discharged from the armed forces for neuropsychiatric reasons was statistical proof of the prevalence of emotional disturbances in the population as a whole.

To the more or less constant group in our society who show either latent or overt symptoms must now be added those whose personality suffered some degree of disintegration as a direct result of their war experience. In the years immediately ahead we are faced with a national problem in mental health which is the concern of the medical profession and of many other groups. The plight of the psychiatrically disabled veteran was more immediate and more pressing because war forced our attention on it and brought it closer to public interest, but the plight of the psychiatrically disabled civilian is no less serious. Sound planning for mental health must consider both groups.

What has been learned during the war period about psychotherapy and the protection and maintenance of mental health has maximum value only when such findings are related to current problems and those anticipated in the years ahead. A brief preview of these problems is presented in Chapter V.

Fortunately, in the course of the war and in the time that has passed since V-J Day, we have gained a fuller knowledge of the causes of mental illness, improved our therapeutic methods, and developed more effective organization for prevention and treatment. We have learned much that is constructive and much that can be used to give a stimulus and direction to work in the field of mental hygiene.

For one thing, we learned how better to select men for service in the armed forces. We saw in the military how important for health and stability were satisfactory interpersonal relations and other environmental factors. We gained new appreciation of the fact that good leadership contributes to good morale. We saw that prolonged combat strains upset normally stable men, as well as those predisposed to neurotic illness. We learned that patients do not function in a vacuum; for even in the military setting and more particularly after return to civilian life, the family, the job, and the community pattern proved to be powerful forces affecting morale and personal adjustment. Psychiatry became conscious of the social implications of mental health. Further, the therapeutic team consisting of the psychiatrist as leader, the psychiatric social worker, and the clinical psychologist was accepted as the most effective therapeutic unit, since no psychiatrist could hope to master all three disciplines or become expert in the management of the complex social and psychological factors that permeate the total emotional milieu of any individual patient. And finally, military experience revealed that the traditional psychiatric therapy based on the establishment and resolution of the tranference was too time-consuming to be practical as a means of meeting the problems of so large a number of patients. We developed of necessity shorter methods of individual therapy and evolved new methods of treating men in groups.

We have seen on a mass scale the effects, on men and on their wives and families, of long separations. We have learned much about the family, work, and community aspects of veteran-civilian adjustments. We have had substantial experience in the psychiatric rehabilitation of veterans who returned with disabilities or developed them in the course of resuming civilian patterns.

We have also witnessed a marked increase of interest in mental health on the part of the public. The war brought home to every community, as nothing else has done, the need to pay attention to mental health. Every man rejected for psychiatric reasons, every soldier or sailor who was discharged because of unfitness or mental or personality breakdown, and every wife, parent, or child whose mental health suffered directly or indirectly from the war increases the number of those who have experienced the tragedy of mental illness and are roused to the seriousness of its threat to our individual and community life. All these people are seeking information; many are eager to lend their support to a program that will better the conditions of those who are ill and avert the danger from those who are threatened. We must be ready to give them information and help. Never was there such an opportunity for public education in mental hygiene.

Along with broader public interest has also come greatly increased interest on the part of the various professional groups, especially physicians (non-psychiatric), clergymen, educators, public health nurses, and industrial counselors. The period of professional isolationism in psychiatry, social work, and clinical psychology is coming to an end. There is nothing esoteric in the understanding of people that these professions have acquired or in the techniques they use in dealing with problems of mental health. Other professional groups have a right to a share in such knowledge, for only by interchange and cooperation can all groups learn how best to apply mental hygiene understanding and methods in their respective fields.

What contributions to treatment and to constructive mental health can be made by family physicians, social workers, and psychologists? What can be done by the church, by industry, by community organizations, and by government? Some of the answers to these questions are given in Chapters VI to XI.

Psychiatric treatment is the responsibility of trained people, and training is a long and rigorous discipline. The material in Chapters VI to XI is in no sense intended to suggest that people without special training can become skilled therapists. It is offered to show how, within the limits of their several callings, many different kinds of professional people can contribute to the resolution of a national health problem by giving those who consult them wise understanding, cooperation, and supportive action.

To build positive mental health, we must move into what we may call the public health phase of mental hygiene. The point of view and the method of the clinician must be supplemented by those of the public health official. Whereas the clinician's concern is with illness, the public health worker is concerned with positive health. His job is keeping people well, not curing their ills. He deals with a large number of comparatively well people instead of with a few sick patients. His effort is directed primarily to finding and controlling foci of infection, not to treating persons who have been infected. By analogy, those who are concerned with mental health will have to deal with ignorance, superstition, unhealthy cultural patterns, and the rigidities and anxieties of parents, as well as with social conditions which foster the development of neuroses and maladjustments. Family living and a sound system of education are of basic importance. Attention must also be given to the development of a philosophy of life and a society which will make for health and stability. This is the goal which we attempt to outline in Chapters XII to XIV.

The book is the result of actual work in the mental health field, in psychiatry and psychiatric social work. Much of it stems from experience in the New York Hospital Rehabilitation Clinic for Psychiatrically Disabled Veterans. Another part is based on field work in many communities and states and the sharing of experience with leaders in the Army, Navy, Public Health Services, Veterans Administration, civilian psychiatry, medical education, social work, the churches, and industry.

Under wartime pressures there have been, in professional groups concerned with mental health, many changes in point of view, goal, method, and organization. The primary purpose of this book is to add up this experience, take a look at the needs and trends in our post-war world, and consider what education, planning, and reorganization are needed to provide prompt and effective treatment to those who need it, and to build positive mental health.

T.A.C.R.
L.E.W.

New York
November, 1947

ACKNOWLEDGMENTS

In the preparation of this book the authors have received highly valued assistance, for which grateful acknowledgment is made:

To Kurt Porges, who, as special research assistant, gave most generously of his time and efforts in compiling source materials, abstracting pertinent information, and aiding in the editing of the book; to Mildred Voorhees Brainard and Melly Simon for valuable contributions to Chapter VII; to Martin H. Bickham, H. C. Buchmueller, Virgil E. Lowder, and Walter S. Pond for case illustrations in Chapter IX; to Gladys V. Swackhamer for review of much of the industrial literature used in Chapter X; to Francis J. Braceland, Oskar Diethelm, Gordon Hamilton, Morris Krugman, Lawrence S. Kubie, William C. Menninger, Elizabeth H. Ross, and Clarence Yount, who have read the manuscript in whole or in part and given the authors the benefit of their criticisms; to Gladys Anzel, Mary Jane Hawley, and Lucille Hoffman Hughes for untiring assistance in the preparation of the manuscript.

Acknowledgment is made also to the following organizations for permission to quote from their publications: American Council on Education, American Journal of Psychiatry, Columbia University Press, Thomas Y. Crowell Company, The Family, Farrar and Rinehart, Federal Council of the Churches of Christ in America, Harper and Brothers, Harvard Business Review, Harvard University Press, Infantry Journal–Penguin Books, International Universities Press, Macmillan Company, Mental Hygiene, New York Academy of Medicine, New York City Committee for Mental Hygiene, New York Times Magazine, Princeton University Press, Science Press, Charles C. Thomas Company, Understanding the Child, and the United States War Department.

The authors wish also to express their appreciation to the Commonwealth Fund for its support of both the Division on Rehabilitation of the National Committee for Mental Hygiene and the New York Hospital Rehabilitation Clinic.

CONTENTS

Part II
POST-EMERGENCY PROBLEMS IN MENTAL HEALTH

Part III
SOURCES OF HELP IN TREATMENT AND PREVENTION

PART ONE
LESSONS FROM THE WAR PERIOD

I

MENTAL HEALTH SERVICES IN THE ARMED FORCES

THE United States was unprepared for World War II in almost every field. This was true particularly in reference to provisions for mental health services in the armed forces. In the main, the pattern of organization of such services developed in World War I was not adequate for the conditions of World War II. We had a grossly inadequate supply of well-trained psychiatrists and auxiliary personnel. The whole task of recruitment and indoctrination of the staff and the organization of services had to be initiated and effected. Under the circumstances, fumbling and failure at various points characterized our early efforts. However, by early 1944, a fairly effective organization had been developed which functioned increasingly well as the war progressed.

Selection of Trainees

It became apparent very early in this war that tough mental fiber would be required of all men who engaged in active combat. The high degree of mechanization, the extreme destructiveness of modern instruments of war, the blitz-like speed, the gigantic size and complexity of organization, all meant that the individual soldier or sailor at one time or another would be taxed to the limit of his mental and physical endurance. In recognition of this fact, psychiatric examinations were routinely required in pre-induction examinations and increasing efforts were made to obtain information regarding the individual's personal history and background and otherwise to improve the methods of psychiatric selection.

The number of men rejected for psychiatric reasons, popularly referred to as the "psychological 4-F's," was about 1,850,000. This represented 12 per cent of the approximate 16,000,000 men examined and 37 per cent of the approximate 5,000,000 rejected for unfitness.[1] The group was made up of men suffering from varying degrees and types of neuropsychiatric illness or unfitness. A small percentage had serious mental illnesses, some had too low an intelligence rating, some were epileptic, but the largest group had a mild to severe psychoneurosis or a tendency to nervousness, with or without symptoms at the time of examination. It should, of course, be kept in mind that the men were being tested for fitness for warfare, not fitness for peace-time living; that very few of the men rejected for psychiatric reasons were so ill as to require hospital care; and that most of them were working at civilian jobs and have continued to work at these jobs, some with outstanding records. The psychiatric rejection rate among applicants for the women's branches was considerably higher, but in view of the selective factor in voluntary applications, we are not justified in assuming that neuropsychiatric disturbances are actually more prevalent among women than among men.

The psychiatric rejection rate of 12 per cent in World War II is much higher than that in World War I, in which only 2 per cent of the men were rejected at the time of induction and an additional 3 per cent screened out during the early training period, making a 5 per cent total. This difference between World War I and World War II cannot be taken as an index of relative mental health, for in World War I psychiatric examinations were the exception rather than the rule, whereas in World War II every man was given at least a very brief neuropsychiatric examination and, during the last two years of the war, social and health information in regard to a large number of selectees was made available to the examiners. This information led to the recognition of many difficulties which otherwise could not readily be detected in a brief psychiatric examination.[2]

Considering the speed with which our armed forces were recruited, the relative dearth of trained psychiatrists available for pre-induction examinations, and the belated acceptance of plans for supplying information concerning the health and social situation of registrants, it is not surprising that selection was less than perfect and that many men inducted lacked the required temperament and stamina. While we do not know the exact number of men thus mistakenly inducted, psychiatric officers in all branches of the armed forces have been unanimous in stating that many with mental health problems were received in the training camps.

Besides discovering those who had been mistakenly inducted, the armed forces had the further problems of keeping men healthy, of maintaining a high degree of morale, and of providing facilities for the early, effective treatment of men who developed neuropsychiatric disabilities. The mental health program in the armed forces, therefore, involved the three major functions of screening, prevention, and treatment.

Professional Services Required

The mental health program required the services of three professional groups. In screening, prevention, and treatment, psychiatrists had to carry the major responsibility, but they received material assistance from the specialized services provided by clinical psychologists and psychiatric social workers. Their work was also facilitated by the cooperation of general medical officers and line officers.

The mental health value of proper assignment and of adequate training for the job was recognized immediately, and the psychologists performed a stupendous task in the classification and selection of men for the many specialties in the aviation, submarine, amphibious, and marine divisions of the Navy, in the Army Air Corps, and in the communications, engineering, motor, and other divisions of the ground forces. In the Navy alone, 250 tests for enlisted men and 14 for officers were developed and used in connection with the selection of men and their evaluation while in training or service. Psychologists also served as personnel consultants and in some units advised regarding problems of leadership and morale. As the war progressed and the number of casualties increased, psychologists participated in the treatment of men in hospitals and in educational and vocational guidance prior to discharge.

Psychiatric social workers played a leading role in the mental hygiene units by making social studies of men who were showing maladjustments. They also counseled the men on problems of military adjustment and, under the psychiatrists' direction, carried on treatment both with individuals and with groups.* We quote Hofstein's summary statement on the functions of the military social worker:

The social worker serves as an outlet for the expression of many feelings and reactions that, within the coldness and authority of military living, it might otherwise be difficult to bring out. As a representative of the Army, the social worker can allow the soldier to measure his personal problems against military needs and to find a means of meeting them compatible with his responsibility as a soldier. The social worker can clarify the course of action that can be taken and can help the soldier to separate out from the confusion of his problem certain things that he can do to meet his problem. Once definite action becomes possible, the sense of futility disappears.

Through his understanding of resources, of the psychology of taking and using help, and of the problems of military living, the military social worker can help the soldier utilize the resources that are provided by the Army. By virtue of his relation to military authority, his sensitivity to the individual soldier, and his knowledge of family dynamics, he can help

* Because psychiatric social work is a relatively new profession and the Army had had no experience with it in World War I, the psychiatric social worker had no Military Occupational Specialist's number or any other special status in the early part of the war. By virtue of the proven value of his contribution, MOS 263 was established in 1944, and in 1945 further recognition was granted belatedly to the profession by establishing an officer MOS for psychiatric social workers, No. 3605, and by making psychiatric social work a branch in the Neuropsychiatry Consultants Division of the Surgeon General's Office.

the soldier to orient himself within the Army while maintaining his orientation within the family.[3]

It is utterly impossible within the compass of this chapter to describe adequately all the mental health services provided in the armed forces, or to give recognition to all the noteworthy contributions, since some of the men who did outstanding work in organizing and directing mental hygiene services and in the training and supervision of staff have written little or nothing. However, numerous articles on military psychiatry, psychology, and social work appeared between the years 1943 and 1946 in professional journals. From a review of much of the literature and from conferences with leaders in several branches of the service, it is clear that the armed forces made consistent efforts to improve the selection of men for military duty, took every reasonable precaution to prevent personality breakdown, and, notwithstanding acute personnel shortages in the course of the war, provided increasingly prompt and effective treatment of men who became psychiatric casualties.[4]

Psychiatric Screening in the Armed Forces

In some men, signs of unfitness for military service became apparent soon after induction. This was true particularly of those whose unfitness for military service could have been detected by better pre-induction histories and examinations.[5]

There was another group of men who presented no apparent symptoms at the time of induction but whose life adjustment had been such that they tended to break down in service. Through a process of trial and error these men had adjusted fairly well in civilian life but were excessively dependent upon extraneous factors. Some had inflexible habits and attitudes, which made difficult the many changes required of men in a military organization. Passively dependent men, with or without functional ailments, whose dependency needs found satisfaction in their homes or at work, could not adjust in an impersonal environment. The "lone wolf," who had carried on research or had been engaged in some other one-man pursuit, often became disturbed when transferred to an organization where there was no opportunity whatever for privacy. Others, who had rebelled against parental authority but had solved their problems as civilians without an open break with their families, found it very difficult to adjust to a succession of superior officers.

Some men who had appeared entirely normal in civilian life showed minor emotional difficulties in the course of military training and service. Others showed serious disturbances only under the severe strains of combat, where fatigue and exhaustion obviously played a large part.

For all these reasons, screening was a continuous process in connection with classification, training, and general medical care, as well as in the preventive and treatment programs in mental health. Through the alertness of psychologists and various classification officers, administrative and training personnel, medical officers and medical corps men, those showing signs of unsuitability were discovered all along the line and referred for special study and disposition.

THE ARMY PLAN OF SCREENING

In the Army, spotting of the unsuited was a function of commissioned and non-commissioned officers of all ranks. Of course, the mental hygiene unit or psychiatric consultation service, available in all training centers, was a major means of discovering those whose mental or emotional handicaps were sufficiently severe to make them poor risks for further training and for full duty. Others were discovered through frequent reporting on sick call and from observation at dispensaries.

Screening occurred at all points in classification and training, from reception center to active foreign service. In connection with classification tests or further medical examination, small numbers of men ill suited for military duty were discovered at the reception center. Many more were found in the basic and technical training centers, as a result of further psychological or educational testing, failure in training, or maladjustment observed by line officers and non-commissioned officers. Maladjusted soldiers were either given brief treatment by the mental hygiene unit or transferred to a station hospital or general hospital for fuller study.[6]

Those who were below standard educationally—illiterates, slow learners, and some foreign-born men whose use of English was inadequate to military life—were assigned to "special training units." In this way the average soldier-students were not retarded by the handicapped, and the latter were spared the risk of mental breakdown as a result of being assigned to tasks beyond their capacity. Eventually most of the men in the special training units made good soldiers.[7]

Through all stages of training, the mental hygiene unit performed a screening function in addition to its main preventive and treatment work.[8] Referrals were made by line officers, non-commissioned officers, disciplinary units, chaplains, and others who had been instructed to look for maladjusted soldiers. Air crewmen were under the continual observation of the flight surgeon, who practically lived with the crew. He checked them frequently and sent those suspected of having developed a psychiatric condition to the psychiatrist for fuller study and disposition.

The next step for the soldier was the overseas replacement or staging area. Here the men went through medical inspection, in which assembly-line techniques were used to handle the enormous number of men. They were passed as physically and psychologically qualified for overseas duty or they were transferred to the post hospital for further study.

Most men with neuropsychiatric disabilities were discharged, at whatever point decided upon, by a medical board, and certificates of disability were given. Individuals of psychopathic personality, homosexuals, alcoholics, mental defectives, and certain enuretics were discharged by an administrative board made up of line officers and one medical officer (AR 615–368 and AR 615–369). A psychiatrist testified before this board, but decisions were made by the board. Where both physical and psychiatric factors were involved, the medical discharge could be given with mention only of the physical condition or of the psychiatric condition, depending on which was the primary diagnosis. Men who were found to have general unsuitability for military service but no specific psychiatric syndrome were discharged by way of the aptitude board, which was made up of both line and medical officers (see Chart 1).

THE NAVY PLAN OF SCREENING

Special attention was given to the screening of men unsuited for naval service. Because advanced training was usually given to small units and because immediately after boot training large numbers of sailors were assigned to duty on ships or in small units where there was no psychiatric service, the Navy developed and used additional devices for selection[9] (see Chart 2).

For example, at each boot camp, new recruits filled out a questionnaire and were examined in three-minute interviews. These interviews were designed to catch any history of psychiatric difficulty or social maladjustment which would make it difficult for a man to fit into one of the small and very compact units which are characteristic of naval organization. About 5 per cent of the men examined at the boot camp were suspected of having a neuropsychiatric condition and were sent to the observation building.

At the observation building these men were under special supervision and study by a professional staff headed by a psychiatrist who was assisted by psychologists and Red Cross social workers. After careful study on the observation ward, three dispositions were possible: (1) assignment to full duty; (2) assignment to trial duty: the sailor was kept under constant supervision for two to four weeks and at the end of the period the officer to whom he was assigned

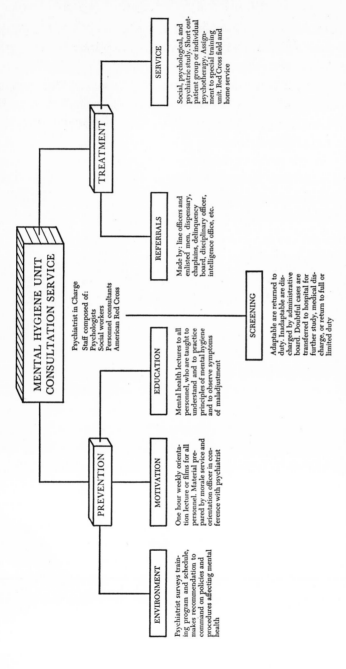

CHART 1. FUNCTIONAL DIAGRAM, MENTAL HYGIENE UNIT, CONSULTATION SERVICE, U.S. ARMY

COMPILED BY KURT PORGES

for supervision reported his progress to the psychiatrist, who then interviewed him again; (3) discharge by an aptitude board composed of two psychiatrists, one psychologist, a general medical officer, and a line officer. The majority of men sent from boot camp screening to the observation building were discharged, but some were briefly treated by psychotherapy, and a very few were transferred to a naval hospital.

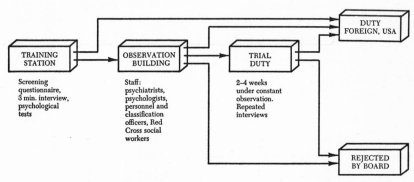

CHART 2. PERSONNEL FLOW CHART, NAVY SCREENING.
COMPILED BY KURT PORGES

The double provision of screening examinations in boot camp and special observation and study of those suspected of having mild psychiatric symptoms failed to discover some men who developed disabling conditions. The disabilities of one fourth of the men placed in the observation building were discovered on the line in some later stage of training or after assignment to duty. Study and disposition of such men were the same as for men who were referred to the observation building as a result of boot camp screening.

Continuous screening took place in all outfits. In the Naval Air Service the flight surgeon paid special attention to early signs of emotional difficulties. On the line, medical officers who had been given some psychiatric training and commissioned and non-commissioned officers who had been given some training in mental hygiene were on the watch for early symptoms of maladjustment.

During the period 1942–46 inclusive the number of men discharged for psychiatric and other personality reasons from all branches of the service and from all points between reception centers and combat zones exceeded 680,000. Approximately 380,-000 army and 77,000 navy personnel were discharged because of psychiatric illnesses. Another 137,000 in the Army and 92,000 in the Navy were released because they could not adjust themselves to military life.

In this connection it should be noted that a special discharge policy prevailed with regard to men suffering from neuropsychiatric disorders or tuberculosis. Men suffering from other diseases or injuries were retained until medical treatment was completed. Because tuberculosis and psychiatric conditions normally require long treatment, it was deemed wise to discharge the men in these two groups prior to the completion of treatment. In fact, in the early part of the war prompt discharge, with little or no treatment, was the policy. This in part accounts for the relatively high discharge rate for psychiatric reasons.

Prevention of Psychiatric Disabilities

Screening, while important, was only the first step taken to insure mental health in the armed forces. As has been pointed out by representatives of the Neuropsychiatry Consultants Division of the Office of the Surgeon General, "Psychiatric screening can weed out only abnormal men. It cannot be expected to have any effect whatsoever on decreasing the rate at which 'normal' men break down. . . . Screening can and must reject psychiatric non-effectiveness."[10]

It soon became apparent that the supply of men of maximum stability was limited and that the great need was for a preventive program which would keep healthy men healthy and remove, as far as possible, conditions which tend to cause breakdown. It was clear that it would be necessary to take psychiatrists out of hospitals and put them in the field where they would be in contact with normal men and could enter into the everyday life of the Army. Consequently, in 1942, psychiatrists were placed at the command headquarters of each basic training center in the Army, called replacement training centers, where, with staffs of varying sizes, they engaged in the triple function of screening, prevention, and treatment. Late in 1943, a psychiatrist was assigned to each combat division, both armored and infantry. As Menninger has stated, "In both of these situations, the psychiatrist's chief function is to help the maladjusting, rather than the maladjusted, man."[11]

This change in the organization of psychiatric services in the armed forces required also a change in viewpoint. As someone has put it, psychiatry for the first time during World War II developed a "social sense." Of course, in civilian life, some efforts had been made to control the environment and to educate the group in the principles of mental hygiene, but for every psychiatrist who devoted appreciable time to these two factors, there were scores, if not hundreds, who limited their activities strictly to the study and treatment of the individual's immediate psychological problem. It became clear almost overnight, when these same practitioners began to work in a military set-up, that the individual approach would be totally inadequate. Increasing emphasis was placed on prevention, and in treatment group methods were developed and used. Preventive mental health programs as developed in the armed forces have included several essential features.

MENTAL HYGIENE UNIT CONSULTATION SERVICE

To promote mental hygiene education and deal more adequately with men showing signs of mental or nervous illness or social maladjustment, whether occasioned by unwise assignment, poor adaptation to the military situation, worry about loved ones at home, or other conditions, mental hygiene units consisting of psychiatrists, psychiatric social workers, clinical psychologists, and a Red Cross social worker were developed in replacement training centers.[8, 12]

These units were the chief instruments used in the preventive aspects of mental health in the armed forces. The staff functioned as a clinical team, just as in civilian psychiatric and child guidance clinics, but in the Army the team worked very closely with line officers, training instructors, and other administrative personnel. Chart 1 shows the functional diagram of the mental hygiene unit.

The psychiatrist in charge of the unit not only directed the clinical work but acted as a member of the headquarters staff. In that capacity he contributed materially to the mental hygiene education of officers and enlisted men, aided in the development of morale, and suggested environmental controls which helped to secure maximum mental health. Great value has been attached to this last function, as indicated by Appel:

Whereas mental hygiene education of enlisted men and officers is regarded as important, we believe that a far more effective means of preventing psychiatric disorders has been through attempts to control the environmental factors which affect mental health of troops. These factors, which include job assignment, leadership, training schedules, danger, climate, punishment, etc., are under control of Army commanders. The psychiatrist functions by advising the commanders on the proper control of these factors so as to obtain the most effective use of his manpower. It is in this sphere that the psychiatrists have achieved the most notable results in preventing psychiatric disorders.[18]

Experimental work was at first carried on in only a few centers, but later units were established in all the larger replacement training centers, both in the ground and service forces and in the Army Air Force. In training centers not having full mental hygiene units, the neuropsychiatric consultant with a smaller staff of assistants performed the various functions just mentioned.

By respecting the rights and personality of the individual soldier in his assignment and training and by giving due attention to health needs and the building of morale, the staff of the mental hygiene unit helped him to become the best possible soldier within the limits of his special abilities and disabilities. Of 1,089 men seen by one unit in a seven-month period, over 80 per cent were able to continue and complete their training in the replacement training center.[12,14] Positive effects accrued for the group, also, through keeping to a minimum dissatisfactions and maladjustments which if allowed to continue would have spread infectiously.

In most training centers the specific functions described in the following paragraphs were integrated into the mental hygiene units. The adviser system used experimentally at a few centers was not officially adopted for general use.

PSYCHIATRIC EDUCATION OF MEDICAL OFFICERS AND LINE OFFICERS

An extensive program of psychiatric education was carried on for medical officers who had not specialized in psychiatry, to increase their understanding and skill in treatment of men suffering from psychosomatic complaints or other nervous or mental disorders. Work in this field was an essential part of the original indoctrination of all medical officers, and the neuropsychiatric consultants of most of the service commands in the United States conducted continuous programs of lectures, conferences, case studies, and the like. Approximately 2,000 battalion medical officers were given special training in the 312th Station Hospital (neuropsychiatric) in England, and hundreds of general medical officers were given a short training course in the Pacific. Technical medical bulletins dealing with the education of line officers and enlisted men in principles of mental health and group psychotherapy were sent to every medical officer in the Army.[15-17]

Obviously the doctors could not do the whole job of developing and maintaining high morale and of dealing with adjustment problems as soon as they arose. The line officers and non-commissioned officers who had more immediate contact with the men were in a more favorable position to observe the beginnings of maladjustment and to deal with organizational problems which, if not solved, would militate against morale. Very soon psychiatrists were asked to give lectures to staff officers, and early in 1944 a series of six lectures was required as part of the training of all army officers. These lectures covered principles of personal adjustment, personality structure, motivation, signs and symptoms of breakdown, fears, homesickness, and particularly measures to maintain the mental health of the group.[18] Discussions of characteristic reactions under various conditions helped the officers to understand the behavior of their soldiers and increased their skill as leaders.[19]

The most effective means of disseminating psychiatric knowledge was found to be informal talks with line officers, either singly or in groups. Here specific cases could be discussed, as well as problems of morale, leadership, discipline, and motivation.[10] In the naval service, indoctrinational lectures and discussions were given not only to psychiatrists of the marine division and those attached to other unit groups, but also to officers, general medical officers, and men of the units.

MENTAL HYGIENE ORIENTATION FOR ENLISTED MEN

Similar but somewhat simpler mental hygiene talks were given to enlisted men. These dealt with the various factors which threatened adjustment to the Army, such as natural civilian resentment toward army life, regimentation, and fear. These talks indicated why each factor was present and offered specific advice on what to do to insure normal reactions.[16, 20]

In 1942, an experiment was made in two replacement training centers and was repeated with five companies. Companies similar in all other respects were used as controls. Results were measured by the reduction in sick calls for psychosomatic symptoms and in the number of hospital days spent for such symptoms. During the basic training period, 995 man-hours were saved in the five companies which received the mental hygiene talks. In each of the five companies there was a decidedly lower number of sick calls and hospital days than in the corresponding control company.[21] There was other evidence of favorable influence on the morale of the total group as well as on the morale of those likely to become ill enough to need medical attention. For one thing, the companies which received the mental hygiene talks used Sunday or other free time to report on sick call rather than miss out on training periods. The experimental groups had fewer AWOL's and the men in them obtained somewhat better grades in their training work.

On the basis of these findings and other evidence of personal benefit and general improvement in morale, these mental hygiene talks were later made a requirement for men in training centers.

Additional activities of a morale-building nature, developed by the Morale Services Division in cooperation with the staff psychiatrist, were carried on in all training centers.²² A good example of this is the work done at Camp Callan, California, under the direction of the consultation service psychiatrist. Basic to the development of this program was the leader's concept of the nature of morale.

It must be clearly understood that under sufficient stress and strain any man may break down. A broad program of preventing neuropsychiatric casualties embraces a definite procedure. . . . Suffice it to say that adequate rest and provision for recreation are both fundamentally important. Meaningless, petty restrictions contribute nothing of constructive value and definitely tend to undermine morale. And speaking of morale, it is perhaps not out of the way to suggest that morale is not something that springs from dances, movies and radio programs alone. While such things are indeed a necessary part of the recreation which must be provided for the men in the armed forces, morale in itself is something of a much more fundamental nature.

High morale springs from a full knowledge of the meaning and significance of this war. It enables an individual or masses of individuals to carry on and persevere in their mission in spite of adverse conditions, disheartening developments, defeatist rumors, fatigue, hunger and physical discomforts. It is a state of mind which can come to a soldier only when special pains are taken to instruct him in the fundamental issues at hand—to make him feel that he is an integral part of everything his nation is fighting for—to arouse in him a social consciousness the like of which he has never felt before. This most necessary condition can be achieved only through a systematic program of education. Men who are imbued with a zeal which springs from a full knowledge of what they are fighting for are less apt to experience emotional or other personality disorders as a result of actual warfare.[23]

Through a column in the camp publication edited anonymously by the psychiatrist, mental hygiene talks over the camp loudspeaker system, lectures, and discussion periods, the men acquired a real appreciation of the issues involved in the war and developed what was generally regarded as maximum morale. The soldiers trained better, and there was a noticeable reduction in the incidence of neuropsychiatric disorders.[24]

Other developments within the Morale Services Division (since August 9, 1944, the Information and Education Division), while not labeled mental hygiene, were nevertheless of great value in keeping soldiers informed and building their morale. An army orientation course stressed six objectives, namely: (1) know why we fight; (2) know our allies; (3) know our enemies; (4) know the news and its significance; (5) know and have pride in your outfit and in your personal mission; (6) have faith in the United States and its future. This course and other activities of the Division helped tremendously to give the soldier an appreciation of what he was fighting for and what he could look forward to in the world he would live in after victory had been won. The stronger his sense of purpose and the more ardently he pursued it, the greater was the likelihood that he would carry on effectively without disabling anxiety or other nervous symptoms.

USE OF ADVISERS AND PERSONNEL CONSULTANTS

Kraines of the Medical Corps, Tank Destroyer Replacement Training Center, North Camp Hood, Texas, developed in that center an adviser system whereby non-commissioned officers were selected and trained to observe early evidences of maladjustment, to act as friendly counselors to the men in their respective barracks, and to encourage those who continued to have problems to take them up directly with their commanding officers and, through them, to obtain consultation with the neuropsychiatric consultant.[25] These advisers, in consultation with the psychiatrist, were able to encourage and reassure those who were shy and timid, to help the homesick make friends and mingle with others, and in other ways to build up the morale of individual trainees, thus raising the morale level of the entire company. The use of this system resulted in a substantial decrease in the number of AWOL's and improved the morale of individual soldiers. Advisers also quickly discovered situations that were acting as irritants for many of the trainees and that were serving to lower the morale of whole companies or battalions. The following quotation from Kraines' statement is illustrative:

One battalion had very poor morale because of the excessive time spent in "detail." In this one battalion, where much work needed to be done, the trainees were called out during their free hours, after their training schedule was finished in the evening, on Saturday afternoons, and even on Sundays. The details involved necessary work, but the difficulty lay in the haphazard way in which men were selected and in the poor organization of this extra work.

In another battalion, according to the advisor, trainees came away from the mess hall hungry most of the time; portions were too small, and the men were not permitted second helpings. It was found that an adequate quantity of food was sent to the mess hall, but that the mess hall organization was primarily at fault.

In one company the advisor stated that the men felt extremely depressed because they did not have time during which to write letters—"the lights in the barracks were extinguished at 9:00 P.M., and the men were often occupied up to that time."

In another battalion, the advisors told how some trainees had to work long hours on KP—not as punishment, but as part of the regular schedule. Some of these men worked sixteen to twenty hours at a stretch, and 50 per cent of these KP's developed blisters from the hot and greasy water. Here again investigation revealed that the morale-breaking situation was the result of oversight in the mess organization.[26]

Monthly meetings with battalion commanders uncovered many situations which if allowed to go uncorrected would have been destructive to good morale. Advisers never reported names of trainees who had registered complaints but merely passed on to their commanding officers information about situations which in their judgment called for investigation or correction.*

The personnel consultants assigned to most military units performed a similar function, although often they had special responsibility for the reassignment of men who seemed to be misplaced.[27] Many a soldier whose initial assignment was for him unhappy and unwise later became, thanks to the alertness of the personnel consultant, an efficient and grateful soldier in a job better suited to his capacities. While the needs in the armed forces were such that not every man could be given the assignment for which he was best fitted, early consideration of those who were very badly placed salvaged many men who, if compelled to carry on in a kind of work for which they were ill fitted, would doubtless have developed mental or nervous illness or proved personally inefficient and a threat to the morale of the group.

POSITIVE AND CONSTRUCTIVE LEADERSHIP

The significance of true leadership in the winning of wars is no new discovery. In the earlier campaigns in which the United States participated in World War II, observations were made which resulted in a helpful analysis of just what is involved in providing leadership. Observations reported by Spiegel, an infantry battalion medical officer, during the Tunisian campaign, made pretty clear the importance of leadership in maintaining mental health and sta-

---

* Over against the obvious merits of this system, there proved to be certain defects: (1) it departed from customary military channels and tended to short-circuit company commanders; (2) it tended somewhat to foster espionage within companies; (3) it placed the functions of junior psychiatrists on relatively untrained men. Because of these limitations, at a conference of more than twenty psychiatrists in ground force basic training units in January, 1944, it was agreed that the adviser system should not be generally adopted in basic training centers.

bility under combat conditions. Two factors seemed to be operative in developing aggressive action: the approval of their comrades and loyalty to their units, both of which depended on good leadership.

It was interesting to observe that most of those cited for gallantry or heroism admitted that they performed as they did because it was expected of them; they had an audience. It is unlikely that many of these men would have risked their lives to perform such hazardous duties if they had not been observed by others, provided, of course, that the performance of that duty was not required for their own personal safety. They expressed little hate for the enemy and they had little desire to kill. Rather, their aggressive action was motivated by a positive force—love more than hate—manifested by (1) a regard for their comrades who shared the same dangers, (2) a respect for their platoon leader or company commander who led them wisely, and backed them with everything at his command, (3) a concern for their reputation with their leaders, and (4) an urge to contribute to the task and success of their group and unit. They were fighting for themselves and for their country and their cause.[28]

The fuller significance of leadership in the motivation of the combat soldiers is revealed in the following statement, in which Spiegel describes what he refers to as the "X" factor:

It was something which corresponds to whatever courage is; it was something which, when present, indicated good morale . . . it was influenced greatly by devotion to their group or unit, by regard for their leader and by conviction for their cause. It seemed to explain why a tired, uninspired, disgusted soldier had the clinical appearance of an anxiety state. It seemed to explain why some units could out-do others; it seemed to aid in controlling the ever-present fear; and it seemed to aid in resisting fatigue. In the most stable fighting men, this factor was not so prominent because of their innate ability to carry on no matter what happened. But in the average soldier, which most of them were, this factor attracted serious attention. Here was a critical, vulnerable, and to be precise, influenceable component that often decided whether or not a man would be overwhelmed by his fear, anxiety or fatigue. Here was a factor that often decided whether or not the man became a psychiatric casualty. It was here that news reports reflecting apparent lack of real appreciation of what they were doing were taken as vicious insults that inflicted their most damaging wounds; but it was here, too, that inspiring leadership played its great role. On the battle field, leaders, especially the junior officers and the noncommissioned officers who had direct personal contact with their men and lived with them, had a great influence upon them, primarily because of intensified comradeship within the unit. Good leadership meant good morale and this, in turn, meant a low psychiatric casualty rate and good performance. It indicated that this X-factor was so strong that it enabled men to control their fear and combat their fatigue to a degree that they themselves did not believe possible.

Good morale seemed to be a labile emotional tone, which at its maximum, enabled the soldier to perform to the very best of his ability, despite the inevitable hardships and threats to his life. That it was labile, the officers soon learned. The maintenance of good morale required constant attention to, and concern over, the factors responsible for it. In combat, the company commander or platoon leader could not, of course, do much about the abstract levels of morale, but he was in a very good position to manipulate morale at the more concrete levels. For instance, he saw to it that his men got the best possible food under the circumstances; he sent blankets up to them at night-time if it were at all possible; he made every effort to keep them well supplied with water and ammunition; he saw to it that promotions were fair; he made certain that good work and gallantry were properly recognized; he got mail, news and information to them when possible; he made sure that violations of rules were treated quickly and fairly; but above everything, by such actions, he made his men feel that they were not alone, that he was backing them up with everything humanly possible. That, plus technical ability, constituted a good leader.[29]

The implications from all this were pretty clear. Pep talks of the usual kind and lectures on the vileness of the enemy were found to mean little. Evidence that their leaders knew their business and cared for their men and their loyalty to one another, were the things that kept the men on an even keel and increased their powers of endurance. One further quotation will suffice:

In essence it [the interest of the combat soldiers] was "me and my gang, how are we doing?—And how about the others?" Sensing this, the battalion commander gathered his men together while preparing for a new offensive, and, in their own language, said, in effect—"I know as well as you do that the going has been tough. Perhaps I sweat it out more than you do because I have more to worry about. But you have done a fine job and I am proud of every single man in my outfit. I assure you that everything possible will be done to give you the best available support and I will not order you to attack unless I am confident that you have a real chance to succeed. The harder we fight now, the sooner we can finish this mess and get back to living the way we wish." This, I believe, demonstrates the wisdom of detecting and utilizing the available forces which can effectively thwart anxiety-producing factors. Had this battalion commander, on that occasion, talked about the advantages of democracy over Fascism, or about the evil things that Hitler had been doing during the past ten years, it would have undoubtedly struck a sour or unresponsive note with the men. Instead, he wisely seized upon one of the strong motivating forces in his men, namely a respect for him as a leader, a desire to maintain a reputation with the other men, and an urge to participate in the accomplishments of the group. And his method was a frank, direct talk. . . . On the battlefield, there were available forces complementing good leadership which effectively minimized anxiety. They were: (1) proper classification and assignment, (2) adequate discipline, and (3) good doctors.[28]

Doubtless we shall never be able to count the number of men who carried on heroically and were saved the devastating experience of a combat neurosis because of good leadership and effective organization. It is reasonable to believe that they number many thousands. When the whole story of World War II is finally told, the value of constructive leadership will probably be confirmed many times over by many units in all theaters of war.

WORK OF DIVISION PSYCHIATRISTS

In 1943, a psychiatrist was assigned to each combat division. Some of the best mental health work in the entire Army was done by these division psychiatrists. They consulted the commanding officers and brought them recommendations on problems of morale and leadership on the field. They instructed general medical officers and medical corps men regarding effective methods of dealing with the mental hygiene problems, both of the wounded and of those suffering from combat fatigue or psychiatric disabilities. By providing maximum rest, food, comfort, and reassurance in battalion aid stations, training and rehabilitation centers, and NP clearing stations in the forward areas, they made it possible for many men to recover promptly and to be returned to their original units, thus averting the threat which is nearly always involved when men are evacuated.

Treatment of Psychiatric Disabilities

In establishing facilities for the psychiatric treatment of NP casualties in the armed forces, due weight had to be given to the exigencies of the military situation and to factors which do not obtain in civilian life. Whereas the civilian psychiatrist is primarily concerned for the individual and the effect which the group has upon him, the military psychiatrist had to be much concerned with the untoward effect which maladjusted individuals have upon the group and had to strive for a high quality of group efficiency. Neither could the military psychiatrist give as much time to treatment as the civilian psychiatrist. He was constrained to discover casualties in the early stages of breakdown and to get them under immediate treatment, both for their own sakes and for the sake of the group.

Because of this need, mental health programs in the armed forces stressed prevention and early and quick therapy. Though the organizational machinery was designed chiefly for preventive purposes, it was also used to discover symptoms of maladjustment as soon as they became evident, and to a large extent the personnel responsible for the preventive phases of the program also administered the treatment. For example, the mental hygiene unit discussed in the previous section was a major instrument both for discovering those who were not adjusting well and for giving them prompt and appropriate treatment.[30]

Another difference between military and civilian psychiatric treatment is the degree of control of the total situation. The whole organized life of the soldier-patient was made to serve the ends of treatment. Food, rest, recreation, and, in the latter stages of treatment, further training and assigned duties were all directed to hasten the recovery. The primary goal was to get each patient well as quickly as possible and return him to full duty as an efficient soldier or sailor, with his original group, if possible.

Other treatment policies have been enumerated by Farrell and Appel as follows:

1. Every case is regarded salvageable until proved otherwise, and, while priority is given to cases expected to return to duty, every possible effort is made to provide treatment for personnel awaiting discharge to their homes or to veteran or civilian facilities.

2. Every case is regarded a medical emergency and treatment is initiated immediately to prevent the fixing of symptoms.

3. Emphasis is placed on outpatient treatment and hospitalization is avoided as far as possible, because of the tendency of hospitalization to exaggerate the concept of the illness in the patient's mind. In a three-month experiment in three training centers, separate battalions for retraining psychoneurotics were set up under the direction of picked line officers, psychiatrists, psychologists, and psychiatric social workers attached to the battalion headquarters. Seventy per cent of the entire group were returned to duty, and of that number at least 75 per cent were still on duty six months later.

4. Because of the significance of situational reactions in many psychiatric cases, every effort is made to remove situational factors which have helped to precipitate the disorder. Special attention is paid in both training and combat casualties to proper job assignment and to training for it. Through Red Cross social service and other agencies domestic problems are given attention.[10]

Because of limitations of professional personnel and the urgency of the military situation, the treatment of neuropsychiatric casualties in all branches of the service was characterized by speed, and facilities were set up accordingly. Case-finding was the function of both medical and line officers at every point, from initial training posts to combat areas, and as much treatment as was practical was given all along the line, at battalion aid stations, NP clearing stations, general hospitals, convalescent hospitals, and reconditioning centers.

ARMY

Chart 3 indicates the organization of facilities for the treatment of both training and combat casualties arising in the Army. Facilities which served the Army Air Force were administered by the Army Air Force. A special feature was the establishment of rest centers, where flying personnel recognized by the flight surgeon as showing signs of exhaustion or combat fatigue could be treated. These centers were close enough to the scene of action to prevent any feeling on the part of the men that they had been evacuated; they stayed with their own branch of the service and were still identified with their specific groups. A large percentage of men recovered and returned to full duty.[31] Those requiring further treatment were sent to station or general hospitals, or returned to the United States for treatment in convalescent centers.[32]

All facilities serving the ground and service forces were under the supervision of the Neuropsychiatry Consultants Division of the Surgeon General's Office. Chart 3 indicates also the flow of personnel and the major kinds of treatment given at the various treatment centers. The method of treatment varied very much with the location of the center. In the initial treatment of training casualties, main reliance was placed on short psychotherapy, both individual and group. For seriously disturbed patients who reached general hospitals, all the usual methods were available.[14, 33, 34]

In the treatment of battle casualties, procedures in forward areas

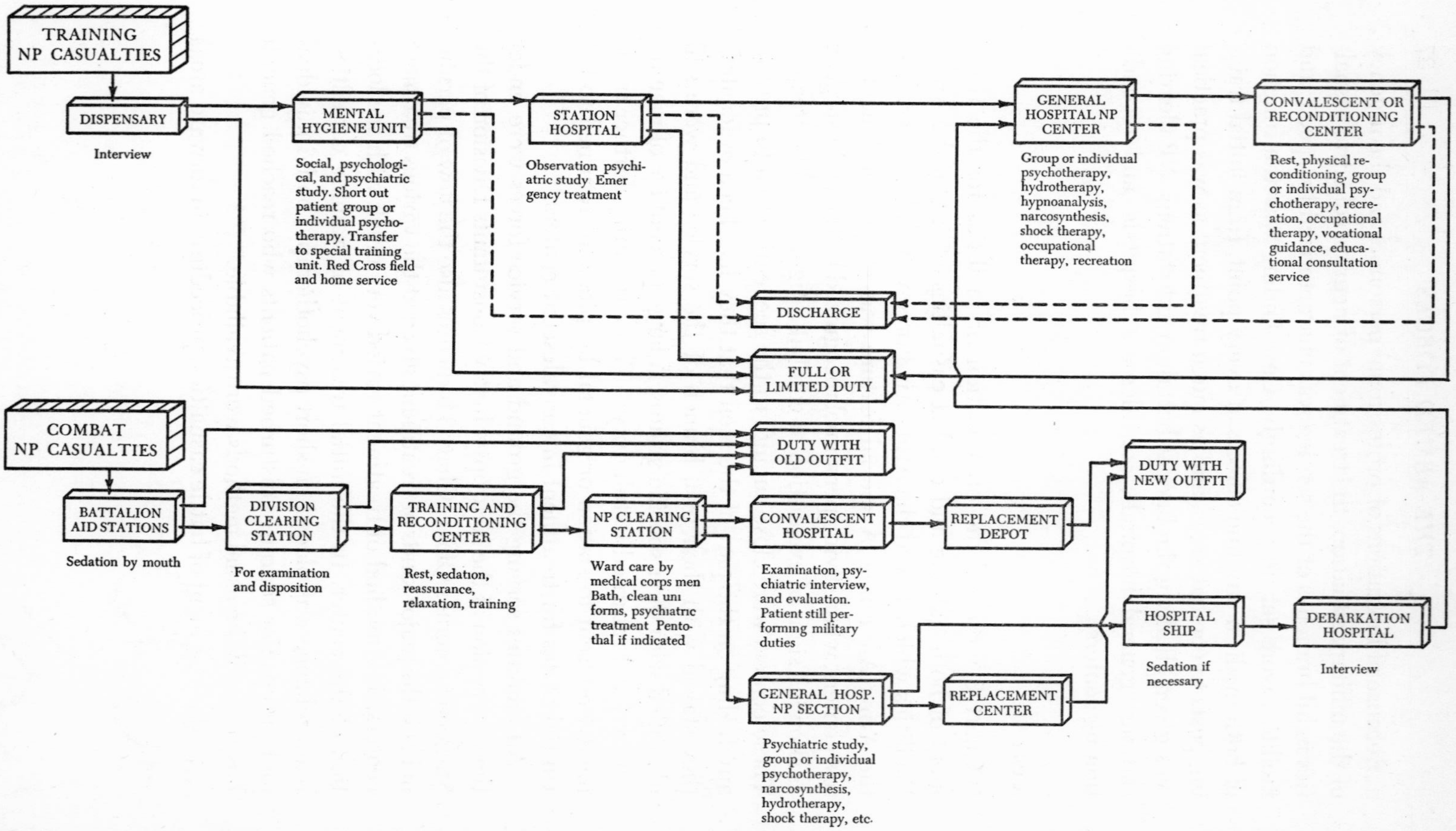

TRAINING NP CASUALTIES

DISPENSARY
Interview

MENTAL HYGIENE UNIT
Social, psychological, and psychiatric study. Short out patient group or individual psychotherapy. Transfer to special training unit. Red Cross field and home service

STATION HOSPITAL
Observation psychiatric study. Emergency treatment

GENERAL HOSPITAL NP CENTER
Group or individual psychotherapy, hydrotherapy, hypnoanalysis, narcosynthesis, shock therapy, occupational therapy, recreation

CONVALESCENT OR RECONDITIONING CENTER
Rest, physical reconditioning, group or individual psychotherapy, recreation, occupational therapy, vocational guidance, educational consultation service

DISCHARGE

FULL OR LIMITED DUTY

DUTY WITH OLD OUTFIT

COMBAT NP CASUALTIES

BATTALION AID STATIONS
Sedation by mouth

DIVISION CLEARING STATION
For examination and disposition

TRAINING AND RECONDITIONING CENTER
Rest, sedation, reassurance, relaxation, training

NP CLEARING STATION
Ward care by medical corps men Bath, clean uniforms, psychiatric treatment Pentothal if indicated

CONVALESCENT HOSPITAL
Examination, psychiatric interview, and evaluation. Patient still performing military duties

REPLACEMENT DEPOT

DUTY WITH NEW OUTFIT

GENERAL HOSP. NP SECTION
Psychiatric study, group or individual psychotherapy, narcosynthesis, hydrotherapy, shock therapy, etc.

REPLACEMENT CENTER

HOSPITAL SHIP
Sedation if necessary

DEBARKATION HOSPITAL
Interview

CHART 2.—ARMY PERSONNEL FLOW CHART, NP COMBAT AND TRAINING CASUALTIES. COMPILED BY KURT PORGES may be summarized to include: "Segregation of cases according to severity, provision for observation, adequate sleep, food and warmth, stimulation of the conscience, bolstering of ego and morale, maintenance of soldier rather than patient discipline, provision for continued contact with fellow soldiers of the same unit and rapid return to duty."[35] In the forward areas, especially at the NP clearing stations, the division neuropsychiatrist was responsible for psychiatric treatment and utilized sedatives, rest, and reassurance as his chief aids.[36-38]

At evacuation hospitals and training rehabilitation centers, treatment was carried on for a period not exceeding five days and consisted of continued rest, warm baths, sedation, explanation of symptoms, and strong psychotherapeutic reassurance. In most combat areas 40 to 60 per cent of the men were returned successfully to combat duty from this point.[36, 38]

In general hospitals overseas, therapy, according to Grinker and Spiegel,[35] included narcosynthesis with pentothol, brief psychotherapy, convulsive shock therapy (with small numbers of selected cases), continuous sleep, general convalescent care, occupational therapy, group therapy, and other methods. Narcosynthesis with brief psychotherapy was used increasingly with good results.[39]

NAVY

Chart 4 shows the organization of facilities and the flow of personnel through the treatment centers, administered by the Navy, which supplied all the medical and psychiatric service to the Marines as well as to the Navy proper. The organization of land installations to serve Marines was very similar to that of the Army: battalion-aid stations, NP clearing stations, mobile hospital units, and so forth.

Both in these stations and in floating facilities, treatment was of necessity limited, whereas at base hospitals abroad and at the NP sections of the general hospitals in the United States, specialized

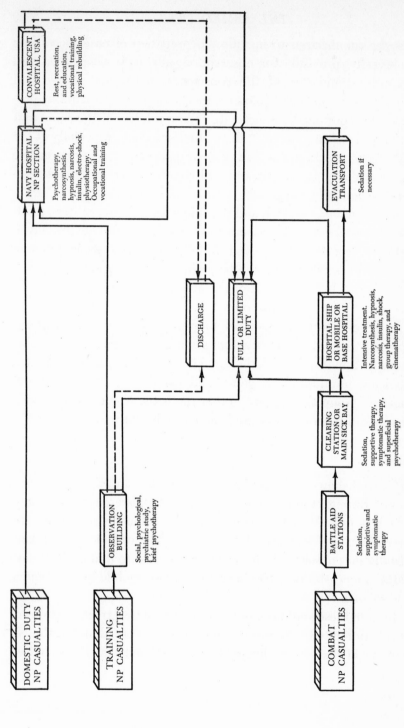

CHART 4. NAVY PERSONNEL FLOW CHART, NP CASUALTIES. COMPILED BY KURT PORGES

DOMESTIC DUTY NP CASUALTIES

TRAINING NP CASUALTIES

COMBAT NP CASUALTIES

OBSERVATION BUILDING

Social, psychological, psychiatric study, brief psychotherapy

BATTLE AID STATIONS

Sedation, supportive and symptomatic therapy

CLEARING STATION OR MAIN SICK BAY

Sedation, supportive therapy, symptomatic therapy, and superficial psychotherapy

DISCHARGE

FULL OR LIMITED DUTY

HOSPITAL SHIP OR MOBILE OR BASE HOSPITAL

Intensive treatment. Narcosynthesis, hypnosis, narcosis, insulin, shock, group therapy, and cinematherapy

NAVY HOSPITAL NP SECTION

Psychotherapy, narcosynthesis, hypnosis, narcosis, insulin, electro-shock, physiotherapy. Occupational and vocational training

CONVALESCENT HOSPITAL, USA

Rest, recreation, and education, vocational training, physical rebuilding

EVACUATION TRANSPORT

Sedation if necessary

treatment of all kinds was available.[40] More specifically, to quote Braceland:

Allowing for variation in each specific situation, in general the following is a fairly adequate picture of the specific kinds of treatment at every point from the battle aid station on. At the battle aid station, either among the Marines or on board ship, the NP casualty receives sedation, supportive therapy and symptomatic therapy. Later at the clearing station or main sick bay on board ship, he may receive these plus rest or superficial psychotherapy. Some men return to duty from here. Later, either on board a hospital ship or at a base or mobile hospital, he begins to receive more intensive treatment with the addition of narcosynthesis, hypnosis, narcosis, modified insulin treatment, some group therapy and even cinematherapy. Later, upon his arrival in this country and his assignment to a regular naval hospital, he receives such definitive treatment as is called for. The above may be used and to them are added electroshock therapy, physiotherapy, intensive individual psychotherapy, and such rehabilitative procedures as occupational therapy and vocational training. Convalescent leave is also used as a therapeutic procedure, but its effects are open to question. Before a discharge or return to duty, the man then may be transferred to a convalescent hospital or may be given a period of limited shore duty for six months. In general the naval treatment parallels the best modern professional practice, with the early stages of treatment limited by the lack of facilities at the front lines and the latter stages of treatment in this country bolstered by much more in the way of rehabilitative procedures than is typical of present civilian practices.[41]

At several of the Navy's large hospitals, special attention was given to occupational therapy. In a few instances, in cooperation with industry, factory installations were made in a section of the hospital, and patients were gainfully employed, often on a part-time basis, in accordance with physicians' orders.[42] This resulted in greatly improved morale, increased rate of convalescence, and early recovery, whether discharge or return to duty was the goal. Regarding the more serious illnesses, Braceland reports:

The number of psychotic illnesses occurring in the Navy is well below the number expected, and far below the psychotic rate in the civilian population. In the two large hospitals to which psychotic patients are eventually transferred, the recovery rate is 65 per cent returned to their homes, symptom-free, within the first three months, and 20 per cent more within the next three months. This is an excellent record, in or out of the service.[43]

In the base and general hospitals in the Navy, all psychiatric social work was carried by well-trained Red Cross workers in the field. It is believed that, because these workers were "psychologically neutral," patients felt freer to denounce anything or anyone they chose. Through the exercise of this privilege and the social work with men and, as far as possible, with their families, recovery was probably expedited. The recovery rate among psychotic and severely psychoneurotic patients at St. Elizabeths Hospital, Washington, and the United States Public Health Service Hospital, Fort Worth, Texas, has been substantially higher than that of many hospitals at which similar types of patients have been treated exclusively by personnel having administrative authority over them.[44] On the average 60 per cent have been discharged free of symptoms at the end of three months and an additional 20 per cent by the end of six months.[45]

UNITED STATES MERCHANT SEAMEN'S REST CENTERS

In a war in which the transportation problem is as large as it was in the recent war, the need for adequate care of merchant seamen is obvious. In the early stages of World War II, the treatment of ill and injured seamen in the large marine hospitals proved somewhat unsatisfactory, and decision was made by the War Shipping Board to recruit commissioned officers from the United States Public Health Service to organize and operate rest centers for seamen suffering from neuropsychiatric disorders. Here seamen were treated for convoy fatigue, and, with a view to prevention, those who needed rest were permitted to remain for a limited period of time. The maximum length of treatment was three or four weeks, with referrals to marine hospitals for those requiring longer treatment. Each center was located in attractive surroundings and accommodated only 30 to 50 seamen. A very informal atmosphere was maintained. The staff consisted of a psychiatrist and nurses who wore civilian clothes rather than uniforms in order to avoid giving the center the appearance of a hospital.

Treatment consisted of medical care, sedation, adequate diet, individual or group psychotherapy, correction of physical difficulties, and extensive occupational and recreational therapy, including games, dancing, community singing and so forth, arts and crafts, and instruction in first aid, swimming, life-saving, the handling of life boats, and other activities valuable for seamen. Eighty per cent of the men were ready to return to full sea duty after three weeks, and a large percentage of the remainder shipped on the Great Lakes and later returned to sea.[46]

TREATMENT OF MILITARY OFFENDERS

In World War II military offenders likewise were studied from the mental hygiene point of view and were given psychiatric treatment. In the first place, the Judge Advocate General frequently requested the psychiatrist attached to his division to examine men accused of military offenses and to testify regarding the mental responsibility of men being tried by court martial.

In the special rehabilitation centers established by the Army for military offenders, the usual mental hygiene clinic team tested and classified men by their ability to respond to treatment and as far as possible taught ways to adjust to military service. Individual and group therapy was provided without weakening discipline. The establishment of honor battalions in which the standards of training were particularly high prepared many men for an early return to full duty. Those unable to adjust under the rehabilitation program were retained in disciplinary barracks.[47] In the Navy, psychiatrists participated regularly in the rehabilitation programs of brigs, prisons, and detention barracks.

Outstanding Developments in Military Psychiatry

As Strecker has pointed out, "In neuropsychiatry, modern war has not devised totally new treatment formulae, but there have been skillful and useful adaptations of known treatment."[48] There have been three outstanding developments during World War II in the methods of treating and reconditioning NP casualties.

The first of these, which has already been referred to, was Grinker and Spiegel's development of shorter methods of narcosynthesis and their wide application of this method in the treatment of severe battle reactions. A dose of 0.25 to 1.0 gram of sodium pentothol was administered to effect a narcosis. The advantage of this particular drug is that the effects wear off quickly, so that psychotherapy may be continued immediately after the discussion of battle experiences. We can quote only briefly Grinker and Spiegel's statement regarding this method:

Narcosynthesis causes the patient to re-experience the intense emotions which were originally associated with the traumatic battle experiences and which have been perpetuated in various stages of repression up to the moment of treatment. At the same time, the action of the drug enables the patient to deal with these revived emotions in a more economical and rational manner, instead of catastrophic defensive technics, which end in serious neurotic crippling. For lack of a better term, we have called this therapeutic process narcosynthesis. Under treatment, the patient actually synthesizes the emotions and memories connected with his experience, putting together what has lain fragmented between consciousness and unconsciousness into a complete whole, which corresponds in almost every detail with the original experience. Under the influence of the drug, and the work of the therapist, there occurs a dosed release of the intense repressed emotions, in quantities small enough so that the weakened or broken ego, strengthened by the therapist, resumes its appraising and rationalizing functions. The ego, freed from the impact of the immense forces of the repressed emotions, in turn gathers new strength; restores its contact between the powerful emotional drives and the world of reality, both past and present. In this state of renewed activity it can approach the traumatic situation and, to some extent, deal with it. Thus a "benign circle" is created. For this reason, we feel that intravenous barbiturate narcosynthesis is immediately indicated in all cases of the severe anxiety states associated with mutism, stupor, regressive somatic manifestations, regressive (psychosis-like) psychological manifestations, and amnesia.[49]

Narcosynthesis was used increasingly in battle areas by psychiatric medical officers in all branches of the service, and as a result the fixation of battle-reaction symptoms was prevented to a degree previously unknown.

The second major development in treatment during World War II was military group psychotherapy. It was a measure of necessity, given the large number of NP casualties and the limited numbers of trained psychiatrists and other well-trained personnel, but it proved to have superior merits in the treatment of a large proportion of battle casualties. In many instances it would have been used in preference to individual therapy even if the latter had been possible, because in group therapy the patients' identification with the military group is sustained and their sense of failure is much less acute.

This method has wide applicability. As is pointed out in the War Department's bulletin on this subject: "Group psychotherapy can be utilized in any setting where numbers of individuals with personality, emotional, adjustment or neurotic disorders are present. It can be used in the neuropsychiatric sections of hospitals and reconditioning facilities, in mental hygiene units or consultation services, in rehabilitation centers, and in tactical organizations."[17] In the words of Rome:

Group psychotherapy has the advantage of combining expediency with the best possible rehabilitation therapy. In small groups of from five to ten participants, all presenting the same symptom-picture, the approach can be specific, i.e., through those symptoms enabling them to gain relief from incapacitating complaints. In still larger groups, (from ten to twenty-five patients) the approach can be more general, i.e., a presentation of general principles of mental hygiene. In both instances a too-penetrating analysis which would uncover earlier traumata is automatically prevented.

The rationale is based on the fact that in all military organizations security rests on collective action; " in union there is strength" is a maxim, not a cliché. The more an individual feels allied to his squad, platoon, company or crew, the less is he vulnerable to a war neurosis. In a group, security is gained by a mutual pooling of insecurity. The group itself is the emotional equivalent of a "kitty" from which all participating are eligible to draw the additional security necessary to fulfill their personal demands.[50]

The nucleus of the plan is a regulated, orderly social existence on a therapeutic scale. It attempts to fuse in the fire of group morale those individual differences and idiosyncrasies which prevent a complete group amalgamation . . . it stresses unified action with the feeling that through a well-recognized interdependence there will be created mutual attitudes of reciprocity. Insecurities which fragment a group by isolating its members can be welded by the reassuring support of a strong group morale.[51]

In group therapy the here and now of personal attitudes and relationships are stressed; language association is used to explain common symptoms, such as "having one's head swim," for dizziness; "being fed up," for vomiting; and "being scared to death," for fainting. Much use is made of group discussion of an extremely informal kind in which frank inquiry and freedom of expression by all participants are encouraged. Discussion is related to the specific goal ahead, be it return to duty or discharge to civilian jobs and family living.[52] Motion pictures, followed by group discussion, are used as audiovisual aids, and with properly selected patients speed up the treatment process. The special merits of group therapy have been summarized as follows:

It is nonspecific in character and cannot be expected to accomplish that which intense individual therapy can do. However, in addition to the economic advantage of group treatment, it can be more effective in removing attitudes of suspicion and hostility. Contrary to what might be expected, it offers a medium for some to express themselves more freely. Personal problems are minimized and seen in a broad perspective. Guilt feelings concerning failure and incapacity without visible organic disease to justify such failures are partially relieved in the recognition that others have similar disorders. The individual problem is partially transformed into a group problem.[17]

Total advantages listed by Rome are: (1) the similarity of symptoms relieves the therapeutic burden from any one individual; (2) tensions based on feeling unique are dissipated; (3) stigma is ameliorated; (4) the doctor-patient relationship is eased; (5) emotional release is controlled; (6) a too penetrating analysis is precluded; (7) individual sessions may be added if indicated; (8) a twenty-four-hour schedule avoids undirected lulls; (9) monotony is avoided by presenting material familiar to the group in a variety of ways.[51]

Rome, in work with NP groups in the Pacific, did much to develop this method and to formulate the principles and techniques. Psychiatrists in other units experimented with the method under varying circumstances. There appears to have been an advantage in the fact that there was no clear-cut theory or formulated set of practices. Consequently, group psychotherapy methods were used with a great deal of flexibility by psychiatric social workers, personnel consultants, and training and recreational specialists.[34, 53, 54]

A third outstanding development—major credit for which must go to Rusk—applies to virtually all types of patients. A new kind of program in the convalescence and reconditioning of military patients resulted in marked shortening of the convalescent period and returned men to duty or civilian life with functions fully restored or maximum reconditioning in case of permanent disabilities. In cases of a typical pneumonia the average period of hospitalization was reduced from forty-five to thirty-one days, with a 3 per cent, in contrast to a 30 per cent, recurrence rate.[55] The reduction in the average period of hospitalization for arthritic patients achieved by applying sound principles of conditioning amounted to over 70 per cent.[56] Reference already has been made to the more satisfactory results obtained in the treatment of the neuropsychiatric group. The period of treatment was shortened and morale was much improved by a combined program of psychotherapy, recreation, education, and military discipline.[57]

This new emphasis on patient activity and adequate motivation for recovery sprang from various sources, one of the most significant of which was the mental hygiene program in the armed forces, where emphasis was placed on the whole man and on his attitudes toward himself and his future. As Braceland has pointed out:

It is the *man* as a feeling person who will recover from the illness and the *man* as a person of sensibilities who will wear the orthopedic appliance, that psychiatry is concerned about. It is the *person* as a whole who should be treated and not only the diseased part. . . . It depends upon *who* is sick or injured and how his personality is affected for better or worse, as to what chances there are of rehabilitating him. In its broadest sense, rehabilitation depends upon whether or not the *individual* as a whole is capable of rehabilitation, and in final analysis we are defied to rehabilitate any man who will not or cannot be rehabilitated.[48]

REFERENCES

1. Testimony of Brig. Gen. William C. Menninger and Major Gen. Louis B. Hershey before U. S. Senate, Subcommittee of the Committee on Education and Labor, 79th Congress, 2d Session, Hearings on H.R. 4512 (National Mental Health Act), p. 58–63. Washington, Government Printing Office, 1946.

2. Medical Circular No. 4, Selective Service System, describes the Medical Survey Program, through which history material was made available to the medical examiners at the induction stations of the armed forces.

3. Hofstein, S. The impact of family forces on the soldier as met by the military social worker. Ment. Hyg. 29:385–394, July 1945.

4. See especially: Grinker, R. R., and J. P. Spiegel. Men under stress. Philadelphia, Blakiston, 1945.

   Rees, J. R. The shaping of psychiatry by war. New York, Norton, 1945.

   Sladen, F. J. Psychiatry and the war. Springfield, Ill., Thomas, 1943.

5. Edelstein, S. E.   Social work in selection for armed forces; types of problem that would have been discovered with better pre-induction screening.   Ment. Hyg. 28:565–567, October 1944.

6. Ebaugh, F. G.   Misfits in the military service.   Dis. Nerv. System 4:293–298, October 1943.

Freedman, H. L.   The services of the military mental hygiene unit.   Am. J. Psychiat. 100:34–40, July 1943.

Layman, J. W.   Problems of adjustment referred to general hospitals of the Army.   J. Abnormal & Social Psychol. 38:155–164, April (supp.) 1943.

Maskin, M. M., and L. L. Altman.   Military psychodynamics; psychological factors in the transition from civilian to soldier.   Psychiatry 6:263–269, August 1943.

Olkon, D. M.   Effect of war and army life contingencies on the behavior and breakdown of the inductee and soldier.   Dis. Nerv. System 5:243–249, August 1944.

Rosenberg, S. J.   The psychiatric service of an army station hospital.   Am. J. Psychiat. 99:864–868, May 1943.

Seidenfeld, M. A.   Clinical psychology in army hospitals.   Psychol. Bull. 41: 510–514, October 1944.

Simon, A., and M. Hagan.   Social data in psychiatric casualties in the armed services.   Am. J. Psychiat. 99:348–353, November 1942.

7. Kaplan, N.   Salvaging illiterates in the Army.   Occupations 23:74–76, November 1944.

McQuitty, L. L.   A program for the classification and training of retarded soldiers.   Psychol. Bull. 40:770–779, December 1944.

Menninger, W. C.   The problem of the mentally retarded in the Army.   Am. J. Ment. Deficiency 48:55–61, July 1943.

8. Freedman, H. L.   The unique structure and function of the mental-hygiene unit in the Army.   Ment. Hyg. 27:608–653, October 1943.

9. Closson, J. H., and H. M. Hildreth.   Experiment in psychotherapy during selection examining.   U. S. Nav. M. Bull. 43:39–43, July 1944.

Gerstle, M., Jr., R. L. Wagner, and T. Lodge.   The inapt naval recruit.   U. S. Nav. M. Bull. 41:480–492, March 1943.

Hunt, W. A., C. L. Wittson, H. I. Harris, P. S. Solomon, and M. M. Jackson. Psychometric procedures in the detection of the neuropsychiatrically unfit.   U. S. Nav. M. Bull. 41:471–480, March 1943.

Hunt, W. A., C. L. Wittson, and M. M. Jackson.   Selection of naval personnel with special reference to mental deficiency.   Am. J. Ment. Deficiency 48:245–252, January 1944.

Kennedy, W. F., F. J. Braceland, and H. P. Rome.   Rationale of naval recruit selection methods.   J.A.M.A. 125:548–550, June 24, 1944.

Wittson, C. L., H. I. Harris, W. A. Hunt, P. S. Solomon, and M. M. Jackson. The neuropsychiatric selection of recruits.   Am. J. Psychiat. 99:639–650, March 1943.

10. Farrell, M. J., and J. W. Appel. Current trends in military neuropsychiatry. Am. J. Psychiat. 101:12–19, July 1944.

11. Menninger, W. C. Psychiatry and the Army. Psychiatry 7:175–181, May 1944.

12. Freedman, H. L. Mental-hygiene first aid for precombat casualties. Ment. Hyg. 28:186–213, April 1944.

13. Appel, J. W. Personal communication.

14. Freedman, H. L. The role of the mental-hygiene clinic in a military training center. Ment. Hyg. 27:83–121, January 1943.

15. Lecture outlines for officers on personnel adjustment problems. War Department Technical Bulletin, Med. 12. Washington, February 22, 1944.

16. Lecture outlines for enlisted men on personnel adjustment problems. War Department Technical Bulletin, Med. 21. Washington, March 15, 1944.

17. Group psychotherapy. War Department Technical Bulletin, Med. 103. Washington, October 10, 1944.

18. Appel, J. W., and D. W. Hilger. Morale and preventive psychiatry. Bull. Menninger Clin. 8:150–152, September 1944.

19. Cohen, R. R. Officers and their relation to a mental-hygiene program for trainees. Ment. Hyg. 28:368–380, July 1944.

Freedman, H. L., and M. J. Rockmore. Mental hygiene aids for the line officer. Issued at New Orleans Army Air Base, August 1945.

20. Cohen, R. R. Factors in adjustment to Army life; a plan for preventive psychiatry by mass psychotherapy. War Med. 5:83–91, February 1944.

21. Cohen, R. R. Mental hygiene for the trainee; a method for fortifying the Army's manpower. Am. J. Psychiat. 100:62–71, July 1943.

22. Schreiber, J. Morale aspects of military mental hygiene. Dis. Nerv. System 4:197–201, July 1943.

23. Stilwell, L. E., and J. Schreiber. A neuropsychiatric program for a replacement training center. War Med. 3:20–29, January 1943.

24. For a full and interesting account see: Schreiber, J. Psychological training and orientation of soldiers. Ment. Hyg. 28:537–554, October 1944.

25. Kraines, S. H. Prophylactic psychiatry in the Army. Bull. U. S. Army M. Dept. (No. 75) p. 77–81, April 1944.

26. Kraines, S. H. The adviser system; prophylactic psychiatry on a mass scale. Ment. Hyg. 27:592–607, October 1943.

27. Cruvant, B. A. Symposium on psychiatry in the armed forces; replacement training center consultation service. Am. J. Psychiat. 100:41–46, July 1943.

Gilbert, G. M. The personnel consultant in an army training center. Psychol. Bull. 41:180–186, March 1944.

Pickus, J. D. The army personnel consultant. The Family 25:209–216, October 1944.

28. Spiegel, H. X.   Preventive psychiatry with combat troops.   Am. J. Psychiat. 101:310–315, November 1944.

29. Spiegel, H. X.   Psychiatric observations in the Tunisian campaign.   Am. J. Orthopsychiat. 14:381–385, July 1944.

30. Menninger, W. C.   The mentally unfit; detection, elimination and disposal. Dis. Nerv. System 6:109–114, April 1945.

United States Army, the Adjutant General's Office, Staff Classification Section, Classification and Replacement Branch.   An army experiment in retraining psychoneurotic casualties.   Psychol. Bull. 41:532–538, October 1944.

31. Grinker, R. R.   Rehabilitation of flyers with operational fatigue.   Air Surgeon's Bull. 2:18–21, January 1945.

Grinker, R. R., and J. P. Spiegel.   Narcosynthesis; a psychotherapeutic method for acute war neuroses.   Air Surgeon's Bull. 1:1–5, February 1944.

Hastings, D. W.   Psychiatry in the Eighth Air Force.   Air Surgeon's Bull. 1:4–5, August 1944.

Kelsey, M. P.   Flying fatigue in pilots flying long-range single-seat fighter missions.   Air Surgeon's Bull. 1:14–15, June 1944.

Murray, J. M.   Psychiatric aspects of aviation medicine.   Psychiatry 7:1–7, February 1944.

Murray, J. M.   Some special aspects of psychotherapy in the Army Air Forces. Psychosom. Med. 6:119–122, April 1944.

32. Gillman, R. D., and G. V. Ramsey.   A.A.F. convalescent-rehabilitation program. Psychol. Bull. 41:548–550, October 1944.

Murray, J. M.   Psychiatric evaluation of those returning from combat.   J.A.M.A. 126:148–150, September 16, 1944.

Rosner, A. A.   The neuropsychiatrist and convalescent training in the Army Air Forces.   Bull. U. S. Army M. Dept. (No. 78) p. 93–97, July 1944.

33. Knight, R. P.   The treatment of the psychoneuroses of war.   Bull. Menninger Clin. 7:145–155, July 1943; also J. Kansas M. Soc. 44:257–260, August 1943.

Menninger, W. C.   Opportunities for treatment of neuropsychiatric patients. Bull. U. S. Army M. Dept. (No. 74) p. 90–98, March 1944.

Moore, M., and P. D. MacLean.   Treatment of mentally disturbed soldiers overseas.   Bull. U. S. Army M. Dept. (No. 80) p. 113–118, September 1944.

Peal, S.   Psychiatric experiences in a tropical theater of operations.   Bull. U. S. Army M. Dept. (No. 73) p. 68–78, February 1944.

Sandler, S. A., and S. R. Rotman.   Adjusting the emotionally unstable soldier. Bull. U. S. Army M. Dept. (No. 85) p. 103–107, February 1945.

Seidenfeld, M. A.   The special training units of the Army.   Psychol. Bull. 40: 279–281, April 1943.

Stakel, F.   Occupational therapy for neuro-psychiatric patients in an army general hospital.   Occup. Therapy 23:225–229, October 1944.

34. Greving, F. T., and M. J. Rockmore.   Psychiatric case work as a military service. Ment. Hyg. 29:435–506, July 1945.

35. Grinker, R. R., and J. P. Spiegel. War neuroses in North Africa. Washington, Office of the Air Surgeon, U. S. Army Air Forces, 1943. Distributed by the Josiah Macy, Jr., Foundation.

36. Carpenter, R. J. Early recognition and treatment of neuropsychiatric conditions in combat zone. J.A.M.A. 123:705–706, November 13, 1943.

37. Farrell, M. J. Development in military neuropsychiatry. J. Iowa M. Soc. 34: 387–391, September 1944.

    McElroy, R. B. Psychoneuroses, combat-anxiety type. Am. J. Psychiat. 101: 517–520, January 1945.

38. Drayer, C. S., and S. W. Ranson. Combat psychiatry. Bull. U. S. Army M. Dept. 4:91–96, July 1945.

39. Grinker, R. R., and J. P. Spiegel. Men under stress. Philadelphia, Blakiston, 1945.

40. Braceland, F. J., and H. P. Rome. Anxiety and fatigue. Connecticut M. J. 7: 827–831, December 1943.

    Farnsworth, D. L., and R. S. Wighton. Psychiatric practice aboard a hospital ship in a combat area. Am. J. Psychiat. 101:504–510, January 1945.

    Lewinski, R. J. Psychological services in the medical department. U. S. Nav. M. Bull. 41:137–142, January 1943.

    Raines, G. N., and L. C. Kolb. Combat fatigue and war neuroses. U. S. Nav. M. Bull. 41:923, July; 41:1299, September 1943.

    Richards, T. W. The appraisal of naval psychiatric casualties by the Rorschach method. U. S. Nav. M. Bull. 41:788–799, May 1943.

    Schwab, R. S., J. E. Finesinger, and M. A. B. Brazier. Psychoneuroses precipitated by combat. U. S. Nav. M. Bull. 42:535–544, March 1944.

    Steele, E. H. Psychiatric casualties. U. S. Nav. M. Bull. 42:1089–1091, May 1944.

41. Braceland, F. J., Captain, M.D., U.S.N.R. Personal communication.

42. The Arma-Navy Program. Brooklyn, Arma Corp., 1945.

43. Braceland, F. J. The role of the psychiatrist in the general rehabilitation program. *In* New York Academy of Medicine, Committee on Public Health Relations, Convalescence and rehabilitation, p. 31–38. New York, the Academy, 1944.

44. Hagan, M. Red Cross recreation; the program for neuropsychiatric casualties. J. Health & Phys. Educ. 16:66, February 1945.

    Hagan, M., and A. M. Duval. A practical Red Cross program for the social rehabilitation of psychiatric casualties in the United States Navy. Am. J. Psychiat. 100:105–108, July 1943.

45. Braceland, F. J., and H. P. Rome. Problems of naval psychiatry. War Med. 6:217–220, October 1944.

46. Blain, D. Convalescence and rehabilitation of merchant seamen. *In* New York Academy of Medicine, Committee on Public Health Relations, Convalescence and rehabilitation, p. 46–50. New York, the Academy, 1944.

Blain, D., and F. Powdermaker. Convoy fatigue and traumatic war neuroses in seamen. J. Lancet 63:402–405, December 1943.

Limburg, C. C. Psychological work in the United States Maritime Service. Psychol. Bull. 41:664–668, November 1944.

47. Berlien, I. C. Neuropsychiatry in armed forces induction stations, rehabilitation centers, and combat divisions. Bull. Menninger Clin. 8:146–149, September 1944.

Lewinski, R. J., and E. J. Galway. Psychological services at a naval retraining command. Psychol. Bull. 42:297–300, May 1945.

Locke, B., A. C. Cornsweet, W. Bromberg, and A. A. Apuzzo. Study of 1,063 naval offenders. U. S. Nav. Bull. 44:73–86, January 1945.

Snow, H. B. Psychiatric procedures at the rehabilitation center, Second Service Command. Address before the 25th Annual Meeting of the Association for Research in Nervous and Mental Diseases. Unpublished.

48. Strecker, E. A. War psychiatry and its influence upon post-war psychiatry and upon civilization (Pasteur lecture). J. Lancet 357–358, November 1946.

49. See above, item 35, pages 157–158. See *ibid.*, pages 159–214, for an interesting account of the use of this method and the results obtained with the various types of casualties and for a discussion of psychotherapy carried on in connection with narcosynthesis.

50. Rome, H. P. Psychiatry as seen in the advanced mobile base hospitals. Am. J. Psychiat. 100:85–89, July 1943.

51. Rome, H. P. Military group psychotherapy. Am. J. Psychiat. 101:494–497, January 1945.

52. Grossman, M. A group therapy program in a neuropsychiatric hospital. M. Bull. Vet. Admin. 21:149–170, October 1944.

53. Schwartz, L. A. Group psychotherapy in the war neuroses. Am. J. Psychiat. 101:498–500, January 1945.

54. Paster, S. Group psychotherapy in an army general hospital. Ment. Hyg. 28:529–536, October 1944.

55. Rusk, H. A. The convalescent training program in the Army Air Forces. *In* New York Academy of Medicine, Committee on Public Health Relations, Convalescence and rehabilitation, p. 81–89. New York, the Academy, 1944.

56. Thorndike, A. The reconditioning of patients in Army service force hospitals. *In* New York Academy of Medicine, Committee on Public Health Relations, Convalescence and rehabilitation, p. 51–62. New York, the Academy, 1944.

57. Barton, W. E. Reconditioning of neuropsychiatric patients. Bull. Menninger Clin. 8:138–140, September 1944.

Covalt, D. A. Rehabilitation in the Army Air Forces. New York Med. (No. 2) 1:13–17, January 20, 1945.

Dynes, J. B., F. J. Hamilton, and R. A. Cohen. A program of the rehabilitation of psychiatric war casualties; role of the convalescent hospital. U. S. Nav. M. Bull. 43:628–633, October 1944.

II

EMERGENCY MEASURES FOR AIDING VETERAN-CIVILIAN ADJUSTMENT

The return of servicemen from World War II to civilian life presented difficulties more grave than those encountered by veterans of previous wars in which our nation has participated. The number of men and families involved in readjustment was five times as large as the number at the end of World War I. The period of service was longer, often extending three to five years. Instruments of war have been more highly mechanized and more destructive and the stresses and strains of war on the men who fought were more constant and severe. The number and intensity of problems in readjustment have been correspondingly greater.

It is true that all successful soldiers and sailors had made a long series of adjustments. They had adapted themselves to new groups of men, new job assignments, new commanding officers, and to all kinds of threatening and hazardous situations. Notwithstanding the fact that some of the influences in a military organization brought changes which made civilian adjustments more difficult, the very experience of making one adjustment after another gave many servicemen skills in adaptation which facilitated their transition from military to civilian life. Most men were able to take the difficulties of home-coming in their stride when these came singly, but when they piled up they often proved to be disturbing. The outstanding need of both veterans and civilians was to achieve mutual understanding.

Civilians knew little about how soldiers had lived and fought, had carried out orders until they could scarcely endure another, had seen their friends killed, had feared for their own lives, and had endured stresses and strains which, if known in advance, would have seemed impossible and which in retrospect remained something of a nightmare. Nor did they understand that at times veterans were reticent about their experiences just because they sensed this limitation.

Civilians had also a too ready tendency to generalize as though all soldiers and veterans were alike, forgetting the individual man wearing the uniform or service button. Our Army and Navy were built up of men from all walks of life and of all temperaments and personality patterns.[1] Years of military regimentation and even years of active combat did not erase these differences. Moreover, while most men acquired some new viewpoints and habits, basically they were still the same people when they returned and they still differed from one another about as much as before.

The veterans in turn had little understanding of the wartime experiences of the people at home. Though the civilians' war in the United States was not hazardous and had not involved serious disruption of accustomed ways of life, it had brought changes in people and situations which many men resented when they first returned. During the hazardous months or years of their military experience, they had dreamed about home and had longed to return to exactly the same situation they had left. But in their absence time and the war had brought inevitable changes. Millions of women had carried the double responsibility of a war job and the maintenance of a home; many thousands of families had moved into war industry centers where they lived in trailer camps or other crowded quarters; some men in industrial positions had doubled their hours of work in the face of heavy responsibility and shortage of manpower; many workmen had done overtime without a day's rest for many months; women had been left without male companionship; and younger boys whose older brothers and group leaders were away at war had felt very much stranded. Veterans did not realize that civilians' curiosity, which sometimes was annoying, was not idle curiosity, but the very natural effort to learn more about the way of life of near of kin in the military; and that, unlike the servicemen, who could see clearly the value of their own units in the war, civilians had had to carry on in a very impersonal way without the advantage of a "morale services division" and with only a hope that their efforts would help some other soldier if not their own.

It was hard for men in the armed forces to understand this partial war of the civilians. In military organizations everything is either black or white; there are no grays or color shadings. Everything is 100 per cent or zero. A man is either sick or well, on duty or off duty. Either he gets orders or he gives orders. As the soldier saw it, either you were in the Army and hence in the war, or you were out of the Army and not in the war. It was easy for servicemen to think of the armed forces as waging 100 per cent of the war and of civilians as having nothing to do with it. The truth, of course, was that both groups had been at war in different ways. The veterans did not realize that most civilians had also made efforts and met with frustrations although of a very different kind.

Notwithstanding the fact that most men while in the service eagerly looked forward to the time they would return home, many of them experienced definite loss of esteem when discharged from the Army. This was especially true of young men who had held minor positions in civilian life but had achieved positions of leadership and responsibility in the armed forces. It was also true of the large numbers who went directly from school and had not become established in vocation or profession.

Every veteran faced the problem of getting on his own, managing his time schedule, and meeting practical details of everyday life. Responsibility had been carried for him so long in the armed forces that it took some time to resume his pre-war habits of making decisions and taking independent action. Similarly, men who had been officers with heavy responsibilities had to avoid the constant temptation to command or direct others.

During their period of separation, veterans and civilians had idealized one another and forgotten the little irritations and annoyances which they experienced when together. This idealization had bolstered the morale of both groups, but now that they were faced with reality, disappointment made cooperation difficult. Both veterans and the people at home had to correct the idealized pictures they had held of each other and catch up with the real changes in each other. Many a man returned to find that his mother appeared older and his girl friend was more independent, his kid sister with whom he used to romp was engaged to be married, and the mechanic's helper at the plant had become a foreman. On the other hand, to the people at home many of the veterans seemed to have changed—to have matured beyond their years, to be more serious, less talkative, more or less decisive, more shy or more aggressive.

Many men showed tension and restlessness soon after their return. This reaction had its natural and adequate causes but was often a source of anxiety to the people at home. In part it was a response to the radical difference between their life in the armed forces and that at home. Just the change in tempo from alternating periods of long waiting and intense action to the even and moderate pace of civilian life was a major adjustment. Memories of lost friends, feelings of guilt that perhaps they had not done everything for their friends' protection, and the loss of companionship with the rest of the men in the outfit tended to make them restless. In many instances further tension came from the need to continue an active life and the difficulty of settling down to sedentary work. The discovery of more radical changes at home than had been anticipated, the failure to find well-paid and satisfying jobs, and the tactless questions or comments of some unthinking civilians were other sources of annoyance.

One of the most common ways in which veterans resolved their tension and irritations was by keeping busy and working at jobs or hobbies that gave them pleasure. Free expression of bitterness or hostility, of fears and worries to some understanding person, proved helpful. But not all veterans understood the need for this or were fortunate enough to have the opportunity to talk it out with some-one whom they trusted. Civilians in turn were often unaware of the help they could give by lending an ear and being considerate. Many a veteran felt as one reported by Carl Rogers: "I think if, when I get out, the world treats me soft, I will be soft. If it treats me hard, I'll be hard and bitter. That may not be the right attitude, but it's the way I feel."[2]

To find adequate goals and shareable interests which would re-place those given up at the time of discharge constituted probably the biggest task of most veterans. Just as the sudden loss of a goal was responsible for much of the "strange feeling" and temporary loss of morale reported by many men during their early days after discharge, so the discovery or creation of clear-cut purposes and reasonable success in achieving them were major factors in re-storing their morale.

Men who before their induction were well established in family life and in a vocation had a decided advantage over those who were unmarried and had had little or no opportunity to be gainfully em-ployed. The former could pick up where they had left off, could get busy promptly, and quickly build their bridges again. The problem was much more acute for the young men who had merely marked time educationally before going into the armed forces and who had not had civilian work experience or arrived at any decision as to what they wished to do. Rogers reports that of a group of aerial gunners who had completed their required number of missions, slightly over 50 per cent had no clear idea of what they wished to do after discharge.[2] In various veterans' information centers from 30 to 50 per cent of the men sought information about jobs or about training which would fit them for jobs. While some of them had clear-cut goals in mind, large numbers sought assistance in arriving at a decision. They needed some time also to explore recreational opportunities and decide upon those which they preferred. In fact, a large part of the task of learning to live together has consisted in finding common purposes which veterans and civilians can share. As Major General Chisholm of the Canadian Army has put it:

The problem of the readjustment of the soldier as a civilian is one which affects all the citizens of any country. It is of the greatest importance that the returned soldier should be assimilated into the social structure and that he should be accepted by civilians, but no more important than that the civilians should prove acceptable to the soldier, and that they should prove capable of fulfilling the criteria by which he judges who are his friends and who his enemies.[3]

Public Education

To facilitate the readjustment of veterans to civilian life a widespread campaign of education was organized. Information was directed to various groups, to the general public, to families, to employers, and later to the veterans themselves, using all available media, namely, addresses, discussion, pamphlets, radio talks, articles in the daily press and in magazines and books. The main problem was to bridge the years when the servicemen who had been away and the people who had remained at home could not possibly keep up with or enter fully into one another's experience. Veterans and civilians alike had to get reacquainted and face the realities of such changes as had come about. In the majority of instances where both soldiers and civilians expected to find some changes and allowed themselves time to get reacquainted, satisfactory relations were soon established.

Most educational efforts directed to the general public were designed to help people understand the psychological factors in the adjustments which both veterans and civilians had to make. Some adjustments had to be made primarily by veterans, others by civilians, but mutually satisfying relationships could be achieved only when there was understanding on both sides. For instance, civilians who were aware that veterans were going through a period of relearning were careful not to rob veterans of the opportunities for this. They avoided throwing too many responsibilities on the veterans and were not critical if for a little while the latter sought help in arriving at decisions. Again, it was only as civilians understood the significance of the veterans' search for worth-while goals and interests that they were willing to give the men the time and freedom to work things out.

EDUCATION OF FAMILIES

Problems of veteran-civilian adjustment, like most problems which touch the lives of large numbers of people, were first and most keenly felt in family life.

Families are the great improvisors. They act as the air-brakes and axle-springs, taking the first unrecognized jars and shocks of change. Families took the frontal assault of unemployment. They had to learn how to survive when suddenly deprived of money, goods, status, dignity. Countless thousands of families had to undergo this paralyzing contraction of living before the community or nation in measurable degree learned the nature of corrective for the economic disease which swept the world like an epidemic.

Families have had to search for ways and means of retaining their psychological cohesiveness despite the distortions of living brought about by world-wide combat and round-the-clock production. As our military personnel is demobilized, families again receive back into their living stream the full impact of personalities who have been disoriented and hurt by warfare. The frustrations and aggressions that have been engendered by war find their first release into family groups.[4]

In December 1944, the National Committee for Mental Hygiene published a pamphlet which sold 80,000 copies[5] and received a substantial amount of editorial and news comment. In simple terms it oriented the readers to the realities of military training and experience and their various effects on different men. It discussed the home situations which require some special consideration as men return, such as (1) the need for parents to treat returning sons as mature and independent persons; (2) the need for young wives to be attentive to their recently returned husbands and at the same time allow them freedom to see their friends; and the need for both wives and husbands to allow themselves plenty of time to get to know each other well and to work out their marital adjustments, which even in normal times require about two years; (3) the need for those who were wives and mothers to restore their husbands gradually but certainly to positions of importance within the family so that they could participate fully in the give-and-take of family life. It suggested a set of constructive attitudes for dealing with both the average veterans who returned without disability and those who had been wounded or were nervous when they returned, such as giving them a genuine welcome, accepting them as they were and creating an atmosphere of expectancy, showing interest and listening well without prying into their personal experiences, allowing plenty of time to catch up with each other's experiences, and learning or relearning ways of getting along together.

In 1944, the Division of Rehabilitation of the National Committee for Mental Hygiene was flooded with appeals from magazine writers, playwrights, radio script writers, and feature column writers seeking reliable and current information about the adjustments and problems of men in the armed forces and those returning to civilian communities. A little later a large volume of informational articles regarding veterans appeared. Most of this material was factually and psychologically sound although there were some glaring exceptions. Whether such public education was overdone is a debatable point. Many men in the service felt it had been overdone and this caused some resentment among them. More resentment, however, was caused by evidence of the public ignorance which they soon discovered upon return. A few civilians wrote articles in which they decried the emphasis on mental hygiene in much of the literature regarding the returning veterans, claiming that this caused more anxiety than it allayed. There is no evidence that this was true of well-written material prepared by mental hygienists or by other well-oriented writers. Even the few lay authors who were critical of the mental hygiene emphasis invariably ended their articles by offering similar advice. In 1945, two books written by psychiatrists and dealing with the family problems and emotional aspects of veterans' adjustments were published.[6, 7]

EMPLOYERS AND LABOR LEADERS LEARN ABOUT VETERANS

It was recognized that full employment was essential if veterans were to make satisfactory adjustments in the post-war period. If large numbers of them were allowed to be unemployed there would be not only bitterness and resentment but loss of faith in the very democracy for which they had fought, a cleavage between veterans and non-veterans, and a lowering and possibly a disintegration of national morale.

Both because of a genuine desire to be helpful to men who had served our country and because of labor shortages, most employers were actively interested in giving employment to veterans. Many firms went well beyond the requirements of the Selective Service Law, extending the time which the law permitted veterans to take before resuming their former occupations, permitting them to shift jobs frequently during the early months of reemployment, and granting vacations with pay soon after reemployment. Employers also tried to up-grade as many veterans as possible. Most large industrial and commercial firms established clear-cut policies and many employed special coordinators to handle problems of reemployment, training, assignment, and follow-up.

Labor unions likewise took an active interest in their members as they came back from the armed forces. Several of the larger unions published pamphlets giving veterans a wealth of information useful to them. Most unions maintained the dues of members while they were in the armed forces and worked to maintain fully the seniority rights of servicemen and to get seniority credit for men who had not been employed before the war. The National CIO War Relief Committee and the Labor League for Human Rights took an active part in many communities in promoting the establishment of veterans' information and referral centers.

The chief deficiency in most of the plans of both employers and labor unions was the almost complete lack of information that would give managers and supervisory personnel fuller understanding of the viewpoints and needs of veterans as they returned to work. Employers, personnel men, and union counselors alike needed to become familiar with the prevalent attitudes and the specific job wishes and fears of veterans.

Many young men who had had only a short period of employment before they went into the armed forces were much concerned lest employers think of them only as they had known them and would not take into account the fact that they had matured, had acquired new skills, and in many instances had assumed heavy responsibilities and acquired leadership ability. Most veterans had a strong need to make up for lost time and therefore were interested in positions which offered both a fair measure of security and opportunities for advancement. Accustomed to group morale in their military units, they wanted to find good working morale among fellow workers. Having experienced the government's provident care while they were in the armed forces, they looked for evidence that the employer was interested in their job satisfactions and personal welfare as well as in production and profits.

To meet the need for such information, and for other material of special value in placing and supervising men who returned with physical injuries or psychiatric handicaps, the present authors prepared a short book dealing with all phases of the subject.[8] A pamphlet on the employment of nervous veterans was widely distributed by one of the insurance companies.[9] Methods and objectives of counseling were discussed in a volume published early in 1946.[10]

VETERANS GET PREVIEWS OF THE RETURN TO CIVILIAN LIFE

To aid servicemen on their return to civilian life, the Army and Navy made efforts at their separation centers to acquaint men about to be discharged with the problems they would face upon return to their home communities, but eagerness to get home quickly militated against effective instruction and counseling at these centers. Late in 1945, the Army prepared a series of pamphlets designed to help men with disabilities get off on the right foot upon returning to their homes. "What's the Score in a Case Like Mine?" prepared by the Neuropsychiatry Consultants Division of the Surgeon General's Office and given to all men discharged for psychiatric reasons, doubtless helped many of them make a good start. "The Psychology of the Returning Serviceman," prepared with the advice of the National Research Council, and a number of simpler pamphlets served to give veterans a look at what was ahead for them and doubtless helped many to get a right approach to the situations they were bound to meet in returning to their families, jobs, and communities. A number of books for veterans authored by veterans appeared later.[11, 12]

Information Centers

It was soon apparent that men returning from the armed forces to the community wanted and needed various kinds of information regarding housing, employment, insurance, processing of disability claims, medical care, and assistance with personal or family problems. Many veterans had had no previous experience in seeking such information, and most communities had not educated their people sufficiently well to enable them to know without assistance where to go for what.

It was found to be very important to keep the focus on services needed and carefully to avoid promoting any organization at the veteran's psychological expense. In communities where men returned from the armed forces and found local organizations wrangling and fighting over services to veterans, they rightly felt that they were being exploited and properly resented this. On the other hand, where the whole community was well organized in ways that were genuinely helpful, their morale was strengthened and they felt they had not fought in vain.

The administrative pattern of information centers varied considerably in different communities. But without exception the most successful centers were characterized by inclusiveness of organization and by the employment of skilled interviewers.

In the summer of 1945, the National Committee on Services to Veterans collected information from the approximate 300 information centers that had then been set up and made a more detailed study of the centers in 45 representative towns and cities.[18] In this study the requirements for an effective program as established by local experience were summarized as follows:

1. There should be a representative, coordinating, and planning committee actively concerned with strengthening existing services and establishing those not available but needed to serve veterans' needs.
2. Community planning must recognize that veterans have varied needs.
3. To those veterans who are disabled or have vocational, medical, or personal problems, quality of basic services is most important in getting back to happy civilian life.
4. If a veterans' information center is established, it should have:
   a. Sponsorship by a community-wide group including representation from all organizations and interests concerned with veterans.
   b. A program whose purpose is primarily to give information and to refer clients to existing agencies with which the center is effectively related.
   c. Staff qualified in the fields of individualized service to people and of community relationships, with knowledge of local agencies and organizations.
   d. Accessible and convenient location, attractive offices, adequate space for comfortable waiting room, and private interviewing rooms.

Educational and Vocational Guidance

The need among veterans for guidance in the choice of job or the type of educational preparation for a job after leaving the armed services was soon obvious. Many veterans wanted to do work different from what they had been doing before the war, particularly work calling for a higher level of skill. In some cases their ambitions outran their capacities and help was needed to spare them the disappointment of failure. Others found it difficult to choose from the many opportunities open for further education in vocational and professional lines the one which would best meet their individual needs. And, of course, educational and vocational guidance was especially needed by veterans who had sustained injuries or other handicaps that made impossible the resumption of pre-war employment or educational plans.

GUIDANCE IN COLLEGES AND UNIVERSITIES

To meet these many needs at the college and university level veterans' guidance centers have been established in approximately 200 educational institutions throughout the country. To these centers disabled veterans who are entitled to free vocational rehabilitation under Public Law 16 are sent by the Veterans Administration for consultation and assistance in selecting appropriate courses. Teachers, vocational experts, psychologists, and doctors interview the veterans and give them tests to determine the type of activity they should undertake in the hope of achieving complete or maximum rehabilitation. Such counseling regarding educational objectives is required by Public Law 16 to prevent the waste of public funds on impractical educational programs. Veterans who undertake educational courses under the "G.I. Bill of Rights" are not required to accept guidance or direction in choosing their courses, but the services of the counselors in guidance centers are available to them if application is made through the regional office of the Veterans Administration.

Of the 65 educational institutions replying to the authors' inquiry, almost all reported special facilities for educational and vocational guidance. This was also true of most of the institutions not included in the group that has set up guidance centers in cooperation with the Veterans Administration. In virtually all instances the institution's maximum facilities for testing and counseling are made available to the student veterans. In two thirds of these institutions, psychiatric consultation and treatment are provided for those who need it, either through the university health service or by special arrangement with private psychiatrists or psychiatrists employed in local hospitals or clinics, the Veterans Administration hospitals, or the state hospital service.

GUIDANCE IN LOCAL COMMUNITIES

If educational and vocational counseling is to be effective, it must be available not only at educational institutions but in local communities as well, for it is there that the greatest need exists and there that it is most difficult to meet it. This need has already been proven conclusively in the work of veterans' information and service centers. In New York City, of the 40,000 veterans who sought information and counsel during the first year of the center's operation, 45 per cent wanted information or assistance in reference to employment, training, or educational or vocational guidance. The Bridgeport (Connecticut) Community Center reported that half of the veterans returning to the community sought some kind of information or guidance at the center; half of these, in turn, inquired about educational possibilities; 46 per cent showed a serious interest in it, although 14 per cent finally decided that they wanted no further training of any kind. Guidance has been sought by men of excellent social status and in good physical and mental health as well as by those who have had less opportunity and those who have health problems.

Other men have no clearly defined objectives and need help in choosing goals which they can achieve. In some instances they lack the necessary ability to pursue successfully more advanced education. As Tyrus Hillway has pointed out:

The fact that the G.I. Bill has been so widely publicized makes a lot of men feel they want to go ahead with their education. Sometimes it distorts their thinking as to what they should really do about it. For example, a man who was a woodworker before the war had heard that the G.I. Bill would guarantee him further education, so he asked to be sent to the best school of forestry. He had no qualifications for admission, and the tests we made indicate no academic aptitude. It was necessary for his good to redirect his thinking to something he could do successfully. We secured him a position with the State Department of Forestry, which has promised him as much training as he can take.[14]

In New York City in a two-year project sponsored by the National Committee for Mental Hygiene and directed by Emily Burr, vocational or educational counseling service was given to 1,200 4-F's and 1,600 veterans. Among these veterans a considerable tendency to overreach was observed. In many instances this occurred in men who had held very routine jobs before the war, who had achieved improved status as non-commissioned officers in the armed forces, and who felt a need to get into some kind of work which would give them a status superior to that of their former civilian jobs. Some had reasonable goals in this direction but the goals of others were out of line. There was some tendency also to seek jobs which carry with them a certain amount of glamour or public attention, such as radio announcing and selling radio time. Photography was a popular choice, perhaps because the armed forces made much use of photography or because there is increasing need for it in newspapers, magazines, and certain kinds of industrial work. For every man who overreached unrealistically in his vocational goals, there were several, in the experience of this guidance service, who were simply in a quandary both as to abilities and goals. They became test conscious while in the service, but too often had not learned the results of the tests that they took. About two thirds of the veterans in this group sought or needed vocational guidance, and the other one third educational guidance. The study shows that the army training did not fully equip many of these men for civilian jobs and that there is a great need for apprentice training, which in many instances would not involve a very long period of time.

Various efforts have been made to provide more educational and vocational counseling in local communities. The YMCA for many years has done some work in this field and is extending its services considerably. A survey made in 1945 indicates that seven associations were carrying on a quite complete guidance and placement service, and that in twenty-five other associations average counseling services were available. Of the most complete services two were in New York City and one each in Cleveland, Ohio; Columbus, Ohio; Boston, Massachusetts; Hartford, Connecticut; and Saginaw, Michigan.[15]

In sixteen cities there are Jewish vocational agencies which give testing, counseling, and placement service to veterans. Advice regarding small business enterprises is available in some of these centers, and in some instances there are sheltered workshops for handicapped men.[16]

The gradually increasing number of special rehabilitation clinics that were set up primarily to give psychiatric service to men discharged for neuropsychiatric reasons and the regular clinics serving veterans quite consistently provide educational and vocational guidance as an integral part of their service. There are about 350 such clinics, limited chiefly to large cities.*

Again in some larger centers of population a fair measure of counseling service is available through public, secondary, and vocational schools. Now that the schools are equipped to give special attention to the guidance of veterans who are resuming education, the need for counseling can be fairly well met in some cities, but most of the 10,000 communities which have less than 10,000

* These are listed in "A Directory of Psychiatric Clinics and Related Facilities." National Committee for Mental Hygiene.

population have little or no service. Some effort is being made through the United States Office of Education and the vocational information and guidance office of the state departments of education to promote counseling in small communities, both for veterans and other adults.[17]

Another major effort is being made in several hundred communities which have established veterans' information centers. Where pronounced need for guidance has been found and adequate facilities are lacking, a carefully selected committee has been formed to test and give vocational guidance to veterans who are uncertain about their educational or vocational goals. The committee is composed of professionally trained and experienced people who, in most instances, serve on a volunteer basis. Unfortunately, professionally qualified personnel in sufficient numbers are available only in communities having educational institutions or industries which employ professionally trained counselors.

Rehabilitation Clinics

Long before the end of the war it became clear that community facilities for treating the psychiatric disabilities of veterans would have to be greatly extended, since this group comprised 37 per cent of all medical disabilities, but because of the lack of personnel it was impossible to establish additional permanent clinics. Many communities found it practical to draw together psychiatrists, psychiatric social workers, psychologists, neurologists, and occupational therapists from wherever they could be found and team them up as special staffs for rehabilitation work.

In order to study and evaluate the various processes involved in providing treatment for veterans with psychiatric disabilities, the New York Hospital Rehabilitation Clinic was set up under the direction of one of the authors in August, 1943. Few other clinics were in operation at that time. The Boston Psychiatric Clinic was already treating rejectees and dischargees by abbreviated psychoanalytic techniques.[18] In New York the Red Cross had established an evening psychiatric clinic. It was quickly evident that more facilities had to be made ready and that impetus had to be given for the development of many such clinics throughout the country.

The first few months' experience of the New York Hospital Rehabilitation Clinic was evaluated and summarized in a pamphlet which served as a guide for those who were planning services in other communities.[19]

VARIATIONS IN CLINICAL WORK AND PRACTICE

Programs of psychiatric rehabilitation varied in the different states and communities. The pattern of the New York Hospital Rehabilitation Clinic, modified to fit particular situations, was used in a number of cities and proved simple and effective in actual operation.

Other methods of making service available to veterans were evolved. An over-all plan for the utilization of all available psychiatrists was developed in Michigan and in Wisconsin. The Duke University Clinic organized a traveling unit to cover the entire state of North Carolina, and it offered some service in South Carolina and Georgia. In Westchester County, New York, nine psychiatrists as a group volunteered their help to social agencies and selective service boards. In New York City, a panel of the members of the New York Psychoanalytic Institute gave free consultation through the Veterans Service Center to veterans who had non-service-connected disabilities. Throughout the country, also, many of the established outpatient departments, community mental hygiene clinics, and clinics associated with state hospitals or with social agencies accepted limited numbers of veterans for treatment.[20]

In an attempt to discover what operational experiences other clinics had been having, the authors, through the Division on Rehabilitation of the National Committee for Mental Hygiene, sent out in the summer of 1945 a questionnaire to which thirty-nine clinics replied. From their replies it was evident that their experience had varied widely. Two of the clinics had an inpatient service only. Twelve had both inpatient service and outpatient service; the majority (twenty-five) were running only an outpatient service. In twenty-eight clinics other medical services were available. Some of the clinics (eighteen) offered entirely free service. An additional sixteen had an arrangement for both free and paid patients. Only three of the clinics functioned on a full-time paid basis with fees ranging from 50 cents to $10 a visit.

The majority of the clinics operated with volunteer staffs. Twenty-four in all had a volunteer professional staff including volunteer clerical help. Fifteen paid all their staff members for their services. The number of psychiatrists in attendance ranged from one to twenty. There was only one clinic which functioned without a psychiatrist, the entire work of the clinic being carried out by a social worker. Three clinics operated without psychiatric social workers. Four clinics operated without clinical psychologists.

The majority of the clinics (twenty-three) accepted every patient who applied. Eleven clinics functioned on a selective basis, each patient being accepted after an interview with the social worker. Among these eleven clinics there was a definite tendency to pick those patients who promised success with short-term therapy. A few clinics referred all service-connected disabilities to Veterans Administration facilities.

Only eleven of the clinics reported problems with broken appointments. The majority (twenty-four) stated that they had no appointment problem. Referral agencies reported in the order of their frequency were community social agencies, American Red Cross, selective service, veterans' information service centers, the Veterans Administration, the armed forces, and the United States Employment Service.

A considerable number of the clinics opened their services to members of the families of men who had had military service. In seventeen clinics 220 patients of the 1,290 registered were wives and other relatives whose difficulties had been induced by induction into the military service of male members of the family. In 30 per cent of all the veterans treated, it proved necessary to counsel with members of the family during the process of the patient's treatment. In the New York Hospital Rehabilitation Clinic, the number of combat cases markedly increased during the last six months of the war. Twenty-six other clinics reported the ratio of combat to non-combat cases as 2 to 5, that is, for every two men who developed their disabilities in combat, five developed their illness during training. Out of 941 cases reported as under treatment, 436 gave a previous history of psychiatric difficulties. Relatively few men seeking treatment belonged in the rejectee group—100 in all.

The type and length of treatment offered varied widely. In the main the trend was toward brief methods of therapy. Therapeutic interviews were usually thirty to forty minutes in length. The number of treatment sessions ranged from 2 to 20, the average number being 6 to 9 (nineteen clinics reporting). Only one clinic used straight psychoanalytic methods and its average number of treatment hours was 25. Only three clinics reported the use of electro-shock treatment in addition to short psychotherapy. All others used short psychotherapy only. Three of the clinics reported the use of narcoanalysis and hypnoanalysis.

Many of these clinics reported special unsolved problems. The outstanding need was for personnel. Inadequate community preparation and organization were stressed and there seemed to be a real problem in getting veterans to seek the needed help. On the other hand, too many veterans were referred to clinics before they had had a chance to adjust to civilian life. Many of the patients needed better preparation and information at the separation centers and some psychotic individuals clearly were too sick to have been returned to their communities. Other problems mentioned were the education of personnel in referring centers, the procurement of sufficient funds, ways of making the rehabilitation clinic permanent, the need to educate the community as to the necessity for treatment of the psychiatrically disabled, and prompter obtainment of the medical records of veterans.

THE TREND TOWARD ALL-PURPOSE CLINICS

In 1945 and 1946 the authors received an increasing number of inquiries from local communities about methods of establishing community mental hygiene clinics which would serve not only returning veterans and their families but also displaced war workers and others, children, youths, and adults who required mental hygiene and guidance services. The policy of the Veterans Administration to contract with community clinics for the study and treatment of veterans further promoted the use of the same clinics for treating veterans and civilians. The problems of veterans revolved increasingly about their new civilian adjustments. Most communities no longer plan facilities for temporary services to veterans but are establishing permanent installations to give service to all groups in the community who have problems in mental health. This trend toward an integrated service for all groups is a healthy one.

Psychiatric Services of the Veterans Administration

The Veterans Administration is specifically charged with full responsibility for the treatment of all veterans with service-connected disabilities and for the hospital care of veterans with non-service-connected disabilities in so far as facilities are available. With the number of veterans increasing rapidly from its pre-war number of 4,000,000 to approximately 18,000,000 at the end of 1946, the VA has greatly extended its services for hospital and medical care. The greatest extension has been in psychiatric service. As of June, 1946, there were 448,235 World War II veterans on disability compensation rolls because of neuropsychiatric diseases, or 29.5 per cent of the 1,519,013 veterans on the rolls. The proportion of World War II veterans on the pension rolls for neuro-psychiatric causes was more than five times as large as the proportion of World War I veterans on the pension rolls in 1922 for the same causes.

The group in greatest need of psychiatric service has been the ambulatory veterans who no longer require hospitalization. Theoretically, outpatient service has been available for those with service-connected disabilities, but the fact that many VA hospitals have been located at considerable distances from large centers of population has militated against the use of such clinics by many veterans who would be legally eligible for follow-up treatment. Early in World War II some psychiatric consultation for such patients was provided in all the VA hospitals. This provision, however, proved totally inadequate.

Only about 10 per cent of all the men discharged from the armed forces because of psychiatric illnesses required hospitalization. The large majority of veterans suffering from neuropsychiatric disorders fell into the psychoneurotic rather than the psychotic group (64 per cent of neuropsychiatric cases were classified as functional). For that reason primary emphasis had to be placed on psychiatric outpatient treatment and social service in their home communities. To meet some of this tremendous need, early in 1945 the VA established the policy of purchasing service from private psychiatrists and from public or private mental hygiene clinics. The results were somewhat disappointing in that much less service was obtainable than had been hoped for. Some clinics were unwilling to make contracts for such work because of the complications with regard to treatment which they feared would arise, particularly from unadjudicated claims and the likelihood of change in pension status during the course of treatment. This reluctance is rapidly disappearing. It is an almost unanimous conviction in medical circles that pensions and medicine do not mix and that the staff which passes on pension claims should be entirely separate from the staff engaged in therapeutic work. This is outstandingly true in reference to men with neuropsychiatric disabilities. For this reason clinics having staffs too small to divide these functions have hesitated to undertake work with veterans under contract with the VA. Then, too, certain clinics soon found that the volume of work to be done was so great that they could continue to give service only if they greatly reduced or eliminated services to other groups which were regularly demanded by the community.

Soon after the appointment of General Bradley as Administrator of Veterans Affairs, plans were made for extending greatly the VA's outpatient psychiatric services. Psychiatric consultation was made available in all hospitals. Neurosis centers for the treatment of veterans suffering from severe psychoneuroses were authorized for all VA general hospitals and plans were made for establishing mental hygiene clinics at regional and branch offices. By the end of 1946, thirty-six such clinics were operating throughout the country.

A number of training centers have been set up to train more psychiatrists and psychiatric social workers. Centers were first established in Winter General Hospital, Topeka (Kansas), under Dr. Karl A. Menninger; at New York University Medical School under Dr. S. Bernard Wortis; and at the University of California Medical School under Dr. Karl M. Bowman. The VA has set up further training programs in its own hospitals located near medical schools. The deans have helped select key teaching personnel, recruited from universities, who serve part time in organizing and directing resident training programs in VA hospitals. Forty VA hospitals and clinics, with thirty-nine medical schools cooperating, are being used as training centers. Inevitably this will be reflected in better care and treatment of veterans.

REFERENCES

1. Pratt, G. K.   Soldier to civilian; problems of readjustment.   New York, Mc-Graw-Hill, 1944.

2. Rogers, C. R.   Psychological adjustments of discharged service personnel. Psychol. Bull. 41:689–696, December 1944.

3. Chisholm, G. B.   Psychological adjustment of soldiers to army and to civilian life.   Am. J. Psychiat. 101:300–302, November 1944.

4. Woman's Foundation, Inc.   The place of the family in American life, p. 6–7. New York, the Foundation, 1945.

5. Rennie, T. A. C., and L. E. Woodward.   When he comes back and if he comes back nervous.   National Committee for Mental Hygiene, Division on Rehabilitation.   New York, the Committee, 1945.

6. Dumas, A. G., and G. G. Keen.   A psychiatric primer for the veteran's family and friends.   Minneapolis, University of Minnesota Press, 1945.

7. Kupper, H. L.   Back to life; the emotional adjustment of our veterans.   New York, Fisher, 1945.

8. Woodward, L. E., and T. A. C. Rennie.   Jobs and the man.   Springfield, Ill., Thomas, 1945.

9. Brown, Meyer.   The adjustment of the nervous veteran in industry.   New York, Zurich Insurance Companies, 1945.

10. Rogers, C. R., and J. L. Wallen.   Counseling with returned servicemen.   New York, McGraw-Hill, 1946.

11. Bolte, C.   The new veteran.   New York, Reynal & Hitchcock, 1945.

12. Droke, M.   Good-by to G. I.; how to be a successful civilian.   New York, Abingdon-Cokesbury, 1945.

13. National Committee on Service to Veterans.   The home town job; a report on community services for veterans.   New York, National Social Work Council, 1945.

14. Quoted by Meyer, A. E.   Community service; the model center at Bridgeport, Connecticut.   The Washington Post, March 30, 1945.

15. National Council of Y.M.C.A., Committee on Placement and Guidance.   Counseling.   New York, the Association, 1945.

16. Jewish Welfare Board, National Veterans Service Committee.   Veterans' Service Information Bulletin.   New York, the Committee, 1945. (Note: Contains a list of agencies in the 16 cities, and fuller information regarding services available.)

17. Jaeger, H. A., and F. R. Zerna.   Community adult counseling centers.   Occupations 23:263–308, February 1945.

18. Deutsch, F.   Civilian war neuroses and their treatment.   Psychoanalyt. Quart. 13:300–312, July 1944.

19. Rennie, T. A. C.   A plan for the organization of psychiatric rehabilitation clinics.   Ment. Hyg. 27:214–223, April 1944,

20. For a listing of all the available psychiatric resources in America see: Directory of psychiatric clinics in the United States and other resources.   New York, National Committee for Mental Hygiene, 1946.

III

THE PSYCHIATRIC DISABILITIES OF WAR:
DYNAMICS AND MOTIVATION

From the previous chapter it is evident that many servicemen had varying degrees of difficulty in their readjustment to the civilian way of life. It was suggested, with no elaboration, that the psychiatrically disabled veteran had particular problems and complexities created by his psychiatric state. It is necessary, therefore, that we understand in more detail the nature of these psychiatric disabilities.

World War I gave us the term "shell shock," a term unwisely used to cover a variety of psychiatric disorders from the simplest anxiety reaction to full-fledged psychotic states. The term came into use early and was abandoned before the end of the war. It was badly chosen, suggesting as it did that physical shock, the bursting of a shell or some undefined physical trauma, was responsible for the disorder. Not for a long time was it sufficiently recognized that the majority of these disorders were emotional in origin. Once that concept had been clarified, the term "shell shock" became useless and even dangerous, since it created in the mind of the patient an erroneous impression of the nature of the disorder which often intensified and prolonged the disability.

In World War II, by far the largest number of psychiatric disabilities fell into the everyday civilian categories of psychoneurotic disturbances: preeminently anxiety states and depressive states and, to a lesser extent, hysterical reactions, neurasthenic fatigue states, obsessive-compulsive disorders. Approximately 10 per cent of the psychiatric casualties were in the psychotic groups; usually schizophrenic and depressive conditions. A substantial group, however, showed a particular kind of reaction which differed in some essentials from the ordinary peacetime psychoneuroses, a reaction which was much more acute, severe, and disabling and was attributable in part to fatigue, loss of sleep, and poor nourishment, and in part to the emotional reactions to combat stress. The term most commonly used to describe this is "combat fatigue," otherwise variously known as "combat neurosis," "flight fatigue," "operational fatigue," "war weariness," or "task-force fever."

Combat Fatigue

There is considerable disagreement among military writers as to whether or not combat fatigue constitutes a new or unique syndrome. Those who believe it does point to the role of physical exhaustion, malnutrition, and lack of sleep in the etiology and to the essentially normal premorbid personality make-up. Combat fatigue therefore deserves further definition. Under circumstances of combat warfare, men react in a variety of ways, most of which have in common the cardinal features of severe subjective and objective anxiety; a striking change in the personality with evidence of becoming morose, silent and sullen, irritable, or alcoholic; a startle reaction to stress or hypersensitiveness to sound; proneness to catastrophic nightmares; and a clinical picture which fluctuates and may have concurrently manifestations of anxiety, depression, guilt, hysteria, obsessive preoccupations, resentment, hostility, or severe regressive phenomena. Symptoms and clinical manifestations overlap and it is only late in the course of the disorder that a consistent picture emerges. There may be a greater or less degree of unconscious elaboration of the difficulties so that there is often a secondary gain from the illness, as, for instance, a striking lack of guilt (except for depression cases) over the termination of military duty. Most of these patients no longer regard the military organization as the parental figure to which they are bound by a sense of moral obligation. In this respect the man is like a child who has not developed to the stage of accepting his parents as authoritative-conscious figures. He begins to conceive of the military situation as a bad one from which he can expect no love or consideration. Instead, he identifies himself with the protective family at home to which he desires to escape. Most of these men seem badly demoralized and some show a decided lack of motivation. While the condition characteristically appears to come on suddenly, it has been reported that as high as 90 per cent of these men function for considerable periods with some degree of incipient neurosis. Intensive scrutiny reveals that the onset has been gradual but the climax reached in an acute traumatic experience, such as the death of a friend, the sinking of a ship, or the news of family problems. The anxiety picture is greatly colored by the anxiety of the actual battle situation. The common clinical findings are the severe depressive reactions, outstanding fatigue reactions (marked exhaustion states often leading to confusion, bewilderment, disorientation, and accompanied by loss of weight, vomiting, and diarrhea), pseudo-psychotic or actual psychotic reactions (schizophrenic-like in their regressive phenomena), and overwhelming psychosomatic responses (including transient stuttering).

The Army Air Corps divides what it calls "flight fatigue" cases into several different categories although recognizing that the descriptions of the symptoms are never clear-cut and often overlap. They view the reaction as taking six major forms: (1) marked anxiety reaction with psychosomatic and phobic complaints; (2) depressive and apathetic reactions with marked guilt feelings; (3) passive dependent reactions whereby the men show a craving to be cared for; (4) irritable, aggressive reactions; (5) psychosomatic reactions; and (6) psychotic-like reactions of schizophrenic-like states, occasionally with delirium, commonly with residuals of fixed inflexible attitudes, flattened affect, paranoid feelings, and lack of insight.

Thus it is seen that there is no uniformity in the clinical picture. The most striking feature of the reaction is its frequent, although not invariable, prompt and dramatic response to therapy. Many times the dynamics are close to the surface and are easily obtained. The clinical picture is modified by many circumstances: the nature of the combat experience, the degree of loss of morale and motivation, the quality of leadership present. Sometimes the reactions develop while men are on leave and at a time when they are presented with new frustrations and new factors in their external environments with which they cannot deal. On a basis of experience there is real reason to believe that these states may be reactivated later in civilian life.

A fairly typical case history will better help to define the combat fatigue reaction.

CASE 1. *Acute anxiety reaction. Precipitating factors: combat experience; violent shelling and anguished cries of buddies.*

The patient is a 26-year-old, stocky, east-side New York man, referred to the New York Hospital Rehabilitation Clinic by the Veterans Service Center because of extreme irritability, temper outbursts, poor concentration, "black-out" spells occurring two or three times a week in which he forgets where he is, and inability to get started at work. He considers his illness a sign of weakness.

He was inducted into the Army October 6, 1941, and was sent overseas, serving in the European, African, and mid-eastern theaters, taking part in campaigns in Tunisia, Sicily, and southern France where he was cited for bravery.

Prior to his induction he drove a heavy truck for a motor express company. He had had no previous neurotic difficulties. He had four brothers in overseas service. The patient was always closer to his mother, and got on poorly with his father who punished him for failures in school. He did badly in school, failing to finish high school. He grew up with a sense of inferiority at his lack of education. He never felt he could bring friends to his own home.

He is married and his wife has been working to support him since his discharge from the Army in 1945.

At his first examination he appeared tense, rigid, his eyes bulging, as he said: "I have days and hours when I feel really wonderful until someone crowds me, pushes against me, or even just touches me, especially in subways or buses. Then I go into a rage and want to strangle the person. I can't work (and they tell me I should 'work or fight'). I can't sit in the movies. I can't sleep. If I sleep an hour I have horrible dreams and wake up—always the same dream, that I'm in a foxhole way out beyond the front lines and around us are our armored cars. They've all been knocked out but one, and that one has blown up and is burning. The men in it can't get out and they're screaming for me to help them to get out. I'm shooting my gun as hard as I can and I can't come to them, can't do anything but shoot."

It seems that something very like this happened on the patient's last day on duty. He had been in advance reconnaissance units—the expendibles who were sent out to draw the enemy fire so the strength and location of the enemy forces could be seen. He loved his friends in these units and felt protective of them. He identified with them as again and again 90 per cent of the unit were wiped out. The patient asks:

"Why was I left? Why wasn't I killed too? The best boys were killed. For officers we always had wise guys—green and fresh. If we ever got good officers they were promoted and taken away from us as soon as they learned anything. Maybe they did care whether we were killed or not but they didn't know enough, and sent us where they shouldn't have. Some of us knew better. They were all alike. Sometimes they'd take our advice but not much of it.

"That's what happened that last day. I had a rough day all that morning. We pushed too far ahead for an infantry division, ahead of our artillery support. We didn't have any support, any defense. I was sent out ahead to look around. I told my officer I thought we should draw back. It looked too good a defensive position for the enemy and no chance of cover for our men. I said draw back, so he did three miles. Just as we did, they let loose on us with artillery. It was three hours before we could get word back to our artillery barrage. During that period, I had to drive a reconnaissance car back under fire to get some messages to Division Headquarters. When I got back the officer said we should advance again and look around. We were still ten miles ahead of the rest of the Division, so I didn't know what his hurry was. He shouldn't have gone ahead again. We walked right into their fire. There were fourteen armored cars, all with my friends in them, and I was in a jeep. The armored cars are built wrong, not thinking of men that have to be in them, only one door. If the car is hit, the door jams and there's no way out. The men just burn in there. But the ones that build the cars don't care about that. . . . It took ten days after that before they could take the sector. The Germans were so strong there. Our cars were all hit, all destroyed. Finally there was just one left, near my jeep. Then it was hit directly and began to burn. The ones in it screamed for me to come and try to get the door open. I didn't dare try. The artillery had the range of that car. I'd just have been killed if I'd tried, so I couldn't do anything with my buddies dying and thinking I could help them. Then three shells came at me, closer and closer, and the last one I didn't hear because it knocked me out. I came to in a hospital in England as a mental case. That was a terrible place. They gave me stuff to make me sleep and the boys told me I'd get up and try to kill the nurse. So I wouldn't take that any more. They tried everything else on me. They gave me stuff in my veins but I never went to sleep. They'd hit on coal buckets, make a hell of a racket and then say to me, 'Now you're in battle. The enemy is here.' That nearly did make me crazy. They tried five times but it never put me to sleep. Why do they do that—just to see how much you can stand? I never did trust the army medics. They don't know you're sick. I never liked any regimentation. I'm not a printed sheet to be stamped. I'm a guy, and other guys like me—the best ones in the world are out there dying so the lousy bastards can have it safe and cozy way back of the lines. All the guys that were worth anything are dead. Why didn't I die too? I don't understand.

"Now my mind works so much. When anybody says anything I notice every remark and I begin understanding it and figuring it out. I think: 'Why did he say that? Did he mean that or something else? Did he say it for effect? Did someone persuade him to say that? Did it have another meaning? What gave him the idea? Is it going to have any effect on the people here?' My brain seems to work very clear and fast.

"I don't trust anyone or anything now. I can only rely on my wife. I examine and weigh everything. I distrust society. I feel unsafe, like I have to look out for my own safety all the time."

Following emergency therapy in a hospital in England, he was returned to this country to an army hospital where he was given electroshock therapy which he felt did not help him. He recalls this period of hospitalization with dread.

When seen in the Rehabilitation Clinic he was extremely restless. He couldn't stand any moment of inactivity. He got a job but he left in two days because he had too little to do. He suspected the Army of subsidizing the project because almost all the workers there were G.I.'s. His identification was with the dead. "All the best guys are dead; the living should be dead instead—why am I not dead, too?" He showed loss of morale and said the officers endangered men through heartlessness and ignorance (lack of love and lack of skill). He believed all officers were snobbish and said they rarely gave the G.I.'s, who were more competent, credit for having sense. He was having torturing nightmares of his last experience in which the incompetent officer sent the best to death— "these guys were killed horribly because of badly planned equipment"— and the patient himself failed to live up to his high ideal of service, not trying to save them because it seemed certain death for him. His dream was an effort to efface his cowardice, to see that *he was doing something for them*. He had no identification with any living person, except possibly with his wife; only hatred and resentment against the living and outbreaks of rage and murder wishes when people encroached on him in the smallest way.

The patient was seen five times with rapid improvement of his severe anxiety state. During the first interview his attitude was completely hostile until the last ten minutes when he seemed to be able to accept the physician as a friendly individual. He was most concerned as to whether the physician was able to maintain interest in him. He asked advice about whether he was ready to go back to work.

In his second visit he was permitted to express again his rage and anger at all army doctors. He described how he was given pentothal, how he felt it was meant to frighten him and threaten him into submission. He reiterated how much braver the G.I.'s were than the doctors. Again the first part of the interview was marked by aloofness and hostility but he more quickly gained a sense of confidence in the therapist. In his third interview he started off again with a hostile, aloof attitude. Suddenly he remembered a companion and beloved friend in service, a man whom he considered competent, adequate, and able to cope with his superiors. He asked if the therapist would like to meet his friend. As he talked about him, he began to relax and decided he would like to go and see his friend. By now, he was discussing his hostilities much more casually and was able to express a warm friendly feeling toward the therapist.

By his fourth visit his tension was markedly decreased and his eyes were not bulging. His attitude was entirely friendly from the opening of the interview. He had found a satisfactory place to live. He was rarely upset any longer. He had gone to work and was making $50 a week. He was proud of the fact that he only had to walk out of the shop twice a day whereas previously he had to leave the machine every hour. His sleep now was unbroken. His nightmares had almost completely disappeared. He had begun now to have pleasant dreams, particularly about his comrades in service and some of the happy events that occurred there. He was discussing more and more his affection and respect for his friends. He felt that the dead were no longer so important and talked of some of his dead companions as if they were living. "I could go back to the trucking business now. I remember now the happy things that happened. I would like to forget everything of three years of war—no, I want to keep the good things I got from people I learned to love."

The patient seems safely out of the acute crisis and largely over his anxiety reaction. His therapy is by no means complete, although he is well on the way toward constructive redirection of living. There remains the resolution of his guilt feelings by a deeper analysis of his aggressive and competitive feelings and by a relating of his contemporary emotions to earlier life experiences and emotional traumata.

This case illustrates well many of the outstanding features of combat fatigue reactions: (1) a "relatively stable" pre-combat personality without evidence of psychoneurotic difficulties; (2) repeated combat experiences and a final one of great traumatic intensity (bursting of a shell near-by, acting as a precipitating event) and overwhelming fear; (3) physical exhaustion; (4) marked subjective and objective anxiety; (5) rapid response to therapy.

The symptom picture is characterized by: (1) repeated, terrifying nightmares reenacting the battle situation; (2) startle reaction and intolerance to stress; (3) irritability, sullenness, aggression, explosive temper, and distrust of people amounting almost to paranoid interpretation; (4) severe guilt feelings; (5) complete loss of morale in service, feeling that the officers have let him down; (6) resentment toward authority.

CASE 2. *Hysterical reaction. Precipitating factors: combat experience and the explosion of a shell; problem complicated by lack of family understanding.*

This 26-year-old man was discharged from the Army after a year and a half in service. He was referred to the Clinic by a psychiatrist in the army hospital. He encountered no difficulties during training. His illness began after landing operations in Sicily. His unit landed under fire, attacking uphill, digging foxholes against artillery fire and strafing by planes. They moved at night and got virtually no sleep. On the seventh day, under heavy shellfire, he was thrown to the ground. His account to the psychiatrist was as follows: "I felt paralyzed and was scared. Everybody was scared. There are no tough guys when bullets are whizzing. I got to the hospital vomiting. I could not eat; was vomiting all the time. They fed me through a vein; that scared me, too." This patient had lost about 50 pounds. When seen at the Clinic, vomiting was continuing, he stuttered some, complained of nightmares every night, was depressed, anxious, impatient, and irritable. He complained of frequent headaches, said that he could not stand any discussion about his experiences, that he flared up easily and sometimes wanted to kill somebody.

When he returned home, his mother and father were terribly upset. They were very resentful toward the Army, blaming it entirely for their son's illness. His father, who had developed a cataract, made the patient feel responsible for this, because he had cried so much about the patient's condition. The mother was tense and upset and immediately urged him to go back to work, resuming her habit of nagging him to seek a better position.

This man's father had been a seasonal worker and the family had experienced some hardship during periods of unemployment. The patient had had only one year of high school, and his academic record was not good. Because of his mother's insistence that he should try to better himself, he had managed to get several jobs. His mother was described as cheerful and wanting the best for her children. Three older sisters and a younger brother seem to be getting along well. With economic insecurity and none-too-good success in school, the patient had shown some lack of security before his induction.

The patient was seen several times by the psychiatrist, was given vocational aptitude tests and vocational guidance, and the family was reassured. The patient spent the first two interviews discussing in detail his military experience, his fear and anxiety, his unhappiness during hospitalization, and his resentment of his medical treatment. He described at length and with ill-disguised pride how he had resisted all treatment efforts. In his second interview he discussed the unhappy family situation, the overconcern of his parents, his inability to get himself oriented, his continued vomiting and stuttering. On his third visit he seemed a little better. He was advised that treatment could be speeded up if he entered a civilian psychiatric hospital. He was vehemently opposed to this plan. That night at home he collapsed on the bed, seemed to faint, but arose dramatically relieved of both stuttering and vomiting. On his fourth visit, he showered the physician with praise for his miraculous improvement. He continued to discuss many contemporary emotional problems relating to choice of employment, methods of dealing with his friends and planning his day to avoid the oversolicitousness of his parents. From time to time, he re-expressed the resentment he felt toward the Army. He discussed in greater detail the anxiety surrounding his combat experience, getting obvious relief in his ability to share his experiences. After six treatment sessions, there was no further stuttering, eating improved, and he gained weight. When last seen, a year afterward, he was sleeping well and getting along well with his family. He then expressed more satisfaction with his civil service job, and was making friends.

More Common Psychiatric Disabilities of War and Military Life

While thousands of men in our armed forces suffered from combat fatigue, the largest group of psychiatric disabilities consisted of psychoneurotic, psychosomatic, and psychotic conditions comparable to those seen in civilian life but brought to acute focus by circumstances and experiences of military life. These conditions must be viewed as aggravated but not caused by military experience. Some were brought to the foreground under circumstances of the training period; others during long non-combat assignments in lonely, isolated areas; and still others during actual combat. A brief series of cases will serve to indicate the dynamic situations in which special conflicts arose within many men as a result of military experience.

Case 3. *Anxiety reaction with reactive depression. Precipitating factors: reaction to lonely assignment and resentment of authority.*

This 29-year-old man enlisted in the Army in 1940, and during the two years that he was stationed in the United States he liked the Army very well and was promoted to the rank of staff sergeant. He was later transferred to the Aleutians, where he found the weather hard to bear. His first attack of anxiety and depressed mood came on at the time of the first Japanese attack. He worried much about his reactions and was afraid of going insane. His fears were of open masturbation, of harming somebody, or of losing complete control of himself. After spending fifteen months in the Aleutians, he was transferred back to the United States for assignment to an artillery maintenance unit, but was granted a month's furlough. While on furlough, he had an attack of palpitation and trembling, followed by repeated anxiety attacks and restlessness. He gradually became somewhat depressed and had broken sleep. He reported to the nearest military hospital, where he was a patient for five weeks and was then discharged. He did not come to the civilian clinic until a year later. His symptoms were less marked than before his discharge, but he complained still of dizziness and a persistent difficulty in concentration. He did not return to his work as a retail salesman, which he had formerly enjoyed, because he was sure he could not concentrate well enough. He admits that he was glad to be discharged because he could not stand so much authority. He has been assisting one of his brothers at a gasoline station. At the second meeting with the psychiatrist, he felt more at ease and showed better concentration. He says he is no longer ashamed of his psychiatric discharge. He can face people better and is planning for recreation at a Jewish center.

CASE 4. *Reactivation of old anxiety neurosis. Precipitating factors: the change of climate, idleness, misuse of talents.*

This 40-year-old man, discharged from the Navy with a diagnosis of "situational psychoneurosis," came to the Rehabilitation Clinic complaining bitterly about being "expelled from the service." He was terribly worried about the psychiatric diagnosis and had told no one about it except his immediate family. He was very fearful that his employer or friends would learn about it. He complained of diarrhea, which he had had also while in the service. He slept rather poorly, waking at 5 A.M. feeling tired and in bad spirits.

This man had been commissioned from civilian life and assigned to an administrative branch. While living on a ship, after being assigned to the Southwest Pacific, he found it extremely hot, had no work to do, and tried to keep busy with reading. During the seven or eight months there he suffered from insomnia, loss of appetite, and fatigue. His symptoms grew worse, and he was later removed from his post and hospitalized in the South Pacific for more than a month before being transferred to a naval hospital in the United States, from which he was discharged two months later. He complained about the misuse of his talents and the failure of the Navy to transfer him to the African area, where he could have put to use his knowledge of French and Italian.

This man had had a nervous breakdown when he was 20 years old, while still in college. He then suffered from insomnia, fatigue, worry, and nervous indigestion. He could not finish college, in spite of going home for a rest and returning four times in successive efforts to graduate. He then transferred to a school in another state, and finally graduated. He secured a good job with a business organization and received several promotions.

Following his discharge from the Navy, he tried to get into the Intelligence Service, but was declined, and returned to his former position. He is cheerful but easily discouraged; sociable but much concerned about the impression he makes on others. He has confidence in his intellectual and business ability, but has been terribly fearful that the firm would discover the basis of his discharge from the Navy.

CASE 5. *Severe tension reaction. Precipitating factor: worry about home.*

This rather tall, well-groomed, 24-year-old ex-serviceman came to the Clinic complaining about tension and occasional "cloudiness." He had also some fear that his more severe symptoms which had developed in the Army might return, such as lack of concentration, some depression, and a compulsion to be always on the go.

This man had grown up in an intelligent family which had been in comfortable circumstances until 1938, when there were severe reverses. Family life was always congenial. He had done excellent work in school, having graduated from high school and gone to college for three years, when he quit in order to earn and assist his family financially. He had bitten his nails until the age of eleven, but showed no other signs of tension, except that it was observed in high school that he seemed to have an inner compulsion to master everything he undertook, and was inclined to become somewhat overwrought. He had had a strong educational drive, which is rather characteristic of the Jewish group to which he belongs. Toward the end of the three years of college when he had taken on additional extra-curricular work he became quite jittery and anxious prior to final examinations. There was no recurrence of this until his military experience.

He was interested in going into the Army, and would have enlisted except for his family's need of financial assistance. Soon after his induction, he was ill for some time and felt much ashamed that he had been unable to go through all the usual physical training. When he was assigned to the radio code division, he became somewhat anxious and tense, and more so later, when he had to take code under pressure of speed. He was not really interested in this work and would have preferred radio construction, in which he had had some training. Upon returning from a visit to his home, during which he saw how his father's health was deteriorating, he was considerably depressed. He then consulted the army physician, because he was "so tense and wound up." After consultation in the mental hygiene unit of the training center, he was discharged as not able to adjust to army routine, and the comment was made that worrying about home had contributed to his anxiety state.

At the Rehabilitation Clinic he was somewhat preoccupied, but not especially tense. He discussed his difficulties quite freely. He reviewed his military history and expressed the opinion that he had adjusted well in the Army prior to his assignment to code work and to his worry about his father's health and family finances. He acknowledged that in civilian life he is sometimes tactless in the way he "tells people off," and realized that in the Army he had to suppress this tendency. He has quite a range of outside interests, including radio, photography, reading, swimming, and dancing.

After resting for about three weeks, largely at a beach, he went back to work for the company by which he had been employed before his induction. On the second visit to the Clinic he reported feeling much better, having more energy, and being better able to concentrate. He has been free of definite anxiety episodes, but told of some diffuse tension feelings. He was enthusiastic about the work he was doing and about his plans to pursue evening courses toward a master's degree.

CASE 6. *Hypochondriacal reaction. Precipitating factors: resentment of military experience and military medical treatment.*

This 29-year-old veteran came to the Clinic one year after discharge from the Army with a diagnosis of psychoneurosis. He joked a good deal while talking about his difficulties, but immediately showed marked resentment toward the Army. After graduation from army radio school as a radio operator, he went to transition school for two months and was then assigned to flying duty in the Air Transport Command, in which he engaged in delivering planes to all theaters of operation. He claims he felt well and his work was regarded as satisfactory until June, 1943, when he developed a severe case of dysentery in Morocco. He was then hospitalized, and upon his return to his post in the United States felt very weak. His major blamed him for unsatisfactory work. This humiliated him greatly and he cried. He became bitterly resentful toward the major, who he claims had the reputation of being inconsiderate and who made use of men for his personal benefit. The flight surgeon sent him to a military hospital, where for three weeks he was placed in a locked ward. Later he was transferred to a semi-restricted, and finally to an open, ward. He especially resented being placed in the locked ward, since he feels that he was normal. He expressed confidence in the army psychiatrist, but said at one point that the psychiatrist had accused him of doing the opposite of what he was supposed to do and of trying to get out of the Army.

When this patient came to the Clinic, he complained of severe headaches which he described as a feeling that his head would burst, both front and back. These usually lasted for one or two days, and sometimes for weeks. He complained also of backaches since a spinal tap was made in the army hospital. He reported that this ache was particularly painful when he shook hands with the right hand. Prior to induction, this man was regarded as easy-going, suffered no hurt feelings, was in good health, seemed at ease with people, and was considered a comedian by his friends. At the same time, he was stubborn and persistent.

His parents died when he was young, and he was brought up in an orphanage. He finished grammar school with high marks and was well liked by his teachers. In his last position before induction he supervised orders and helpers. During five years he received salary advances from $25 to $63 a week. He has been married for the past three years and has a child two years old. His wife has a sharp tongue and is very jealous. He has not been able to get along with her for the last two years, and at times shows real hatred of her. He feels she is inconsiderate and cannot understand why he goes to clubs and is active in the Jewish war veterans' organization instead of spending most of his time with her.

After a few treatments he lost his headaches and generally felt well. He still showed resentment of the attitude of some people toward veterans and of black markets, but had no other complaints.

Section VIII Dischargees

Two groups of patients occasioned military and civilian psychiatrists real concern. The first consisted of men who had received a discharge without honor, though they should have had a certificate of disability discharge. It is to be hoped that they will be given an opportunity to appeal their cases and to alter their status, which is so crippling to civilian adjustment. The second group consisted of overt homosexuals for some of whom marriage and a presumably satisfactory heterosexual adjustment had prevailed prior to the military experience. With this group as with the first, the military policy has been inconsistent. Some of them have been given an honorable medical discharge; others a Section VIII blue-paper discharge, based largely on the personal bias of the commanding officer or the examining psychiatrist. It would seem only fair that all these men should be accorded the same discharge status, and that the Army should decide whether it considers the problem a moral one or a medical one.

This blue-paper discharge is not to be confused with the Section VIII white-paper discharge, which is given to persons who have mental limitations that make it undesirable for them to remain in the service. The former is a discharge without honor which is given to certain individuals whose behavior does not measure up to military standards and who, therefore, cannot be retained in service. Sometimes, however, this behavior is predicated upon psychiatric causes and the genuine psychiatric disability is not recognized. This appears to have been true of the following man (Case 7), who received a blue-paper discharge. Had his full psychiatric status been appreciated, it is likely that he would have received an honorable medical discharge (CDD).

CASE 7. *Section VIII Dischargee. Demoralized by military experience.*
Since early adolescence, this 19-year-old boy had had a great urge to fly. He had planned to complete college and then go into aviation. With the war on, he made every effort to enlist in the air corps and passed all physical and mental examinations, but was turned down on the technicality of not having been a citizen of this country for ten years. He had been raised in the Orient until the age of twelve. While there his father died. After his father's death he came with his mother and brother to the United States. His rejection by the air corps was a bitter disappointment to him. He became much depressed, and at that time the family considered obtaining psychiatric treatment. About three

months later, he was drafted. He asked for immediate induction and was accepted. He was advised that if he went into the infantry, he might later get a transfer to the air corps. After long and painful attempts to get transferred, however, it became clear that there was no possibility of this. As soon as he was convinced that transfer would be impossible, he became bitter, depressed, and defiant. He made one secret suicidal attempt by taking medicine, and was so depressed that he offered to sign his life away for experimental purposes. He became antagonistic and uncooperative to the point of ignoring the corporal's orders on one occasion. He was examined by a military psychiatrist, but by that time his attitude was so despairing that he asked for a court martial. The army psychiatrist considered him immature, and when he appeared before the discharge board, he was given a Section VIII blue discharge, on the ground that both the commanding officer and the corporal indicated that they would not want him in their overseas outfit as they felt he could not be trusted with responsibility.

This man had always been subject to mood swings, characteristically being either very happy or depressed. Upon his return from the Army, these moods were more intense than ever. While he had always talked with his mother at great length, he now gave her the fullest details about everything he had been doing without consideration for her. On one occasion, after attending a dance, he kept his mother awake till 3 A.M. talking it over. She felt he should work, but he was so ashamed of his discharge that if the application blank called for reason for discharge, or if the interviewer asked him about it, he gave up in despair.

This boy had been brought up by governesses, but had developed a very close relationship with his mother; so much so that the mother showed constant concern about him. The mother believes that the boy developed a too demanding attitude throughout his childhood, when the family always had an abundance of servants, so that between the governesses and the servants, all his needs and many of his whims were satisfied at his demand.

This boy is intellectually brilliant and always obtained very high grades in school at all levels. He has always been a great reader, but has had few friends. He is devoted to those he has. He has always been easily discouraged when he is not successful. He has been very shy about making friends with girls, and admits that he does not get along with them as well as he would like to.

During a series of treatment interviews with the psychiatrist, he developed a strong transference and obtained considerable relief from his depressed feeling. With some aid from the social worker, he was able to develop new social contacts and he decided to resume his college education at one of the local universities, rather than to return to the school where his younger brother had been establishing a very good record. This brother had always been more or less the opposite of the patient as to personality, being a very friendly, cheerful, outgoing boy. Meanwhile, he managed to get a job. Once back in college, he did excellent work, having an average grade of A, and was one of five to be received into an honor fraternity.

Notwithstanding the fact that he was able to get employment and that he later was doing well in college, he still felt stigmatized by the Section VIII discharge, and requested the Army Review Board to change the discharge to a CDD. The case was officially reviewed, but the boy's appeal was denied. Notwithstanding a fair adjustment at the time of our last contact, he still felt disgraced by the discharge and was considering making efforts to reenlist.

As the war progressed, an increasing number of patients with problems of overt homosexuality presented themselves. Usually, of course, this condition existed before entering the service and was not discovered by Selective Service or the pre-induction examiner. When their condition was known, such individuals were not accepted by the armed services. In some, however, overt homosexuality was a new problem, apparently brought to focus by the all-male environment of military life. Some of the men fought valiantly against the temptation. A few experienced homosexual stirrings for the first time in their lives. A considerable effort was made by the army medical staff to have this condition considered as a genuine medical problem, but this was not achieved. Nevertheless, considerable latitude prevailed in the manner in which these individuals received their discharges. When the commanding officer was psychiatrically wise, the man sometimes got a medical discharge. Many others, however, were given Section VIII discharges. The following case illustrates this kind of problem.

CASE 8. *Section VIII Dischargee. Homosexual stirrings associated with all-male surroundings in the Army.*

This 27-year-old dischargee is a slender, sensitive, good-looking man who spoke quite frankly about his problems. He was discharged from the Army about a month before coming to the Clinic, after having been involved in a homosexual affair with a fellow officer, who denounced him. He was pressed to resign his commission "for the good of the service." He was referred to the Clinic when he applied for a teaching position and disclosed his army difficulties.

This man had always had homosexual tendencies. In high school he experienced strong physical attraction for one boy and had daydreams of mutual masturbation. During several months of enforced idleness, he became restless, engaged in some drinking, and felt homosexual pressure which led up to the incident which occasioned his discharge. For a few months after his discharge, there was a good deal of homosexual practice, during a period when he was working in a shipyard at kinds of work in which he had never engaged before. He and a girl fell in love, and they went away for a week and lived together. Heterosexual experience was mutually satisfactory. He told the girl about his homosexual tendencies, but she did not mind. The possibility of marriage was discussed, but the patient was not sure that he was ready to marry, and so they separated and he came East. Steady correspondence was maintained, and her picture and letters seemed to mean much to the patient. There were further homosexual practices after separation from the girl and before coming to the Clinic.

This man's father had been a successful businessman who later lost his business and drank heavily. He never made friends and was hated by the patient and his two brothers and sister. His mother was a quiet, small-town girl of artistic temperament, but with little education. Because of the father's business, the family moved from city to city, so that the patient attended many different schools. In college he was very active in student activities. He obtained a scholarship in a graduate school. He later passed a civil service examination and for a year and a half before his induction was employed as an assistant in his chosen field.

After induction he worked for six weeks in a classification office, then took basic training, and later went to officers' training school, from which he was graduated and commissioned a second lieutenant. The incident that occasioned his discharge occurred about a month after he received his commission.

During the interviews with the psychiatrist, he discussed his problems quite frankly, but did not develop much insight into the basis of his difficulties. He was advised not to focus his preoccupations exclusively upon his sexual problem, and he was able to follow this advice. Plans for suitable work and living arrangements were discussed and he obtained employment which he liked very much. When last seen, he was keeping regular hours and living well, had gained weight, and was feeling much better. His work took him away from New York and therefore treatment was brief. A couple of months later he married the girl from the West. Both of them have faced the possibility of marital problems, but feel certain that they can manage.

Very frequently the knowledge of a psychiatric discharge has produced new and disturbing problems for the psychiatrically disabled. This is well illustrated in Case 9. Actually, the psychiatric diagnosis of his condition was unjustified.

CASE 9. *Section VIII Dischargee. Ashamed of psychiatric diagnosis.*
This patient, 24 years old, came to the Clinic at the suggestion of a military psychiatrist at the camp from which he was discharged with a diagnosis of psychoneurosis. He complained of continuous and serious diarrhea, which began nine months after he was inducted into the Army. He complained also of pains in his legs and groin. He described one other symptom of "feeling that I am going through various actions, but at the same time I am standing on the sidelines watching myself."

This patient was born in Europe but had lived in this country since he was one year old. There were no unusual features in his health, educational, and family histories. He had had no emotional difficulties previous to his military experience. He had been employed as a mechanic before entering the Army. He was happily married and was eagerly awaiting the birth of his first child.

He expressed great embarrassment over the Army's psychiatric diagnosis and complained that "If they don't understand anything in the Army, the first thing they do is to chase you to a psychiatrist." He regarded a psychiatric condition as a disgrace, and believed that it involved a "defect of the mind."

Several months after he went into the Army, he had two operations for hydrocele. He showed some anxiety after the second operation, because the purpose of it had not been clear to him and he worried lest he had lost his "manhood." The pain in the legs and groin was a natural aftermath of these operations. Although many laboratory tests had been made, both in the Army and subsequently, all of which were negative, the doctors of the Clinic still suspected a possible organic basis. The lack of emotional difficulties in the man's history combined with the lack of symptoms during the first nine months in the Army pointed to some other explanation. Careful and repeated stool examinations finally revealed a severe *Giardia* infection. Arrangement was made for appropriate somatic treatment.

Etiology

As one reviews these cases, certain situational factors and constellations of emotional problems begin to emerge as having dynamic significance in the development of the disorder. Why, one may well ask, does military life contribute to or produce these reactions? To understand this one must realize that, while on the surface the various factors may not seem adequate to explain the reactions, since a large majority of men survive them without disability, still there are powerful emotional factors at work, often unconscious and unrecognized by the individual, which represent basic conflicts, the true nature of which is frequently hidden from the victim himself. One sees these men breaking down under all kinds of emotional impacts. Some factors begin to operate before induction. The mere anticipation of being drafted can constitute a traumatic experience to certain individuals. This results from the disruption of secure family patterns and established ways of living and applies particularly to those men who have an abnormal fixations to their mothers. The fear of losing the mother is sometimes rationalized as concern or responsibility for her or for the family. The threatened disruption of family security starts off a pattern of anxiety. Another cause of anxiety is the man's anticipated fear for his own welfare. Transfer to an environment with its exclusively male connotation can result in disturbance to the man's traditional attitude toward masculine society. This is particularly true of men who have failed to integrate the homosexual libido into the personality structure. Such individuals are unconsciously afraid of contact with other men, especially men who seem stronger or superior. For them the defense against their unconscious desire to be loved and appreciated by men breaks down. In other men, the unconscious aggressive feelings are so strong that they cannot be successfully integrated into the newly formed superego. In the vast majority of men military life results in the heightening of their ego strength, pride in their identification with military activities, and the achievement of a new contentment and purpose in life, all of which permit the justification and acceptance of their aggression.

It is not surprising, however, that some individuals develop disabling anxiety just before or immediately following induction into service. Indeed, there are cases on record where men have broken down between the hour of induction and the hour of arrival at an army camp.

There are multiple factors which begin to operate immediately after induction which are inherent in the subsequent military situation. These center primarily around the disruption of personal security and the breaking down of neurotic defenses that have been successfully utilized by the individual to keep him at a functional level in his civilian existence. We may briefly enumerate these factors. (1) Separation from the secure family environment and family ties is a frequent and potent source of continuing anxiety. In many this anxiety is expressed as a need to write and hear frequently from home, inordinate concern for the welfare of the family, disturbance over the news of illness among its members. When these anxieties are great enough, men sometimes go away without leave in order to restore immediate contact with the home situation. (2) Soon after induction, a man is faced with the necessity to accept a completely new authoritarian world and a break with many of his established normal routines. He is faced with the unconscious struggle surrounding the acceptance of authority and discipline; lifelong patterns of resentment of parental authority are reactivated. (3) Some of the previous histories have dramatically illustrated the reaction of men assigned to unwanted tasks and of men whose specific talents were misused, when in the rush of military life they were unwisely assigned to tasks for which they felt unprepared. In the main, the armed services did a superb job of placing men with special talents and abilities. It is not surprising, however, that in the rush of mobilization and with millions of men to assign, some individuals rightly or wrongly felt themselves inappropriately placed. (4) Some men found the lack of any semblance of privacy particularly trying. (5) Others were consciously or unconsciously disturbed by the exclusively male environment and the lack of normal sexual outlets. (6) In others inordinate guilt was stirred by the need for aggression. (7) There was also the ever present anxiety concerning the possibility of physical injury, mutilation, or death. Many of these factors began to operate at once and became more exaggerated as the training period progressed. Under these circumstances it is not surprising that conditions which gave no trouble while they were latent strikingly came to the fore.

Certain factors occurring in the life of the individual seemed definitely to predispose to neurotic breakdown. In the main, the following factors seem significant. Younger men broke down more rapidly than men in the older age group. Patients who had had previous psychiatric hospitalization or other psychiatric treatment were less likely to stand up. Previous antisocial behavior, resulting in a poor adjustment in school and at work, made for less likely success. Many individuals who developed neurotic disabilities had come from broken homes, or families with a history of nervous, emotional, or mental illness. This factor of predisposition existed in the background of most of the psychiatric casualties and is emphasized by most writers on military medicine.

Combat experience brought in additional dynamic factors which operated singly or in combination: fatigue, increased responsibility, the diverse changes of climate, new somatic diseases, intense anxiety and fear, states of dwindling morale and sometimes loss of confidence in leaders, guilt feelings toward the death of comrades, exposure to explosions and blasts and repeated exposure to danger of various kinds, the need to appear courageous in the face of overwhelming fear, the inevitable conflict between duty and the instinct for escape or aggressive release. The experiences a man had in a military hospital often induced an emotional attitude which militated against his later seeking or accepting further psychiatric help. Also, it has been shown that the formulation and advice given him strongly determined his willingness or unwillingness to undertake therapy. If he had been psychologically well prepared at separation centers, he was more likely to seek treatment. If he had been given poor advice, such as to avoid physicians, ignore his illness, and rest indefinitely, he was little likely to seek treatment. While some orientation toward civilian life was given before discharge, the major task of civilian rehabilitation had to be done after the man's discharge from service.

Following discharge and upon his return to civilian life, a whole new set of factors began to operate—loneliness, desire to be back in service, remorse that his fighting buddies had either been killed or had remained in the line of duty, a changed social and economic scene, powerful family attitudes of anxiety or misunderstanding, lack of companionship, lack of general social and recreational outlets, the need to get reoriented in satisfying employment, over-expectation of the remunerative returns from work, frequent floundering and overreaching in work selection, knowledge of the psychiatric status and diagnosis, the stigma associated with the NP discharge, the inability to formulate it to friends and family, and the necessity to relinquish authoritative military discipline and to find in its place, at least temporarily, a strongly supportive figure who would not be a disciplinarian. It is at some point in this progression that psychiatric therapy must be started. As has been shown in a study made by the New York City Committee on Mental Hygiene, some 80 per cent of these psychiatric casualties are in need of help, but only 25 per cent are willing to accept it. This may mean that the bulk of these individuals feel no need for treatment, are antagonistic to seeking treatment, or feel able to meet their own problems without professional help. Yet once the patient has accepted help, he has to be shown that he has a large role to play in the therapeutic process and must be encouraged to assume full responsibility for his own recovery.

Motivation

The fundamental dynamics involved in all these disorders are best understood in terms of anxiety, especially in terms of its disrupting effect on the total personality and the many mechanisms and defenses developed against it. The clinical forms in which anxiety will manifest itself vary and depend upon the individual's constitution, family history, specific personality organization, and prevailing pattern of dealing with anxiety. When the defenses become ruptured as a result of overwhelming conflict, the reaction may be an overt expression of anxiety, a denial of anxiety by hysterical dissociation and mounting rage, or the displacement of anxiety by paranoid projections, or by regressive disorganization and overwhelming submissiveness.

Freud[1] stressed the fundamental distinction between the war neuroses and peacetime neuroses. In peacetime, the usual conflicts arise between the ego and the repressed forces of the libido. In war, the struggle is precipitated by the hostile forces of the external world. The fundamental conflict arises out of the soldier's desire to be successful, to prove himself as strong as his comrades, to meet the demands of his conscience in the face of his mounting fear of death or injury, and the disruption of his peacetime living. As the anxiety mounts, the patient is no longer able to deal with it or to release it in constructive activities, and he is forced to resort to substitutive behavior. The anxiety may manifest itself in the disturbance of his sexual functioning; unconscious infantile fears of sexual incapacity may then be revived as a fear of impairment of sexual potency. The soldier may turn his anxiety and anger upon himself with the development of depression. In his search for a method of dealing with anxiety, more primitive mechanisms may be reactivated. He may develop self-centered, self-protective behavior, acting much like a child in his search for environmental protection and affection. In its severest form this may result in schizophrenic regression. In others the unrelieved anxiety and rage lead to increasing aggression, anger, resentment, and projection of self-blame to others.

Anxiety of sufficient intensity invariably results in profound physiological and psychosomatic disorganization of the entire organism. Involved in this is the disruption of the functions of the autonomic nervous system. These disturbing physiological reactions in turn provoke secondary anxiety leading to greater subjective insecurity and disorganization of the ego, and there may be a massive explosion of anxiety manifested at the psychological, physiological, or psychosomatic level. The end result is a disorganization of the total personality with total loss of the capacity to deal as a mature individual with the manifestations of anxiety. Various degrees of regression occur in the attempt to meet the overwhelming threat. It is these infantile regressive mechanisms which we must understand and with which we must deal in the therapeutic situation.

These are the more immediate reactions. They suggest two immediate goals of therapy: first, fundamental anxiety must be relieved and, second, the disturbed and weakened ego must be restored. Because of its contribution to both these goals, narcosynthesis is an effective technique: it brings about relief of anxiety before dissociative and repressive mechanisms begin to operate and, through the strongly supportive encouragement and reassurance of the therapist, effects the restoration of the ego strength.

The conditions we have been describing are reactions to an emergency. Where they are not successfully dealt with, the original threatening situation may be duplicated in all future prospective dangers. Faced with his own helplessness, the individual may revert to the techniques of infancy and reach out for continued and automatic support. In this lies the main danger for his future. Rather than face new anxiety situations, he constantly seeks protection against further anxiety or menacing situations, resorting ultimately to attitudes of submission, dependence, chronic invalidism, and potential deterioration. In a group of chronic neuroses in a veterans' hospital, Kardiner[2] was able to show that all chronic cases, however diverse, are characterized by irritability, proclivity to aggression, repetitive dream-life recreating the war situation, a lowering of personality function, a change in the patient's conception of himself and the world, and a craving for compensation. Kardiner saw the lasting damage that was done to the patient's adaptive capacity and describes a continual and often fruitless struggle to recapture the tools of mastery ending frequently in the acceptance of defeat.

The motivations are commonly unconscious and unrecognized by the patient himself. Without some knowledge of fundamental dynamic mechanisms the physician is little likely to be effective in treating any but the more superficially traumatized individuals.

REFERENCES

1. Freud, S. Beyond the pleasure principle. New York, Psychoanalytical Press, 1922.
2. Kardiner, A. The traumatic neuroses of war. New York, Hoeber, 1941.

IV

THE PSYCHIATRIC DISABILITIES OF WAR: PRINCIPLES, METHODS, AND RESULTS OF TREATMENT

WORLD WAR II developed only one outstandingly effective new technique in the treatment of the war neuroses, narcosynthesis, so ably employed by Grinker and Spiegel; but the vast experience of applying established psychiatric methods in the armed services points the way to more effective utilization of sound techniques in civilian work.

Treatment of Psychiatric Casualties in the Armed Forces

A few basic principles governed the regulations concerning psychiatric procedures in the armed services. First and most important was the requirement that the patient be treated immediately and as near to the combat area as possible. Secondly, it was found imperative to segregate the psychiatrically disabled soldier from his healthy comrades as soon as possible in order to avoid the undermining of the group morale. Thirdly, acute emergency therapy was limited to as short a time as possible, usually five to seven days, rarely longer than three weeks.

The Army's plan, which is well described by Farrell,[1] was designed to salvage as many psychoneurotic individuals as possible for some type of duty. Recognizing that long periods of hospitalization tend to consolidate the neuroses, this plan aimed at the shortest possible period of treatment, carried out under a military (optimistic, stern, not-too-sympathetic) rather than a hospital atmosphere. Those who did not respond promptly were evacuated to a base area. At the clearing stations, sedatives, rest, and reassurance were the chief tools. At the evacuation hospitals the policy was to treat those men who required five days' treatment or less. All others were treated in hospitals removed from the front, where they received rest, warm baths, explanations of their symptoms, strong psychotherapeutic reassurance and suggestion, and were then sent to bed for three or four days. They were given phenobarbital routinely so that most of their time was spent sleeping. Patients were required to be up for meals and military discipline was strictly enforced. Intravenous barbiturate medication to aid psychological catharsis and suggestion were used in selected cases. Following this regime, the decision was made whether to return the patient for further duty or to evacuate him to the communications zone.

Therapy, therefore, for the acute and combat neuroses consisted mainly of complete physical and mental rest, the restoration of normal metabolism and nutrition by the use of food and fluids in large amounts (intravenous fluids and plasma if necessary), the restoration of lost weight, and psychotherapy.

The main psychotherapeutic tool was psychological catharsis, which was most effective when begun immediately. The patient was encouraged to describe or relive his combat experience in an atmosphere of understanding and respect and thus to release anxiety and rage. Sometimes in addition hypnoanalysis and narcoanalysis were necessary in order to induce the patient to express feelings of which he may have been only vaguely aware, to reactivate emotional memories that may have been largely unconscious, to relate such feeling to deep unconscious attitudes and emotions, and specifically to penetrate the amnesic areas, thus bringing into consciousness the unrecognized material and fusing it with appropriate emotional expression and restored adult ego-function.

This work is well described by Grinker and Spiegel: "Without equivocation it can be stated that the only knowledge newly applied to the prevention and treatment of war neuroses up to the present, whether in forward hospitals, general hospitals overseas

or at home is a sound, rational understanding of the dynamic conflict between the unconscious sources of anxiety and the ego forces
and an understanding of the symptoms produced by psychological
defenses, regressions and collapse."[2] Grinker has outlined the aim
of the narcosynthesis therapy carried out under sodium pentothal
as follows:

> Release of repressed emotions in a process of so-called "abreaction";
> support of the patient's weakened and regressed ego through identifi-
> cation with the therapist's strength; desensitization from the memories
> of the anxiety producing situations by repetitive recounting of trau-
> matic experiences, as the therapist helps the ego to discriminate be-
> tween past danger and present safety and between dangers of the world
> of reality and inner anxieties; neutralization of the severe superego re-
> action of guilt to the actual, or sense of, failure; instilling insight into
> the relationship between the neurotic reactions to war and the past
> character and personality trends; encouraging the ego in its experi-
> mental attempts to regain mature attitudes and to attempt adult activi-
> ties, thereby giving new confidence to the weakened and regressed per-
> sonality.[3]

Psychotherapy, therefore, "consists largely of uncovering the
basic problems, the process of which is facilitated by the use of
pentothal. Under partial narcosis the patient is able to abreact his
hidden emotions and synthesize them within his ego, hence we
call the method narcosynthesis. Aided to understand his inefficient
adjustment and braced by the therapist's support, the patient can
undertake the problem of reeducation. The use of these techniques
makes possible the return to full duty of 95 per cent of officer patients and 80 per cent of enlisted patients."[4]

While psychotherapy was always the preeminent tool, certain
other psychiatric techniques derived from sound psychiatric practice were also used. "In hospitals insulin and electro-shock are
proving of value for the treatment of psychoses. For psychoneuroses, subcoma doses of insulin are used in combination or consecu-
tively with barbiturate narcosia. . . . Group psychotherapy is

being adopted rapidly and increasing use is made of adjuvant therapy; occupational therapy, recreation, athletics and music. . . .
All general hospitals in this country now have a program of graduated convalescence in which full use is made of military discipline, technical and vocational training, education, recreation and entertainment. Neuropsychiatric patients participate in this program as a separate group."[5] Priority was given to the acute cases who could be expected to return to duty. Every case was regarded as a medical emergency; hence treatment was begun immediately. Every effort was made to keep psychiatric patients out of hospitals since it was recognized that hospitalization was likely to exaggerate the concept of illness in the patient's mind. Since many of the reactions were largely situational, every effort was made to modify and remove the situational factor, particularly in the choice of an appropriate job assignment. Increasing use was made of Red Cross workers and of social service workers in other agencies in the solution of significant domestic problems.

These basic principles of emergency therapy were confirmed by the experience of the United States Public Health Service in the treatment of traumatic war neuroses in merchant seamen. Blain and Powdermaker reaffirm the wisdom of the procedures outlined:

Traumatic war neuroses of all degrees are seen in merchant seamen who have been subject to more strain than they are physically and emotionally able to bear. They occur in men who are neurotic and in those who seem to have been relatively stable and do not always seem to be in proportion to the strain involved. The symptoms may include all of those which the psychosomatic mechanism is capable of producing. Treatment should be instituted as early as possible and include (1) sleep, induced if necessary; (2) removal of all strain in the environment; (3) adequate diet; (4) psychotherapy directed toward the full expression of the traumatic events coupled with the expression of the emotions associated with them and toward an understanding of the causes of the breakdown; and (5) treatment of physical difficulties.[6]

The treatment of other than the acute combat reactions utilized the well-known principles of general psychiatric care. Psychotherapy aimed at giving the patient a genuine understanding of the emotional nature of his reactions and encouraging a complete expression of anxiety, resentment, and aggression. Occupational therapy, vocational training, and educational training were additional useful tools. Shock therapy, and particularly modified insulin therapy, was used increasingly. For excitements, use was made of prolonged sleep therapy whereby the patient is put soundly to sleep with sufficiently large doses of sedatives for twenty hours a day and is aroused only for meals, fluid, and elimination.

Group psychotherapy, described in a number of comprehensive articles, was used increasingly.[7] In the main, the results reported were satisfactory. The specific techniques used by different therapists differed rather widely. Some depended upon the lecture-discussion method, in which specific orientation talks were given on the meaning of military life, the cause of nervousness, body-mind relations, and so forth, followed by free discussions within the group. Other therapists utilized the question-answer method whereby the patients submitted written anonymous questions for group discussion. In general, the greater the freedom and spontaneity maintained within a group, the better were the results. These are some of the advantages of the method as reported: it permits dissipation of tension and anxiety feelings; it helps relieve the stigma of the NP diagnosis; it offers a control of the emotional release; it permits full, and for some patients easier, expression of aggression and resentment; it affords opportunity for attaining insight; it encourages group solidarity and security; it offers patients who have been reluctant to discuss their experiences an opportunity to talk freely in front of others; it tends to depersonalize problems by making them part of the large group problem; it is in itself a socializing process.

Group therapy methods proved so valuable in the Army that a directive describing methodology, types of patients to be treated, and expected results was issued.[8]

RESULTS OF TREATMENT

It is difficult to evaluate the results of all the therapeutic methods used in the armed forces. Foremost among those published is the report of the results obtained with combat reactions by Grinker's method of narcosynthesis. As previously stated, 95 per cent of officers and 80 per cent of enlisted men treated by this technique in combat areas were returned to active duty after a few days of therapy. Grinker and Spiegel report further that 60 per cent of the cases chosen for narcosynthesis in rear areas were returned to combat duty. It is important, however, to add their own note of conservatism in the interpretation of these striking finds:

We shall not indicate to you the basis of our doubts regarding these statistics or our observations on the rate of relapse. Sufficient is it to say that at least for a time troops are returned to combat, effective or not is hard to say. Furthermore, the end result in many of these soldiers carrying a reservoir of repressed anxiety will be a post-war problem, if not before. There can be no doubt that the work is necessary and if done early, close to the front lines and with therapeutic enthusiasm, it will return many men to combat. But it requires a fine psychiatric sense to determine the end result in the man—if that is important. Its goal should not be the statistical result.[2]

It is obvious that the results of therapy are dependent in part upon the degree of disability and the nature of the psychoneurotic casualty. On this latter point, we again quote Grinker and Spiegel:

Let us now see what clinical syndromes in general are efficiently treated. The free-floating anxiety states offer a good prognosis although many severe cases require longer time only available at home. This holds true when severe somatic regressions are also present. The conversion states, phobias, many types of depression, likewise promise well for recovery. Psychosomatic visceral disturbances unless very mild and without history of previous similar illness usually have to be sent home. The same holds true for those showing paranoid trends. We believe that with adequate facilities, proper use of adjunctive treatment such as shock and narco-synthesis and the proper use of psychotherapy of the uncovering type, based on sound dynamic principles, followed by a sound work rehabilitation program, most of even the severe cases can recover in hospitals in this country. These men need more time for the working-through process.[2]

The findings of the Navy in the treatment of combat cases are equally encouraging. Raines and Kolb[9] report of their treatment of the combat-induced or aggravated emotional disorders that 13 per cent were restored to full duty, 19 per cent to selected duty, and 30 per cent to duty within the continental limits. Thus a total of 62 per cent was returned to some form of duty.

Unfortunately for many of these disabled men, adequate treatment resources did not always exist in the armed forces. The medical corps of the armed services was seriously handicapped by a dearth of competent psychiatrists. While late in the war determined efforts were made to correct this deficiency, particularly by the establishment of brief, intensive three-month training courses in psychiatry for young medical officers, there were never enough psychiatrists to do the vast job that needed to be done. Significantly, too, the Chief of Psychiatry for the United States Army was belatedly promoted after V-J Day to the rank of Brigadier General, a recognition which was long overdue and an obvious failure to give psychiatry its rightful place with the other medical specialties. That this finally happened was due to the valiant efforts of the meager number of psychiatrists and to the inspired leadership of Brigadier General William C. Menninger. With a service so handicapped, it was little wonder that many psychiatrically disabled individuals received little or no therapy. The plans and efforts and successes of the psychiatrists of the armed services, which we have reviewed in these chapters, deserve our fullest praise. Nevertheless, it would be a serious mistake to assume that the plans were always effected as they have been outlined, that the efforts were always appreciated or acceptable, or that the successes were as widespread or effective in total numbers of individuals rehabilitated as the published statements might imply. Some of the results reported were based on hopes sincerely expressed and sincerely sought by the able men who led psychiatry in the services. For many reasons, however, the performance sometimes fell far short of the goal.

Because of inadequacies in the psychiatric services many men were discharged though severely disturbed, psychotic as well as psychoneurotic. Indeed, the common complaints of a considerable number of discharged veterans center around their treatment during their army hospital experience. Many tell of hospitalization periods of three to six weeks, during which time they had little or no opportunity to talk with a psychiatrist. Many psychoneurotic individuals have complained bitterly about the traumatizing experience of a six-week stay in a "locked" ward with disturbed patients. They have found it difficult to forget the fear, embarrassment, and sense of stigma that pervade such an experience. Commonly it has been this experience that has caused some individuals to refuse further psychiatric hospitalization in civilian life.

Treatment of Psychiatric Casualties as Civilians

The treatment of the psychiatric casualty once he becomes a civilian offers new and different problems. It is this that we explored and tested in our two years of experience at the New York Hospital Rehabilitation Clinic. Civilian psychotherapy, too, must be incisive. It must focus immediately on the disability. It must draw upon a full understanding of the effect of military life, but it must work within the framework of the family and community setting with all its additional attendant emotional complexities.

TRANSFERENCE

Treatment now becomes purely optional or voluntary. There is no longer any power to enforce it. Hence the success of the therapeutic process depends to a considerable extent upon the establishment of a strong, positive bond of transference between therapist and patient. The speed and ease with which positive and utilizable transference occurs is extremely striking. It is one of the features that is most surprising to the average civilian therapist. In the following case the immediate transference formed was the most significant aspect in the patient's treatment. Indeed, it was so strong that with surprisingly little psychotherapeutic investigation this man's main difficulty was quickly resolved.

CASE 10. Prior to his enlistment in the Marine Corps, this 25-year-old man was a successful newspaper reporter. He had been assigned as a special correspondent in the Marines. He saw about five months of action in the Pacific area. He had attached himself to several outfits which had participated in six or seven major engagements. His last engagement was a particularly grueling one, in which he was exposed to prolonged and heavy artillery fire. He commented, "Planes have only a certain number of bombs, but artillery just goes on and on." Two men were killed within fifteen yards of the patient. He kept on going, but felt "shaky."

A few days after this experience, he went to the hospital, not for his nerves, but for a very sore wart on the plantar surface of his foot. He expected that this could be taken care of in a few days, but it was found to be more serious than he thought and he was sent to a base hospital. He remained on the surgical ward for a few weeks, when suddenly, walking about on crutches one day, he had an "all-gone" feeling, began to tremble, and was found to have a low-grade fever. He had had malaria once before, and thought that this might be another attack. Various tests were made, all of which the patient understood were negative, and the next thing he knew, they were beginning to call him "NP" and sent him to an NP ward, where he stayed for two months. He was finally given an honorable non-medical discharge on the ground that the Marine Corps at that time had too many correspondents.

Since his return to this country a few months before coming to the Clinic, noises bothered him. Sirens reminded him of his battle experience, in which he waited for bombs to fall. He also had a number of combat dreams, especially one recurrent one in which four Japanese leaped out of a plane on the beach and slugged him mercilessly, whereupon he waked up, "scared as hell."

There was nothing in this man's history prior to enlistment to give any indication of a neurotic trend. He came to the clinic largely because he felt he had lost his touch in writing. He reported that, whereas everything he had written before his "crack-up" had been well received, what he had written since lacked that extra something which is required to make it sell. For that reason, he had been worried about the future of his career.

The patient was seen by the psychiatrist five times during a six-week period. He talked out his traumatic experiences in some detail, and he was also helped through a specific approach to his writing problem. There was some discussion of the uncertainties and difficulties in a writer's world. By the end of the six weeks, he expressed the opinion that he had really gotten back his confidence in himself. He thought that the last story he had written was the best he had ever done.

CIVILIAN ENVIRONMENTAL FACTORS

The second important principle easily determined is that without due recognition of the powerful role played by the attitudes of family, friends, and community, therapy can be doomed to failure. The contemporary civilian situation with its complexities and new problems must also be dealt with. For this reason, therapy of all these disorders must of necessity involve many factors other than the patient's emotional turmoil, although psychotherapy focused on relief of the traumatic experiences constitutes the most important part of treatment. One must deal not only with the patient but with all the factors in his social situation which can speed or hinder the restorative process. It is striking how many of the men come to the clinic accompanied by mothers or wives who have to be drawn into the treatment process, often to receive orientative therapy themselves. The first aim is to help the individual eradicate infantile attitudes of dependency and to restore the normal adult self-directing energies. For this reason the veteran's fullest cooperation must be elicited at the outset, and he must be made to understand the vital role he must himself play in active self-help. The first contact is of greatest importance since it can determine or break the attitude toward treatment. It begins with the taking of a complete psychiatric and personal history. In our experience it has been of very great help to have first a thorough social history taken by a trained social worker. This permits the psychiatrist, whose time is limited, to get more quickly into the therapeutic situation at his first interview. Frequently the social worker, who in most instances is a woman, is able to establish the first friendly relationship with the patient, to explain the function the psychiatrist will perform, and to serve as a bridge toward a quick, positive, and therapeutic relationship with the physician.

Very frequently an initial physical examination is necessary to clarify uncertain physical or psychosomatic problems. Through this, anxiety over somatic symptoms can best be allayed. In unclear fainting or syncopal attacks, the electroencephalogram is of value in ruling out epilepsy or the results of head injury. As part of the initial survey psychological testing is of importance to determine intellectual limitations or unrecognized assets, special aptitudes and skills for training and education, and appropriate employment; in unclear cases, the Rorschach test is useful to clarify the depth of personality involvements.

Specific efforts may have to be made to obtain appropriate recreational outlets and companionship, to provide occupational therapy and hobbies, and to aid in the actual choice of the first job where the patient can function in an understanding and sheltered situation in spite of as-yet-unresolved symptoms. At this point, the help of a vocational expert can be extremely valuable in interpreting the man's temporary limitations to the employer and in securing work which will be satisfying, while at the same time sparing the individual emotional hazards that may reactivate the entire neurotic picture. Restlessness and intolerance to noise must be weighed carefully in the choice of employment.

INDIVIDUAL PSYCHOTHERAPY

The aim of psychotherapy is to permit full psychological catharsis and to bring to the foreground emotional feelings of which the patient may be only dimly aware. In this catharsis the memory of experiences normally or pathologically forgotten may be reactivated. The anxiety induced by traumatic experiences can only be borne in consciousness if the man succeeds in strong identification with the therapist as an authoritative and kindly figure whom he can trust and through whom he can restore the forces of his own disturbed ego. Reassurance and strong support from such a figure are imperative in enabling the man to make his first orientation to the disturbing world of occupation and friends.

The first interview, therefore, is aimed directly at a review of the army experience, the onset and development of the illness, the particular emotional factors operating during army life, and a tentative and brief résumé of the past life and personality structure with the aim of formulating a specific plan and program of action. During this interview and in succeeding ones, every encouragement is given for a ventilation of resentment, anger, guilt feelings, anxiety, and disappointment. A very quick and strong positive transference usually results even in the most hostile patient as soon as he recognizes that the therapist is exclusively interested in his welfare. The following case shows clearly the extent to which the patient must often test the therapist for his dependability and understanding before a relationship of trust and confidence can develop. Once formed, however, it becomes a major tool for therapeutic effectiveness.

CASE 11. This veteran seaman, 34 years old, seemed more mature than the usual young sailor. There was resentment in his manner which he was trying obviously, and with difficulty, to keep under control. He came here with a "convenience of government discharge" about which he was most disturbed. He had a bitter feeling of injustice that this should be given to him after 15 months of service in the Navy with a tough overseas assignment and combat duty in the Mediterranean. In addition, he felt that he had lost hold of himself. "I have to get some help. I can't go on like this. I have an awful desire that comes over me to scream out loud, and I can't control this desire. Civilian life seems different and hard to get used to."

Before telling his story he spent some time in testing out the therapist. "I am afraid to talk about myself. I am afraid that if I tell you what has happened, you will think I am yellow." And finally: "OK; I guess you are going to treat me all right."

In three clinic interviews, which covered a period of three weeks, he gave excerpts of his story very much in the manner of a modern movie—cutbacks from present to past, from past to present. There was evidence of growing confidence in the physician and of a remarkable decrease in tension.

"I've always been a real guy on my own feet, and I've done big things and had big responsibilities. I was selling papers on the streets of New York at the age of 11. I've earned my own way ever since. I've supported my family. I was dead broke in 1927, but I've made a come-back. I've put a brother through college, and I've had big family responsibilities. I've had to come up the hard way. I never had trouble with my nerves before I went into the Navy unless you call a pain over the heart once in a while nervous trouble."

Following boot training in the Navy he was given a radar course and after three weeks went into active sea duty on a cruiser. He spent many months on convoy duty during which he was on communications bridge in charge of radar. "You have to be on your toes every minute, watching that screen. You can't even blink your eyes. I stood my watch all the time. I never broke any of the rules, and I had a 4.0 record all the time when I was in the Navy." The ship was almost hit several times. "I got along all right. . . . The guys that I was with in this radar outfit were all 18 or 19 years old, just kids trying to be tough guys." They amused themselves while he felt the responsibility and seriousness of his assignment. "They'd razz me and say, 'What's the matter, Pop—they always called me Pop—getting scared, Pop?' and I never could get to first base with them."

Then this happened: "We were just going through Gibraltar at night. It was a fifteen-mile channel. There were 128 ships in our convoy, and there was another convoy of 90 ships coming at us. Get the picture, Doctor, all those ships had to pass each other and not crash in a fifteen-mile channel. It was my watch, and I was responsible. I had to pick up the friendly targets ahead and send the message to the Lieutenant who passed it on to the Captain on the bridge. Somehow or other I made a miscalculation. I don't know how I did it, but I did it.

"Suddenly all hell broke loose up on the bridge. The Captain, who knows his stuff, had a third piece of apparatus down below, and he picked up the error. God knows what would have happened if he hadn't. Can you imagine 128 ships piling into 90 ships coming the other way in a fifteen-mile channel? God! What a smash-up that would have been. So the old man bawls out the Lieutenant, and the Lieutenant let me have it. He slung everything he had at me. I had it coming to me, and I took it, but it wasn't too easy with those guys below later on. They made me feel it plenty. They razzed me even though they continued to horse around the way they always had on the radar deck. Our Lieutenant was too young to have any authority over them, and I didn't have any rank on them so I couldn't do anything, but I felt plenty bad about the whole thing."

On coming back to the States following this experience, "I was on edge. I was jittery and irritable as hell. I had a dry throat and knotting stomach." He was sent to Florida and later to Virginia for reassignment.

While sleeping in a tent when the thermometer was around zero, he developed pneumonia, was sent to a naval hospital, and seemed to recover in a few weeks. On his first liberty, however, he walked out as far as the gate and suddenly felt "all in and blacked out." They took him back to the ward and found that he had a fever of 104° and a strep sore throat. In the ward his tenseness and jittery feeling increased, and on one occasion when the radio was playing in the ward he shouted, "Turn that God damned radio off." One day when he could control himself no longer he ran to the lavatory and screamed at the top of his lungs, feeling dazed afterwards. He was interviewed by a young psychiatrist, "a Land Admiral of 22," who treated him as though he were "a criminal," calling him "yellow." The Medical Survey Board to which he was later brought, gave him little chance to state his case and discharged him with a "convenience of government discharge." "That, Doctor, is how I parted company with the Navy after a 4.0 record."

This veteran had made so good an adjustment previous to his time in service that one was encouraged to believe that he could work out his problem successfully. He married a "swell girl" (with whom he was able to talk over his feelings with considerable relief). There were many assets to build on. Continually throughout the interviews he returned again and again to his experience with the doctor at the naval hospital. "Honest, Doc, do you think he had a right to say things like that to me?"

Psychiatric treatment with this man was only in its initial stages, but with his increasing ability to handle his own affairs and his relief in being able to express his resentment to an understanding person, he seemed to be on the road to recovery. There was considerable discussion of the discharge, "for the convenience of the government." It was pointed out to him that the Navy probably recognized his good service record and preferred to give him this kind of discharge rather than a medical survey. He accepted the fact that even to a "regular fellow" things of this kind might happen. At the time of his third visit he said, "I have been thinking about it. I want to go back to work. I have got a chance now. I can go out on the road for a while and see where I stand, see whether I have got the old stuff." Now he plans also to join the American Legion where he can be of help to other veterans. "I am very much encouraged, Doc. When I go away from this clinic, I am all relaxed. I expect to be out on the road next week, so I will be coming back to see you in two weeks."

Many men, like this patient, seem to be lost without the authoritativeness of military existence and are ready to form a relationship of trust and dependence with their civilian physician. Obviously no physician can fill this role and at the same time act as an adjudicator of compensation claims. The man's confidence must be implicitly respected and no outside facts should be obtained or given without his full permission. It is most helpful to have the military record to check against the man's own account of his experiences. In the initial interview considerable time must be devoted to the understanding of the military situation and the man's reactions thereto. At the end of this interview the physician will have made notes of the main areas to be explored in subsequent interviews. It is here that his knowledge of unconscious dynamics is of greatest importance since he must anticipate that certain material remains yet to be explored or elaborated or more thoroughly understood in terms of earlier life patterns. This process is relatively easy and the traumatic material is quickly accessible when it has not become completely repressed. Considerable care must be given to the patient who has a completely bland story, since he may offer far more investigative difficulties.

A study of the dream-life and a knowledge of dream-symbolism are the best ways to get immediate clues to the fundamental nature of the traumatic experiences. Where such ventilation is not easily possible, other techniques must be employed.

HYPNOSIS

Hypnosis is used in certain selected cases for the alleviation of hysterical symptoms by direct suggestion, and used also to facilitate the reliving of highly traumatic experiences. Lorand[10] sees hypnosis as a method of therapy which heightens the child-parent relationship, thus permitting a direct access to the repressed unconscious material and enabling the therapist to exploit the transference situation more easily and quickly than in long analysis. Others, more traditionally, have used hypnosis primarily for the alleviation of symptoms in the monosymptomatic hysterias. More recent work by Erickson and others has utilized hypnosis for the re-creation of attitudes and feelings of earlier life periods, wherein the patient is given suggestion under hypnosis to revert to a specific earlier age period and reenact the pertinent emotional experiences of that age level. With this uncovering technique, Karl Menninger and associates,[11] Lindner,[12] and others have succeeded in abbreviating the usual psychoanalytic procedures. In our experience hypnosis has been utilized to abreact traumatic material which was not accessible by direct psychotherapy. The following case will indicate its usefulness.

CASE 12. The patient is a 26-year-old former electrician, separated from his wife, who was referred to the Clinic by the United States Employment Service. The patient had served in the Coast Guard for four months in 1942 and then had been a ship's electrician with the Merchant Marine. He got into difficulties with an officer who deducted his pay because he said the patient had not been on watch. The patient said he had been and struck the officer. His papers were taken away and the Merchant Marine excluded him from all vessels.

This man was described as a constitutional psychopath with intellectual retardation and impulsive behavior. On examination, the patient seemed irritable, impulsive, and primitive in his way of thinking and in his reactions. He realized that he had only harmed himself by striking the officer. However, he seemed full of hatred for him. The patient admitted having done a lot of fighting in his youth. He also admitted it was difficult for him to get along with others in any kind of job. He did not like to work and he tried to make up for his vocational shortcomings by exaggeration and "tall tales." It was obvious that lying and inventing strange stories served as a means to cover up his deep anxiety.

During the first examination, he seemed irritated. He opened his eyes very wide as though he were trying to frighten the examiner to conceal the fact that he was frightened himself. Even when the examiner succeeded in making him smile, his expression remained rather uncouth and primitive.

The patient felt that since his service in the Merchant Marine he had become much more irritable and in particular very sensitive to noises. He was reluctant to talk about his battle experience, and all he ventured to report about it was that he was torpedoed three times; he begged not to be questioned about it since it made him terribly nervous.

The patient's childhood and youth seemed to have been dominated by intense hatred against his father. He said he would like to kill him. His father was always very strict and intolerant. His mother was good and kind and couldn't get along with the father. They were separated; one month after her death the father remarried. The patient is fond of his stepmother but hates to go home because his father is there. He is separated from his wife, who will not return to him while he is not working. He has a long past history of lying, unsatisfactory work adjustment, and support by social agencies.

The patient claims that he had one year of college. Since his marks were not too good, his father took him away. He worked for two months repairing small electrical appliances. He then spent several months at home. He was getting an allowance of $15 a week from his father and found it satisfactory. He then spent the spring and summer on a farm working for his keep. This poor work record is corroborated by the examination of his intellectual processes and by his psychometric examinations. His intelligence was found to be dull (IQ 89), and his thinking processes confused and impaired by his tendency toward anger and resentment.

The tentative diagnosis made was that of a psychopathic personality with poor intelligence and acute anxiety. It was felt that the latter was caused by his battle experiences, and hypnotic treatment with abreaction was initiated. It was hoped that the superimposed anxiety could be relieved by this treatment.

Treatment was begun at the second interview. The patient was put into deep hypnotic sleep by verbal suggestion. In this condition it was suggested to him that he relive his experience of being torpedoed. He promptly displayed a tremendous amount of anxiety. The deeper he went, the more he tried to defend himself against further memories. He perspired profusely and one could see how he was fighting against the return of the traumatic experience. He spoke of how vividly he was seeing the scene when he was torpedoed and saved in a life boat. He was witnessing some of his friends perishing in the sea. By strong positive suggestion, he was urged to tell how his ship was bombed and his friends burned to death. After hypnosis he felt quite exhausted but recovered quickly. He felt grateful. He was not asked whether he remembered the hypnotic experience.

A week later this therapy was repeated. The patient was given the suggestion of subsequent amnesia for events which would occur during hypnosis. He was much calmer about his ship being torpedoed. He refused to go into the traumatic experiences which had been the topic of the previous session. When awakened, the patient reported that he had had a fine sleep and had a very pleasant dream about fishing.

The next week, the patient reported considerable improvement. He felt much calmer and his sleep was good. Hypnosis was again given and the patient was asked first to tell about his experience with the superior officer he had knocked down. The patient acquiesced to this request without much affect. He then was asked to dream in connection with both the officer and his father. The patient became irritated, almost woke up, and complained that he could not sleep because he was irritated by his "old man." He spoke with great irritation about his father, who was always after him, who never did anything the right way, and who never approved of anything the patient did. Now the patient was ordered to fall deeply asleep and not to mind his father. It was also suggested that after awakening he would be able to report about the dream and this would help him to get the father out of his system. The patient fell deeply asleep and was awakened after twenty minutes. He reported that he had had a dream about his "old man." He wanted to go home to see his stepmother because she was nice to him, but "Why must

my father always be there? . . . He is not worthy of this nice woman.
. . . Why must I find him always in my way?" It was explained to the
patient that he had to put up with this situation which could not be
changed and the suggestion was offered that after all this was his
father's home and he had to build up a home of his own. The patient
seemed to accept this and left very much relaxed.

The patient returned again three weeks later. He gave the impression
of being relaxed and considerably improved. He said that no doctor had
ever helped him as much; the treatment helped him to get things off his
mind which had been bothering him for a long time.

The patient was twice given a Rorschach test; the first before the
treatment and the second upon the completion of the treatment. Definite changes were found between the two periods. The test results
showed real improvement in integration and expansion—he was less con-
stricted and more mature in his approach to the situation. The character
of his answers changed from psychopathological (paranoid) to normal.

Little more than this alleviation of anxiety could be expected from
treatment. The fundamental personality remains unchanged. At the
present time he is working and exhibits somewhat explosive temper, but
is managing to convert some of his aggression constructively into his job
as a longshoreman.

SODIUM AMYTAL INTERVIEWS

Much more commonly, and after many years of experience in its
use, we have relied upon the intravenous injection of sodium
amytal as an uncovering technique in interviews with our ambulatory patients. No untoward effects have resulted. At the evening
clinic, the patient is given the injection at 7:30 P.M. By 10:30, with
the use of black coffee or specific stimulants if necessary, the patient is sufficiently aroused to return home. One or two patients,
however, were still so drowsy that it was safer to send them home
with a social worker. It is advised that 10 mgm. of benzedrine
sulphate be administered one hour before the amytal interview is
begun. Customarily we ask a relative to accompany a patient to
the clinic and send the patient home in the relative's care. The
main advantages of the method lie in the overcoming of resistance,

the fuller emotional abreaction of traumatic events, the establishment of a closer relationship to the therapist, and the resultant speeding up of the total psychotherapeutic process. The following case history will show the value of this process.

CASE 13. A 28-year-old unmarried veteran sought treatment eight months following discharge from the Army for a condition of psychoneurotic depression. He came to the Clinic weeping and in a suicidal state, following rejection by his fiancée who had just announced her intention to marry someone else.

The story of his army life was quickly obtained. He enlisted before Pearl Harbor in 1941 in the hope of getting his military service over with and returning to his civilian occupation. He spent two and a half years in the Army, the first year in training and the rest of the time in the Southwest Pacific. He objected to military discipline from the first. He was assigned to the Medical Corps as a corporal. He developed increasing nervousness and quick temper and felt that he had to assume too much responsibility for his corporal rank. He resented his sergeant for his open interest in alcohol and women. In a burst of anger he assaulted him, but he was not court-martialed. His resentment grew after he was made sergeant and he had to act as "doctor" to 500 men despite the fact that he himself was ill with malaria. Fatigue and sleeplessness accentuated his mounting resentment. He lost weight. He became increasingly depressed, wept frequently, and found himself unable to concentrate. When he was rejected from OCS, to which he had been recommended, because of renal glycosuria, his symptoms rapidly became worse and his resentment of his treatment and lack of recognition became outstanding. Upon return to civilian life, he immediately fell in love. He had returned to his previous occupation but soon found himself unable to work. When the girl he loved refused to marry him, his depression became acute and he sought help.

His past history was one of loneliness and rejection. Following his father's death when he was only 3, he was placed in the care of a succession of relatives, living most of the time with a grandmother who was a strict disciplinarian and who showed him little affection. He finished high school at 17 and would have gone to college but discovered that his mother had squandered his trust fund. With the little money left he entered a trade school. After graduation, he was promptly thrown out of the house to care for himself. For the next few years he rarely saw his mother. He was preparing to start his own business when military service intervened.

At the beginning of his first interview, he was tense, suspicious, and on guard. He sat stiffly on a chair making random and impulsive movements. He had marked concentration difficulties and described depression and constant preoccupation with his unsuccessful love affair. With agitation and at great length he ventilated his resentment toward the Army and his mother.

Under the influence of the first injection of sodium amytal (0.5 gr. in solution, injected slowly, over a period of 20 to 30 minutes) he recovered an episode which he had completely forgotten. During this interview he expressed extreme resentment toward his grandmother for her lack of affection and understanding, death wishes for his mother, and sibling rivalry of his younger sister, who he felt was the sole recipient of his mother's affection. He gave more details about his traumatic overseas experiences, recounting his resentment toward his superior officers, many of whom he felt were his inferiors and did not deserve his respect and loyalty. The forgotten memories concerned an episode when he and a friend set out into the jungle to collect Japanese souvenirs. They came upon a tent from which protruded the feet of two soldiers. The patient promptly shot them, thinking they were Japanese combatants, only to discover that it was a hospital tent, and that they were wounded Japanese soldiers.

Following the revealing of this forgotten experience and further ventilation of resentment toward his family, his depression rapidly cleared within two weeks. By that time, he was symptom-free and had embarked upon a private enterprise with a close friend. He planned to start college night school. He appeared cheerful, optimistic, and confident of his ability to adjust to civilian life.

This patient, like many other civilians treated in the Clinic, suffered from an involved emotional problem that was no longer acute and had had many months to consolidate his symptoms. With such patients, amytal treatment may not permit as immediate release as with patients suffering from acute reactions to combat. Moreover, amytal catharsis cannot be considered the sole agent in the treatment of the patient under discussion since preamytal psychotherapy was also used.

PROGRESSIVE STEPS IN BRIEF PSYCHOTHERAPY

This case illustrates well, however, the value of sedation in releasing profound and underlying hostility directed at the Army but stemming more immediately from lifelong repressed aggression toward the family. It is only through the release of such basic hostility that anxiety and guilt can be freed. In sharing such material the therapist plays a strong supportive role through reassurance that these emotions are common and acceptable and rebuilds the ego strength by stressing the similarity of the patient to other men in the same situation and by convincing him that these reactions are understandable and acceptable and that he has not been a coward in experiencing his particular degree of fear and anxiety. Very often, too, if the patient was working in an essential war industry, his identification with the Army was perpetuated by the formulation that he was still contributing to the war effort. This reassurance was of heightened value because it came from the therapist and was combined with general reassurance that the patient could recover and return to productive living.

In ambulatory therapy the time lapse between interviews gives an opportunity for the settling down of emotional stirrings and permits new emotional problems encountered in the interval to be brought to the foreground for additional discussion. The time lapse permits the new insight to be integrated and makes use of concrete opportunities for the testing of reality and the establishment of new emotional relationships with increasing confidence. It is for these reasons that ambulatory therapy is the therapy of choice. The protected life of a hospital or a rest home offers little opportunity for this testing process. As the interviews proceed, it is surprising how quickly the discussion of the military experience gives way to a free expression of the more common emotional problems as related to the early family pattern and constellations, to unsatisfied sexual strivings, and to the previously established patterns of resentment, dependence, and affection which one sees in civilian practice. The early interviews, therefore, are devoted to a thoroughgoing review of the individual's past life and give him ample opportunity to relate current emotions, feelings, and attitudes to past behavioral patterns. Thus the military experience soon comes to be seen as part of the larger personality problem. At the same time the specific problems in the current adjustment to civilian life are becoming focused.

The analysis of symptoms and their relation to anxiety stemming more basically from these remote emotional difficulties frequently succeeds in removing immediate symptoms and permits the more general problems to emerge. As treatment proceeds, the man is increasingly encouraged to assume full responsibility for his own active reorientation and is expected to make his own decisions, once the issues are clarified for him. In this way his own ego-functionings are bolstered and strengthened so that he can handle successfully the contemporary situation. Such therapy can be brief, as long as it is kept incisive and focused. Successive interviews of half an hour may suffice, but these require careful planning on the part of the physician in order to elicit new material. It requires caution on the part of the therapist to prevent the fixation of certain attitudes into permanent patterns and full awareness on his part of the current reality situation as well as the dynamic importance of past traumatic experiences in the early life period. There is little time for the orthodox free association procedures. Every opportunity is given for spontaneity of expression but the therapist must keep constantly in mind his knowledge of personality dynamics in order to keep new material flowing.

Very soon many of these patients are ready to return to work. They are encouraged to do so at the earliest possible moment but are protected from the disappointment of failure which might occur if work were undertaken precipitously. Most of these men can find work and, with properly selected employment and with strong reassurances and support, they are capable of working effectively during the treatment process. It is surprising to see how effective many psychoneurotic individuals are when at work, particularly under sympathetic and appropriate guidance by the employer, and we have seen some schizophrenic individuals who were working successfully and inconspicuously in spite of sweeping delusions.

We have emphasized brevity in treatment. A word needs to be said about actual length of treatment. Patients who do well show improvement in a remarkably brief period of time. On the average, about six interviews suffice to resolve the most immediate problems. By that time it is clear whether long-term uncovering techniques are necessary. For such patients we try to obtain the services of established outpatient departments or private psychiatrists. In other cases, the essentially chronic nature of the disorder becomes clear and the prognostic evaluations help to eliminate cases with poor potentialities. Fortunately, compensation issues have not yet loomed large. Not more than 10 per cent of these patients have been seriously involved in compensation litigation. When this happens the prognosis is inevitably worse. Fortunately, too, most of these men prefer occupation and self-support. This picture may change later if opportunities for employment become scarce.

Psychotherapy, therefore, is the crux of treatment. Special psychotherapeutic methods include the use of hypnosis and narcoanalysis. The method of the hypnogogic trance, as developed by Kubie, deserves investigation. A few patients with severe depressions have been referred for ambulatory electro-shock treatment. The possibility of utilizing subcoma insulin in the treatment of ambulatory patients needs investigation.

GROUP THERAPY

Group therapy methods can be successfully employed if the cases are selected carefully on the basis of comparable symptomatic picture and general intellectual level. Here we have found, as in individual therapy, that the same transference phenomenon is evident. Many factors enter into the success or failure of group therapy. Difficulties arise when the group represents too wide a range of intellectual differences and too diffuse a range of cultural and emotional patterns. A seriously depressed patient can retard a group of psychoneurotic individuals and an intellectually retarded man can slow up a group of intelligent patients. Ideally the members of the group should be selected. The therapist should have some knowledge of the psychiatric status of each member and he may have to allot a brief period of time for individual discussion at the end of the session. Discussion should be as free and spontaneous as possible, but some lecture material can be given which covers the normal range of emotional expression and common conflicts, the nature of anxiety and fear and their somatic expression, the conflicts between instinctive strivings and moral standards, the problem of goals and ambitions versus inherent ability, and the utilization of various psychological mechanisms in meeting personal problems. Group therapy deals essentially with the interreaction and response of multiple personality patterns in the relation of individuals to one another and to the therapist. At the same time it permits the gratification of the real emotional need for group acceptance and belonging, removes the sense of isolation, and encourages the development of mutual insight. The method permits of emotional discharge and resolution of difficulties encountered in recent experience. Unconscious factors cannot be dealt with except as they emerge in the motivation of contemporary behavior within the group. The method is deserving of more intensive study as it offers a procedure of unquestionable value in dealing with groups of men who have experienced comparable situations and anxieties, the very nature of which tends to hold them together in common sympathy and search for help.

At the Red Cross Clinic in New York City, Ackerman has utilized group therapy as a psychoanalytic tool, using the therapist's analytic orientation for active interpretation of unconscious dynamic motivation in the individual's behavior and responses toward the group and toward the therapist.

The size of the group may vary. Usually it consists of ten members, which permits of greater intimacy, but there can be twenty-five or more. Group methods must be developed increasingly in civilian practice if therapy is to be made available to the increasing numbers of patients who need it and for whom individual work is impossible because of the dearth of psychiatrists.

RESULTS OF THERAPY AT THE NEW YORK HOSPITAL REHABILITATION CLINIC

Results in the treatment of the neuroses are extremely difficult to evaluate. The types of cases chosen, the length of treatment, and the varieties of psychotherapy utilized make it most difficult to evaluate comparative studies. Thus far, there have been so few civilian reports of the results of therapy with psychiatrically disabled veterans that it is impossible to draw any definitive conclusions, and comparisons with the results obtained in the treatment of civilian psychoneuroses have questionable validity.

Approximately 1,300 veterans applied for psychiatric treatment at this Clinic between August, 1943, and August, 1946. A follow-up survey was made of the first 200 cases to determine the results of treatment six months to a year following termination. The cases were unselected except that they were admitted mainly from the east side of Manhattan. No attempt was made to exclude unfavorable or difficult cases. The problems they presented can be considered representative of those encountered in the total group of psychiatric dischargees, except that they include a much smaller proportion of combat fatigue symptoms than were found among those treated later.

Every effort was made to evaluate the subsequent status of these patients by clinic interview, home visit, letter, or telephone. If the patient himself could not be seen, information was obtained from the family, social agency, private doctor, or employer. We were successful in obtaining current information on 179 cases. Of the remaining 21 cases, information was not secured because the physician had asked that no attempt be made to reach the man (7 cases), because the nature of the problem made follow-up inadvisable (5 cases), and because the patient had moved without leaving a forwarding address (9 cases).

These patients represented a broad range of cultural and social background, from the sixth-grade, foreign-born citizen to professional men with university degrees. At the time of follow-up, 71 per cent of the group were working. Many men had not returned to their old occupation but had found more interesting and more lucrative employment. Some refused six or seven jobs before accepting the one they wanted. Some clearly expected more than their qualifications merited, or complained that they were not getting their just due.

The types of illnesses represented the entire range of psychopathology, although the overwhelming majority fell into the psychoneurotic group. One hundred cases (56 per cent) were suffering from some form of psychoneurosis, outstandingly from anxiety reactions. Other reactions were hypochondriasis (9 cases), hysteria (8 cases), obsessive compulsion (6 cases). Two showed post-traumatic syndromes. In 32 the psychoneurotic disturbance was diffuse and could not be placed in an exact category. The next most common type was psychopathic personality (24). Schizophrenic reaction ranked third (22 cases). True manic depressive reactions were found in 10. Six evidenced overt homosexuality and six were mental defectives. Thirty-two men in all were frankly psychotic. Most of them were in need of hospitalization, but the majority refused it and had to be treated in rehabilitation clinics.

The illnesses of most of these men developed rather soon after induction, 64 per cent occurring during the first six months. Of the total group, 148 (74 per cent) gave a history of previous personal difficulties. In 41 cases (20 per cent), there was no clear-cut evidence of such difficulties before induction. Illnesses were precipitated by a wide range of emotional factors. Fifty-three patients were quite unable to adjust to service because of previous personality traits of rigidity, immaturity, overdependence, and resentment of military authority.

Fortunately, the majority of these men who came to the Clinic were reaching out for help. Many of them harped on somatic disturbances as their sole complaints and demanded physical treatment in preference to psychiatric. Some came primarily for help in finding work. Many had to be persuaded that psychiatric treatment was indicated. Hospitalization was necessary for 14, and 23 required long and intensive psychotherapy for which they were referred to other established outpatient services. One hundred and sixty-three were considered suitable for therapy at the Clinic.

In more than half of the 179 patients (104 cases, 58 per cent), we feel justified in speaking of improvement. In 72 cases (40 per cent) improvement was very marked. Including a few additional cases showing slight improvement, we have a total of 113 (63 per cent) who benefited from their contact with the Clinic. The best results were obtained in the combat reactions.

It should be stressed that these patients averaged six visits and that the time spent by the psychotherapist in most cases was brief. Very few patients wanted to return indefinitely. The majority terminated treatment as soon as they were feeling better.

A few illustrations will serve to indicate how problems created by military service can be effectively resolved.

CASE 14. A 21-year-old man was discharged from the Army, after three months' service, because of severe anxiety symptoms: palpitation, choking, inability to concentrate, broken sleep, severe anxiety dreams. When first seen by us, he appeared discouraged and indecisive about his future, and complained of anxiety so marked that he could not wear his vest. Psychological tests were recommended and the patient was found to have very superior intelligence. A scholarship was obtained for him at a college where he could pursue his ambition to study sociology. On his second visit to the Clinic he reported that he was sleeping well, without dreams, and he was able to discuss his lifelong sexual insecurity. By his fourth visit, his anxiety had almost entirely disappeared, he was engaged to be married, and he had registered for college night school. He stated he felt better than before he entered the Army.

The same response was evident in another patient whose problem, if it had developed in civilian life, would have made one pessimistic about the outcome.

CASE 15. A 35-year-old unmarried man was referred to the Clinic in a state of great anxiety and evident depression. He was one of nine children in an Italian family, with two brothers in the Italian Army. He was inducted into the service in 1942. While doing calisthenics he fell, lacerating his right temple; the diagnosis was "contusion." Two weeks later he began to sleep poorly and to develop depressed feelings, poor concentration, and fear of unconsciousness. Later an x-ray revealed a linear fracture of the skull. He was hospitalized and finally discharged after one year in service. On returning home he was given financial help by a family service agency. His depression grew worse and he developed the fear of committing suicide by jumping out of a window.

His illness was formulated to him as a depression. He was referred to social service for recreational outlets. He very shortly changed his employment. One week later he resumed seeing his friends. His appetite and sleep began to improve on mild sedation. At his third visit he said he was perfectly comfortable during the day. In a total of six visits, he discussed his sexual difficulties in detail. He was content with his work and had been referred for artistic and recreational outlets. His phobias had almost entirely disappeared.

Sometimes effective therapy seemed to be accomplished in one consultation, as in the following case.

CASE 16. A 34-year-old man applied for admission to the Clinic because he wanted to discuss his illness and his vocational adjustment. The man was a college graduate, discharged seven months after induction with a diagnosis of "psychoneurosis." He had hoped for a commission but had been assigned as a private in the infantry. All the other men were younger than himself and less well educated. He felt unable to adjust.

The patient was seen only once in consultation. He discussed his difficulty in social adjustment, his resentment of his experience in the Army, his increasing fatigue and depression. He was given advice about seeking different work. Two months later he stated that he felt perfectly well, had been transferred to a personnel job. He said he felt he was on the way to a real accomplishment and had no more need for psychiatric help.

The same immediate response was evident in the next case. It seems likely that both these men were ready to accomplish their own recovery but were enabled to complete the process by the understanding of the psychiatrist and simple supportive help.

CASE 17. This man was 31 years old when he was discharged from the Army and seen at the Rehabilitation Clinic. A diagnosis of anxiety reaction with hysterical features was made. He was born in this country of foreign parents, and was the oldest of four brothers, with whom he got along well. At the age of 5, he returned to Europe with his parents, and there obtained his education through three years of high school. His early development was normal in every way. He was a sociable person and not unduly sensitive. He rarely lost his temper and showed little anxiety before entering the armed forces. He played hockey, baseball, and football, liked to dance, and had numerous dates with girls. After his return to this country, he attended night school to learn more English while working first in a factory and later as a laborer on a construction job. His work record was good, and he got along well with his fellow workmen.

Early in 1941, he enlisted in the Army. He did well during training in several camps, and was a staff sergeant when he was wounded in the North African campaign. He was hit in the chest by a falling rock dislodged by a nearby explosion. His chest was bruised and was painful for some time, but he did not report this injury to his medical officer and kept on with his unit until a week later, when he was knocked out by the concussion of a shell that exploded near him. He was unconscious for six days, and on regaining consciousness found himself in a military hospital. He suffered an amnesia for about twenty-one days, but later could remember everything up to the time when the shell exploded. During the seven months that he was in the military hospital in North Africa he was nervous, slept poorly, was tense, and had frightening battle dreams. After being returned to the States he was hospitalized for a few weeks more. During this time his condition improved somewhat, his nervousness and tension decreasing. He began to sleep better, but required sedatives. His appetite was quite good.

When seen in the Rehabilitation Clinic about three months after his discharge, he was still startled by noise, especially if he could not immediately see the cause. He was sleeping less well than he had a few weeks earlier. He attributed this to not having enough to do and to worrying over lack of sufficient money, and particularly over his parents in Europe, from whom he had not heard since 1939. He was eager to get well and go back to work. He had refused a job as a guard, because he felt he was not fit, in his nervous condition, to carry a gun. He continued to have frightening battle dreams about twice a week. During the day, he was rather nervous and tense and, since about a month after leaving the hospital, he had been troubled intermittently with sharp pains in his side, legs, and feet. He was also troubled with heartburn, which was relieved by taking food or soda. He had tried a job as bartender, but left after a few days.

This patient was seen by the psychiatrist only once. He was permitted to elaborate his story in considerable detail and to ventilate his army experiences. His illness was explained to him as a reaction to an overwhelming experience and he was reassured that because of the basic stability of his personality the illness would not persist. He was then given an explanation of the role of anxiety and tension as it was reflected in his physical complaints. He was told that his physical status could be carefully checked over if he had any further doubts about his wellbeing. He was given a formulation which stressed the need to keep occupied and to maintain an adequate balance between work and recreation. He was allowed to discuss his worry about his relatives, but was urged to abandon this preoccupation in view of the fact that he could not do anything about it. He was told that the social worker would procure him opportunity for recreation, and stress was placed on the necessity to undertake social activities. He was advised that aptitude tests were available and that they would be helpful in leading him to a wise choice of appropriate employment. With such brief ventilation and strong reassurance and support, he seemed greatly relieved. He then spent several weeks in an adjoining state at the home of an uncle. He liked his uncle very much, and in his uncle's home he had a good balance of rest and normal activities. When seen by the worker in the social agency who had referred him to the Clinic, he appeared much more relaxed and seemed to be enjoying life.

It is of special interest to see how much constructive therapy can be given in a relatively brief time. Cases showing improvement were not necessarily mild conditions. A few individuals were suffering from schizophrenic illness; some presented severe depression or a marked degree of psychoneurotic involvement.

Scrutiny of the 57 unimproved cases shows clearly that they presented the most difficulties. Nine were schizophrenic, 9 were psychopathic personalities, 3 were mentally defective, one had lues. The remainder were severely psychoneurotic individuals with deep-seated neurotic backgrounds.

As we look over all these cases, it appears that the Army sometimes discharged as unfit for duty soldiers who could have been restored at least to modified service. This seems to have been true of Case 18, a soldier whose illness bore no relation to his military experience and of Case 19, a sailor who developed symptoms in reaction to unsuitable duty assignment.

Case 18. This was a 26-year-old German-born man who had served as a cook in the Army for sixteen months prior to the development of symptoms of a definite depression. He was discharged for this, following which he became more tired, sleep fell off, he lost additional weight, felt constantly depressed, and complained of frontal headaches. He had gone back to his pre-induction work. His actual depression was related to the fact that his girl friend had married another man while he was in service. Following a single interview his symptoms rapidly cleared up and he declared himself ready and eager to go back into service.

It seems likely that this man need never have been discharged had prompt treatment in the Army been instituted.

Case 19. A 40-year-old lawyer, earning $9,000 a year, applied to the Clinic for help in adjusting to his discharge from naval service for "psychoneurosis." He was particularly concerned about this in view of a history of a nervous breakdown when he was 20. He reacted to discharge with tension, depression, "mental shock," sense of shame, and embarrassment. He was gifted in languages, and had tried hard to be trans-

126   MENTAL HEALTH IN MODERN SOCIETY

ferred to the North African area, where he might have been of great assistance. Instead, he was sent to the Pacific, where with idleness, inactivity on shipboard, and a growing sense of uselessness and frustration, his symptoms began.

His illness was formulated to him in an attempt to correct his resentment toward the Navy and his inordinate sense of shame. It was felt that he need not return to the Clinic.

In some cases prophylactic mental hygiene has prevented the development of more serious difficulties. It seems likely that the same preventive psychiatry could be effective within the armed forces. A certain number of our patients have been men in the armed forces, home on furlough, who were eager to find help but were unwilling to report to the military psychiatrist. The following case is illustrative of this function of the Rehabilitation Clinic and also of the value of preventive work.

CASE 20. This 23-year-old sailor came to the Clinic on his own initiative. He said he found it impossible to talk with the navy psychiatrists, but that he felt he must talk to someone. He could not stand the idea of going overseas again. He had been through three major invasions, including Salerno and Normandy, and had become depressed and more or less in a state of panic over the thought that he might again be assigned to sea duty. He was eating poorly and could not concentrate.

In his first interviews, both with the social worker and the psychiatrist, he kept repeating over and over, "Life is nothing but death and destruction. That is all that fills my mind. I can't remember when life wasn't death and destruction. I cannot believe it will ever be different again." He appeared to be on the verge of a schizophrenic illness. He described the horror of seeing dead people around, especially in Normandy, where he had to fire at a house which he believed was full of civilians. He was sure they had all been burned to death and could not stand the thought of what he had done, although it was to defend the ship and his unit. The memory haunted him.

This man had always been afraid of his father, who drank heavily. He hated authority and for that reason blocked completely when he attempted to talk with naval officers, medical or others. He had always been shy and had never bothered with people. He recalled having had only two friends, both of whom were somewhere in the service. He enlisted in the Navy, partly to get away from factory work, which he disliked very much. His experience in the Navy was disappointing because he never grew to like it. He tried hard, however, to make it go. He did well while in Diesel school, but was unhappy after his assignment to duty on landing craft. He felt picked on by his commanding officer, but in spite of this and strong fear, he carried on faithfully through three invasions. When he first showed difficulty in adjusting, his officer discussed the possibility of discharge, but the sailor refused to consider it.

Two weeks after he was first seen in the Clinic, he appeared without appointment early in the morning, after having walked the streets all night. He was then two hours overdue on his leave. He had learned that he was to be assigned to a different post. He appeared to be so sick that a social worker accompanied him back to the naval hospital. By telephone communication with the commanding officer of the hospital and with his doctor, arrangement was made for prompt review by a CDD board. Within three days, discharge was recommended. On a later visit, before the actual discharge was completed, he remained tense and anxious, and spoke of his distrust of the navy doctors and fear that his discharge might not come through.

The one satisfying outlet for this man had been his art work, which he did while on leave, during evening hours. He did both sculpturing and painting and expressed the opinion that the enjoyment he got out of this was the only thing that carried him through from day to day.

This man had never felt close to his mother or to his three brothers and sisters. He was concerned about his family's welfare, and sent money as he was able. Upon discharge he did not return to his home, but kept bachelor quarters with another man. He was seen by the psychiatrist twice after his discharge from the Navy. He was no longer depressed, and said he felt fine. He slept better and had no disturbing dreams. He was enjoying his art work and was employed part time, but was planning later to pursue his art studies full time. He seemed very cheerful and was much at ease, smiling and speaking freely. We believe that an acute schizophrenic outburst was averted. A second Rorschach test showed marked improvement and dropping out of bizarre schizophrenic answers.

It is evident that many of the discharged men achieved their own rehabilitation spontaneously without help. Another small group was helped in one consultation aimed at orientation to the problem of discharge, discussion of resentment, help in finding social contacts and appropriate employment, and general supportive reassurance. Of 70 cases who have described themselves as either well, symptom-free, or much improved, one fourth required repeated brief interviews. Over one half were not seen oftener than three times, and of these, one third were actually seen only once. The remainder required prolonged psychotherapy.

While brevity of treatment and rapidity of response have been discussed, it would be unfair to give too optimistic a picture of the ease of the therapeutic process. In a survey made by the New York City Committee on Mental Hygiene of the experiences of eleven clinics, certain real difficulties are emphasized.[13] Outstanding among these is the large number of patients who do not keep their referral appointments. In our experience 20 per cent of the patients referred for help never showed up. In contrast to these findings in New York City only 9 out of 38 rehabilitation clinics outside of New York City who replied to our questionnaire reported difficulties with broken appointments.

Striking, also, is the number of patients who visit clinics only once or fail to return after a small number of visits. This appears to represent a common clinical experience, particularly with veterans. It may be due in part to the manner in which patients are referred or to mistaken judgment regarding the timing of a referral or the patient's readiness for participation. Such errors arise because data from separation centers are inadequate to guide a proper referral. In other cases veterans are referred for psychiatric treatment when actually they are looking for a different kind of help, such as finding a job. Some veterans accept referrals more as a response to pressure than as help they feel they require. In some cases a sense of guilt over the military experience may lead to a false feeling of obligation rather than a genuine need. Other patients have to test themselves out in civilian adjustment before they are convinced they need help. In some cases the acuteness of the problem may subside in the interval between the referral and the first interview at the clinic. In others the refusal to turn up may reflect an unconscious resistance to authority. Clearly, some patients have a resistance to psychiatric treatment in marked contrast to their willingness to accept medical treatment. An extremely interesting fact is the paucity of referrals by general practitioners. The whole process of referral with its time-lag can be discouraging. On the other hand, the psychiatrist himself may fail to grasp the patient's true and immediate needs and so fail to use methods which the patient can see as helpful. The pertinent conclusions to be drawn are that referral is a process which requires considerable skill because it involves genuine appreciation of the patient's readiness for treatment and his capacity for real participation. Equally there is a need for adequately trained psychiatrists who can differentiate patients' needs and adapt their treatment skills accordingly.

On the positive side is the fact that of the veterans who are willing to accept therapy, many respond in a fashion that is constantly surprising to the physician who has had no other than civilian therapeutic experience. A considerable number need more intensive therapy, but these are usually seriously involved individuals with long-term disabilities. The majority of those with the more acute reactions and particularly those suffering from combat fatigue can be expected to recover after a reasonably brief period of treatment.

RESULTS OF THERAPY IN OTHER CLINICS

Our experience and results are in no way unique. A group of 38 other clinics have reported tentatively on their results of treatment.[14] Sixteen of these clinics had an opportunity to study their results and have reported their findings. These 16 clinics have treated a total of 996 patients. Of this total, 50 per cent were classed as having had a favorable outcome. However, the findings of individual clinics showed a wide variation. One clinic reported a favorable result in 11 per cent of the cases treated whereas 3 clinics reported a favorable result in all cases. Two of the latter group based their findings on series of 45 and 71 cases, respectively. None of these figures can be taken at their face value, since the criteria used for evaluation must vary considerably. In some of these clinics the work was largely diagnostic in type. It must also be noted that little time elapsed between the completion of therapy and the analysis of the cases and that further follow-up might show a recurrence of disturbance. Nevertheless, if even half of all the psychiatrically disabled veterans could be salvaged by rehabilitation efforts, the work would eminently justify itself from a human and economic standpoint.

Deutsch,[15] who has had a longer experience than most, having begun a treatment clinic in October, 1942, believes that the neuroses of the discharged veteran are essentially family neuroses, centering around the individual directly involved in the military service, who then becomes either the contagious member or the target and victim of the neurotic reaction of others in his environment. The whole family may be affected by an incident of this kind. The treatment process is essentially directed toward the conflict between passivity and activity, hostility and peacefulness, aggression and submission. "Success depends on the redistribution of the libidinal factors which produce narcissistic self-esteem, the capacity to develop aggression, the ability to project that aggression adequately and appropriately, and the courage demanded by independence and activity." Deutsch believes that mental health and peace of mind in the years ahead depend on the skill of responsible leaders in transforming these aggressions.

Terhune[16] considers the problem essentially one of community responsibility and advises the organization in each community of a group of able and responsible citizens who are trained and stand ready to assist the psychiatrist. He believes that the rehabilitation of the war-traumatized soldier is inevitably a part of the general practitioner's job. The practitioner must accept the challenge, provide additional community psychiatric facilities, secure additional training in psychotherapy, and enjoy being a part of a new and interesting phase of medicine.

Malamud and Stephenson[17] have reported on their studies of 42 neuropsychiatric dischargees who were treated at the Worcester State Hospital. They found the removal of the military stress situation, plus intensive psychotherapy, was sufficient to clear up the mental symptoms in many patients. They found that assets favorable for therapy included positive factors in the personality and social setting and in the attitudes of the patient and his family. Factors which hindered were certain personality features and pronounced negative attitudes on the part of the patient and community.

Summary

There is good reason to believe that psychotherapy in America will not entirely revert to its pre-war status. The insistent demand for prompt treatment of large numbers of men developing psychiatric conditions in the armed forces has resulted in further development and effective use of shorter methods of therapy: prompt catharsis, hypnoanalysis, narcosynthesis, short individual psychotherapy, group therapy, control of environmental factors. While these methods are not intended to supplant psychoanalysis and other protracted methods in selective cases, it is the belief of the authors that the shorter methods developed during the war should attain increasing prominence. The number of people needing psychiatric help is and will continue to be so great that methods and techniques which reduce the length of treatment will be at a premium. The results obtained both in the armed forces and in civilian rehabilitation work justify substantial confidence in the use of such methods.

REFERENCES

1. Farrell, M. J.   Development in military neuropsychiatry.   J. Iowa M. Soc. 34: 387–391, September 1944.

2. Grinker, R. R., and J. P. Spiegel.   Brief psychotherapy in war neuroses.   Psychosom. Med. 6:123–131, April 1944.

3. Grinker, R. R.   Treatment of war neuroses.   J.A.M.A. 126:142–145, September 16, 1944.

4. Grinker, R. R.   Psychiatric disorders in combat crews overseas and in returnees.   Proc. Inst. Med. Chicago 15:218–220, January 15, 1945.

5. Farrell, M. J., and J. W. Appel.   Current trends in military neuropsychiatry.   Am. J. Psychiat. 101:12–19, July 1944.

6. Blain, D., and F. Powdermaker.   Convoy fatigue and traumatic war neuroses in seamen.   J. Lancet 63:402–405, December 1943.

7. Bion, W. R., and J. Rickman.   Intra-group tensions in therapy; their study as task of group.   Lancet 2:678–681, November 27, 1943.

   Blair, D.   Group psychotherapy for war neuroses.   Lancet 1:204–205, February 13, 1943.

   Braceland, F. J., and H. P. Rome.   Anxiety and fatigue.   Connecticut M. J. 7: 827–831, December 1943.

   Hauptmann, A.   Disorders of the nervous system.   Dis. Nerv. System 4:22–25, January 1943.

   Jones, M.   Group psychotherapy.   Brit. M. J. 2:276–278, September 5, 1942.

   Paster, S.   Group psychotherapy in an army general hospital.   Ment. Hyg. 28: 529–536, October 1944.

   Rome, H. P.   Military group psychotherapy.   Am. J. Psychiat. 101:494–497, January 1945.

   Rome, H. P.   Psychiatry as seen in the advanced mobile base hospitals.   Am. J. Psychiat. 100:85–89, July 1943.

   Snowden, E. N.   Mass psychotherapy.   Lancet 2:769–770, December 21, 1940.

8. Group psychotherapy.   War Department Technical Bulletin, Med. 103.   Washington, October 10, 1944.

9. Raines, G. N., and L. C. Kolb.   Treatment of combat induced emotional disorders in a general hospital within the continental limits.   Am. J. Psychiat. 101: 331–335, November 1944.

10. Lorand, S.   Hypnosis as a method of therapy, p. 200.   The fourth in the eleventh annual series of conference talks at the Institute of Living (Hartford, Conn.), February 28, 1945.

11. Hypnosis Research Project.   Progress report.   Bull. Menninger Clin. 9 (No. 1), January 1945.

12. Lindner, R. M. Rebel without cause; the hypnoanalysis of a criminal psychopath. New York, Grune & Stratton, 1944.

13. Levine, R. Unpublished study. New York City Committee on Mental Hygiene.

14. From replies to an inquiry of the Rehabilitation Division, National Committee for Mental Hygiene.

15. Deutsch, F. Civilian war neuroses and their treatment. Psychosomat. Quart. 8:300–312, July 1944.

16. Terhune, W. B. The psychiatric problems of the returning soldier and their medical management. Connecticut M. J. 9:29–36, January 1945.

17. Malamud, I . T., and R. Stephenson. A study of the rehabilitation of neuropsychiatric casualties occurring in the armed forces. Applied Anthropology 3:1–15, March 1944.

PART TWO

POST-EMERGENCY PROBLEMS IN MENTAL HEALTH

V

CONTINUING MENTAL HEALTH PROBLEMS
AND NEEDS

THE war lessened some of the injustices with which the people of the world were concerned. Millions who had been enslaved were liberated as a result of the Allied victory, and though it may be years before all can resume their normal pursuits, at least a start has been made in building the peace. Basically the war solved few problems; in fact, it accentuated some of those already in existence and created many new ones. This is as true of the field of mental health as of any other phase of life.

In the rush and go of the war period, we almost lost sight of the round-the-clock, year-in-and-year-out problems of mental health. But the problems did not disappear by virtue of our inattention. In fact, with the drawing off to the armed forces and war industries of trained personnel engaged in the care of the mentally ill, both the quality and quantity of the professional service provided took a definite slump.

Conclusions drawn from pre-war figures indicate that one out of twenty people counted at the age of fifteen will in the course of a lifetime enter a psychiatric hospital on account of a mental illness. Another one out of twenty will be too ill to work for a shorter or longer period, but will not go to a hospital. In short, one person out of ten in the course of his life will be in need of treatment on account of a mental illness or incapacitating psychoneurosis. One per cent of our population are so mentally defective as to need hospital care throughout life or special provisions for supervision and training. Another 2 per cent are so retarded in intellectual development that they need special education and training if they are to become marginally effective. Three to five persons out of every thousand suffer from epilepsy, and on that account are in need of constant medical care and supervision. Some of these mentally ill, feeble-minded, and epileptic people require hospitalization; others do not. At the end of 1944, the last year for which complete figures are available, there were in hospitals in this country, 714,213 patients suffering from mental disease, mental defect, or epilepsy. This is more than 50 per cent of the average daily census (1,299,474) of all hospital patients during that year.[1]

Various other groups not usually hospitalized suffer from mental or emotional disorders of one classification or another. There are a million chronic alcoholics in this country. A sizable group, comprising several types of people medically classified as "psychopathic personalities," constitutes another tremendous need for rehabilitation work. Some current researches indicate the likelihood that this group in reality consists of three or four somewhat distinct clinical groups. It is hoped that further study will lead not only to more accurate classification but also to more effective methods of treatment, for until now rehabilitation methods have seldom been successful. Because persons in this group express most of their difficulties socially, they are an outstanding source of annoyance and disturbance to other people, thereby creating a social as well as a medical problem. Some who are addicted to alcohol or drugs belong in this group. The need for their rehabilitation is obvious.

There is no way of determining accurately the number of people who suffer from psychoneuroses of mild or serious nature. Statistics of the British National Health Insurance Scheme prior to the recent war indicated that of fifteen million insured, one half sought medical attention each year, and that of these, 30 per cent suffered from nervous disorders. Internists in this country have estimated that from 30 to 60 per cent of people who go to doctors are suffering primarily from psychoneurotic difficulties, and that one person in five goes to a doctor yearly for some nervous ailment.

Strecker estimates that 75 per cent of the patients consulting the general practitioner have psychiatric disturbances. Five per cent of these have psychoses. The remainder have one or another of the following psychiatric disturbances listed in order of frequency: (1) psychoneuroses, (2) organic disturbances complicated by psychoneurotic conditions, (3) psychopathological complication of chronic organic disease, (4) mental aspects of convalescence, and (5) partial or complete psychopathological problems in children.[2] McLean points out that 27 of 100 consecutive patients admitted to the medical services of the outpatient clinics of the University of Chicago Hospital were found to be neurotics, 23 had questionable organic disease, and only 50 had clear-cut organic disease.[3] It has been estimated that from 12 to 20 per cent of all patients admitted to a general hospital present conditions and problems that are primarily neuropsychiatric in spite of careful screening on admission to keep psychoneurotic patients out of the hospital. In the face of this tremendous need, it is disturbing to note that of 4,309 general hospitals in the United States only 112 provide for the care of even the mildest nervous, mental, or emotional disturbance.[4]

A recent study of 450 admissions to the medical and surgical wards of New York Hospital showed that 45 patients (10 per cent) were appraised as having severe or moderately severe personality disturbances and 90 patients (20 per cent) as having mild personality disturbances. In one ward for disorders of circulation the percentage was as high as 75 per cent. These disturbances were grouped as follows:

Preexisting personality problems aggravated by infection or trauma (30 per cent).

Personality disturbances precipitated by or first becoming evident in association with infection or trauma (37 per cent).

Personality disturbances with serious defects in structure or function (20 per cent).

Personality disturbances in patients without gross structural defect but with excessive complaints and disturbances of function (8 per cent).

Trauma resulting from personality disturbances (4 per cent).[5]

Many people who have nervous symptoms are productive, some of them brilliantly so, yet most of them are potentially, if not actually, in need of help. In addition there must be many who are too sensitive or self-critical to seek a doctor's help, and who muddle through as best they can. There is, too, a vast group of individuals suffering from somatic disease whose best chances of recovery are effected by the combined efforts of the internist and the psychiatrist.

The treatment of the war-wounded and those who have sustained industrial or other accidents has also its mental hygiene aspect, since a major factor in successful treatment is the development of a healthy attitude and the maintenance of the will to recover. In view of the high accident rate, the number of people who develop startle reactions, reactive depressions, or other symptoms following personal accidents and the number of those who develop symptoms following accidental death of near of kin constitute a problem of considerable size.*

There are still other inadequacies of personality which do not necessarily fall into medical classifications. In a study made some years ago at Harvard University of several thousand people who repeatedly failed in business or profession or were repeatedly out of employment, it was found that 62 per cent of them failed because of personality difficulties or undesirable attitudes, and that only 38 per cent failed from lack of ability or skill. Unhealthy attitudes and personality limitations are also important factors in the high incidence of separation and divorce and the increasing rate of juvenile delinquency.

The findings of Selective Service and the armed forces induction stations confirm these evidences of multiple mental hygiene needs

* Accidental deaths in the United States from the time of Pearl Harbor, December 7, 1941, to June 1, 1946, numbered 355,000, a considerably larger figure than the total of 275,338 lives lost in the armed forces during World War II. Injuries through accident totaled 36,000,000 as compared with the 670,584 wounded in war. The figures for accidental deaths and injuries were compiled by the National Safety Council.

in our population and of the numerical importance of the less serious conditions. Only about 10 per cent of the men rejected suffered from grave mental or personality disorders or major abnormalities of mood; 29 per cent were diagnosed as psychopathic personalities; 54 per cent suffered from psychoneurotic disorders; 4 per cent were addicted to chronic inebriety or the use of drugs; and about 2 per cent were listed as not classifiable.[6]

Psychiatric Residuals of the War

One of the incalculable costs of war is its psychiatric residuals. Just as the human body has no natural protection against bullets, the mind and emotions have no safeguards against breakdown or distress when exposed to the long and severe strains of war. The mental and emotional stability of various groups of people, both military and civilian, has been weakened by the war.

MENTAL HYGIENE PROBLEMS OF THE WOUNDED

Wounds account for our largest group of disabled. According to present statistics about 70 per cent of these battle casualties involve damage to legs or arms, and about 15 per cent involve damage to major nerves. Certain disabling diseases, such as tuberculosis, arthritis, rheumatic fever, and possibly liver disease, will account for another large group. About one soldier in every thousand casualties has his hearing affected. And not even one soldier in every thousand casualties returns home blind.[7]

In the main, the morale of our wounded seems to have been good. But among men with similar wounds there are wide variations in emotional reaction and in the ease with which adjustment is made to continuing handicaps. The specific problems of veterans who have returned with disabilities depend not only on the particular disability but also on the characteristic attitudes and personality of the individual and on his particular situation in life. As Child points out:

In many ways, a disabled person's ability to handle the problems that arise from his disability will depend upon his prior adjustment to certain other problems that have no special connection with it. To what extent, for example, has he learned to depend upon his own resources in dealing with other difficult situations, or to what extent does he expect to take a passive role while those in authority solve his problems for him? How soon will he give up trying when confronted with a problem that seems at first to have no solution? It is only because of this general fact—the interdependence of the disability and other circumstances of life—that the problems of disabled veterans are likely to be any different from those of other persons with similar disabilities.

One man may develop a host of vague but forceful anxieties which may or may not be justified in view of what later actually remains of the man's disability. . . . To some men the loss of any part of the body or of its functioning signifies some sort of loss of integrity. . . . In other instances there are positive reactions, such as pride in an injury as evidence that one has done more than his part in what was expected of him as a soldier or sailor. . . . Again, for some men, injuries have special value in terms of satisfying a peculiar personality need, such as a desire for punishment or an excessive desire for dependency upon other people.[8]

Some men have acute discomfort or very severe difficulty in dealing with the physical environment. Frustration in social activities and loss of self-esteem are experienced to a greater or less degree by virtually all men who have disabilities of either a physical or emotional nature. Men who carry with them residuals of battle reactions or who suffer from nervous ailments or physical disabilities that are not obvious are especially apt to suffer from loss of self-esteem and have special difficulty in relating themselves satisfactorily to other people. From the reading of scores of articles by professional men working with military personnel within the armed forces or with veterans in civilian capacities, one is impressed with the fact that without a single exception the writers emphasize the attitudes of members of a man's family and of others with whom he associates in work or other relationships.[9] Psychiatrists working in army convalescent centers reported marked relapse of some men when they returned from thirty-day furloughs, and it was not an uncommon experience in hospitals where men with amputations were treated and taught how to use their new prosthetic devices to have men refuse proffered furloughs until they had acquired skill in the use of artificial hands or limbs and restored their functions as fully as possible.[10]

Fortunately, the medical profession in recent years has acquired great respect for individual variations among patients suffering from the same disease or similar injuries. Moreover, in the recent war, much more attention was given to the mental hygiene and morale factors in the treatment of men during both the critical and convalescent periods. Most rehabilitation programs have stressed motivation and the stimulation of initiative, self-confidence, and resourcefulness. Procedures such as those suggested by Deaver have been carried out with fair consistency:

1. Make a careful evaluation of the physical capacity of the subject.
2. Motivate the patient to exert conscious effort in his own behalf every hour of the day.
3. Require strong, progressive muscle-developing, "self-actuated" activities.
4. Success comes in working *with* the person and not *on* him.
5. Develop a program of interesting activities which the person can see have a value in his physical, mental, social and vocational rehabilitation.[11]

VETERANS WITH PSYCHIATRIC DISABILITIES

Reference has already been made to the fact that more than 680,-000 men were discharged from our armed forces because of psychiatric illness or inability to adapt to military life. Some of these men with "unseen wounds" adjust to civilian life without unusual difficulty; others who continue to be anxious or suffer from other symptoms will be in need of treatment or special consideration. It cannot be determined at this time exactly what proportion of men will adjust without any kind of professional assistance. But the hope that the disorders of all of these men will promptly pass upon their return to civilian life seems to be based on wishful thinking. In repeated discussions with physicians of the military forces, it has been their unofficial but firm conviction that many of these disorders cannot be expected to clear up without treatment and that they may indeed increase as men return to the complexities of civilian life. Reports of a few factual studies that have been made yield the same conclusion.

Raines, Hohman, and Kolb in discussing severe combat reactions state:

In spite of the situational precipitation of these disorders, relief from active duty alone does not result in recovery. No one of our combat fatigue cases whose illness has outlasted the Naval hospital stay has recovered by being handed a discharge from Naval service. Good evidence for the ultimate recovery of these cases is coming to hand, but the reports are convincing that time and assiduous care are required to effect the return to pre-illness adjustment and mental health. . . . It should be stressed that even in the mildest cases of combat fatigue, separation from the service does not result in recovery, and may in fact aggravate symptoms to produce a degree of illness requiring hospitalization. Many sailors, returned from combat, including those who have not sought treatment in service, will require supervision and psychiatric help after demobilization until complete recovery for their unspoken combat fatigue does take place. . . . These are facts of instant importance in plans for demobilization, and now is the time for concentrated psychiatric planning in those agencies charged with the handling and treatment of men discharged from military service.[12]

Brill, Tate, and Menninger[13] conducted a follow-up study of 5,937 men discharged from the Army between May 1, 1943, and January 1, 1944, because of psychoneurosis. The group studied by the Office of the Surgeon General was made up of men who had been out of the service at least six months. In all, 4,178 men replied. There was no demonstrable qualitative or quantitative difference in the replies from those men who signed their names to the questionnaire and those who returned it anonymously. While the replies represent only each man's own evaluation of his health, they indicate an awareness of illness, the extent of which is very striking. In general, these men considered their health to be adversely affected by their military service. They believed themselves to be in poorer health than at induction. They considered their health impairment chiefly in terms of physical disease and in general did not recognize the psychiatric aspect. Of those who had considered themselves to be in good health, 93 per cent stated that their health had deteriorated to fair or poor. Of those who had considered themselves to be in fair health prior to induction, 42.5 per cent regarded their health as poor at the time of the inquiry. Of those who had considered themselves to be in poor health, 80.7 per cent still described their health as poor, and only 19.3 per cent reported improvement in their health status. About 72 per cent of the entire group reported some deterioration in their health as a result of army service. Only 2.1 per cent of the entire group reported improvement in health as a result of service.

Nor did the mere passage of time result in any demonstrable improvement. Some 62.3 per cent considered their health to be the same as at the time of discharge, but 21.2 per cent believed it to be worse than it was at discharge. Only 16.5 per cent believed their health improved since discharge.

A few other points in the study are worthy of comment. The longer these men served in the Army, the more likely they were to consider their health to be affected. Similarly, men who served overseas considered themselves to be sicker than those who did not see overseas service. In addition to poor health, the group reported a need for medical and hospital care which was far beyond their pre-army requirements. For example, since discharge 75 per cent of the entire group have consulted a physician one or more times, generally for the same medical conditions for which they were discharged. Further, 14.6 per cent of the entire group were hospitalized at least once after leaving the Army.

The vast majority of those studied (85.9 per cent) were working full or part time, but definite changes in their employability were apparent. The incidence of their unemployment had increased appreciably in spite of the manpower shortage. More men were unemployed at the time of the study than at the time of induction. Most of the men who were unemployed attributed their failure to work to poor health. There was little indication that they were discriminated against by prospective employers because they had received a medical discharge. While the results of the questionnaire may not be a reflection of the true state of their health, and while these men may consciously or unconsciously exaggerate their disability, nevertheless in the words of this study, "The veterans' own evaluation of their conditions is important and cannot be ignored. The findings indicate that there was little tendency for them to report change in their conditions between discharge and the follow-up study. There is a distinct suggestion of permanence of their disorders in their own minds. Active measures will have to be taken if this attitude or state of affairs is to be influenced."[13]

Social and psychiatric study of groups of neuropsychiatric rejectees and dischargees in New York City in 1944 revealed a high percentage of need of professional service of various kinds. At the time this study was made, few soldiers who had combat experience had then been discharged, so that conclusions drawn from this study may not be applicable to the large group of men who became psychiatric casualties under the stresses of combat. It should be noted further that whereas 82 per cent of the men studied were found to need psychiatric treatment, only 21 per cent were aware of this need or would accept it if offered.

If these percentages were applied to the total number of psychiatric rejectees and dischargees, it would mean that a total of more than 1,900,000 young men may need psychiatric treatment and 475,000 would accept it if available.

We have no corresponding facts regarding the mental health needs of the women in our nation, but on the basis of some experi-

Neuropsychiatric Rejectees and Dischargees in New York City during 1944 with Proportion Needing Each Type of Help[14]

Type of resource needed or being utilized for help	Total (623)	Rejectees (314)	Dischargees (309)
	Per cent	Per cent	Per cent
Psychiatric	82	82	82
Medical and surgical	54	48	60
Vocational	49	44	54
Neurological	11	15	8
Family case work	9	7	10
Group or recreational	4	5	3
Educational	10	5	15

NOTE: Number in parentheses indicates number of persons in group studied.

ence in the women's branches of the armed forces and civilian clinical experience in the past, it is probably valid to assume that a similar percentage of them would profit by some attention to mental hygiene needs.

In a 1945 survey of 5,000 WAC's, one third indicated the need of advice, three fourths of these expressed a desire for information about training and employment opportunities, and one fourth wanted help in reference to personal attitudes and problems. Preston has reported that the higher incidence and more severe degree of breakdown occurred among women whose placement failed to take into account emotional needs.[15] For example, many of the most severe psychiatric problems arose in the cooks' and bakers' school, among women who had entered the WAC particularly to escape that kind of work. By far the lowest percentage of referrals to the mental hygiene unit came from the motor transport section, which is a masculine type of occupation and probably went furthest in fulfilling the needs of many women who enlisted in the Army. Since their return to civilian life many have complained of the reluctance of employers to place them in types of jobs for which they had been trained while in the armed forces.

Rusk reports a comparative study of 455 employees in one company who had been discharged from the armed forces for NP reasons or had been found upon psychiatric examination to have NP tendencies, and a control group of the same number of so-called normal workers. At the end of eighteen months, 250 of the NP group were still employed by the company as against 245 of the control group. Of those whose employment was terminated by the company because of unsatisfactory performance of duties, more than three so-called normals had to be dismissed for one NP.[16]

It is fortunate that some of the men who suffered psychiatric disabilities during their period of military service recover sufficiently upon return to their home communities to be successfully employed, for it would be impossible to provide psychiatric treatment for all. As it is, the Veterans Administration and local communities have been unable fully to meet the demand for appropriate treatment. As of June, 1946, there were 448,235 veterans of World War II on disability compensation rolls because of neuropsychiatric illness and 57.6 per cent of the patients receiving hospital care through the Veterans Administration were suffering from neuropsychiatric illnesses.

Since the autumn of 1945, when large numbers of combat soldiers began to return home, increasing numbers of men discharged on points have been seeking psychiatric consultation from private physicians and community clinics on account of tension which developed after their return. How extensive such delayed reactions may be among men who weathered the entire war without disability cannot be accurately determined, but if experience following World War I can be taken as a clue, it may be expected that the total number of World War II veterans who will suffer from serious psychiatric illness will probably increase annually for the next twenty-five or thirty years, although military experience cannot, of course, be held accountable for all of this increase. At the present time, 68 per cent of World War I veterans being cared for in VA hospitals are psychiatric. The proportion of such patients has been increasing gradually and will, it is believed, continue to increase for another year or two. The number of World War II veterans with psychiatric disabilities is not expected to reach its peak until 1975 or later.

EFFECT OF THE WAR ON THE CIVILIAN POPULATION

It is very difficult to determine what the total effects of the war on civilian mental health has been. But there is little evidence in terms of gross and unquestionable mental illness that the war has been a hazardous experience for civilians. In three representative states, all of which have well-organized departments of mental health, an inquiry revealed little if any tendency toward increase in the number of patients in mental hospitals during the war years. In 1943, the last year for which national figures are available, the number of new admissions to hospitals for the mentally ill declined slightly for the first time in ten years. This decline is not necessarily an indication of a decline in the incidence of mental illness. It may mean only that some patients who in normal times would have been in civilian hospitals were being cared for in military hospitals, or that with the postponement of expansion programs facilities were not available to take care of more patients. It is thought, too, that the labor shortage and greater opportunities for the aged and other marginal groups to obtain employment gave some people a new lease on life and increased their stability.

On the other hand, there is some evidence that the war has resulted in an increase of mental illness and other serious psychiatric disturbances in certain groups of the population. Olkon[17] reported: "At the Cook County Psychopathic Hospital since the war began, a great number of females—wives, mothers, grandmothers, sisters and sweethearts of soldiers—have been committed. Many of these mental breakdowns are traceable to fears and apprehensions for the safety of son, husband, sweetheart or brother. This fact impresses one with the possible remote effects of war on the population at large."

Perhaps the group that has been hit hardest are the young war wives. Kasanin[18] studied a group of war wives in San Francisco, most of them displaced from mid-western areas, who had been left stranded by their husbands' departure for the Pacific. Fortunately a great many of these women had the sense to go back to their home communities. A considerable number of them became outstanding workers in defense plants. A small percentage of them drifted into semi-prostitution and alcoholism. Some of them developed severe psychoneurotic problems, including reactive depressions, psychosomatic disorders, reactivated compulsive states, and marital maladjustments. Most of this group were dependent, immature women who had marked, unrecognized hostility toward their husbands and who reacted to separation with depression, frigidity, a sense of unreality regarding their husbands, and, in a few instances, with unconscious denial of their marriages. With psychiatric treatment most of them recovered. In a series of 50 cases only three were failures.

Bossard[19] has pointed out that in some instances the war effected better family relationships and improved mental health, and Levy[20] has shown that the war had both positive and negative results. In some instances, families were drawn together with a new sense of loyalty and solidarity. Increased opportunities for the very young and the aged were helpful to these groups. Family heads who had lost status during the depression regained their positions. Opportunities for volunteer service enriched family life on an altruistic basis and broadened the contacts of many who had formerly led rather ordinary lives. Mothers who had made household slaves of themselves or whose nerves were frayed by the noisy activity of children in many cases found relief from tension or guilt in war work, and became better parents in consequence. But, to quote Stevenson:

These positive values of the war are to a degree balanced by disadvantages. Privation in some cases has become a liability and increased income has become a basis of demoralization for those unable to deal wisely with abundance. Emancipation has been unduly accelerated in the case of some adolescents and children have been frequently neglected because mothers have been drawn off into war work. The spiritual impoverishment of the home through the loss of members in this way has deprived growing children of the sort of contact with parents that is so essential to full development. And parents have found children running wild on this account. The higher incidence of juvenile delinquents, at least in many places, is an expression of the rapid effect on mental health that is more apt to show itself in the statistics than are the gross psychopathological disorders. Since some of the disturbances are disturbances of growth that incapacitate the individual for future functions, it may be expected that the toll of war will have to be reckoned in years to come.[21]

Considering mental hygiene needs in the years to come, we cannot overlook the fact that approximately three million babies, in addition to the normal number, were born during the war years. Many of these children had a very difficult infancy and childhood. Many suffered from the absence from home of one or both parents, the father at war and the mother at work, from the insecurities of wartime, or from the death of a father (the fathers of 150,000 children lost their lives in the war). These war children, who are entering or about to enter the schools in large numbers, will probably require far more extensive facilities for guidance than are normally provided for in many localities. Among those already appearing in nursery schools and kindergartens, an unusually high incidence of overactivity, aggression, withdrawal, and other symptoms has been reported. Similar expectations are held for the younger group of children who will be the product of the current plethora of divorces and separation growing out of the war, at least in part.

Moreover, as Frank has pointed out:

If we are to judge trends in family life from what is being told us by students in the field, there will be a continued high rate of marriage but with an increasing frequency of divorce, separation or marital conflict. We know there are going to be many full or half orphaned children and adolescents, some from war casualties and others from living with one of the divorced parents. . . . There will be more working wives and mothers compelled to work outside of the home if they are to have marriage, a home and children, because apparently our very efficient business and industry either cannot or will not pay wages sufficient to permit a full time home maker and a full time mother even for children under two. And there will be a housing shortage for several years or longer.

It looks highly probable that the instability of family life will continue and probably get worse with more strains and stresses, both from the socio-economic insecurity and adverse conditions under which people are trying to live, and from the anxieties and conflicts inside the family due to the confusion of masculine and feminine roles, the inability to classify the patterns of relationships within the family, especially with the marriage of people coming from different backgrounds and traditions and with women demanding recognition of themselves as personalities and acceptance of their dignity and worth as persons. As we already know the children and youth will show the impact of that.[22]

Several lines of activity are required to cope successfully with these many mental health problems. The most immediate needs are for research, increased facilities for treatment, and the recruitment and training of additional psychiatric and auxiliary personnel. The orientation and use of other professional groups and the outlines of a constructive mental health program will be discussed in later chapters.

Research

Psychiatry is a relatively new science and while considerable progress has been made in better understanding the psychology of normal personality development and in learning many of the contributing factors in mental and emotional illness, much remains unknown. Except for a few psychoses, such as paresis and alcoholic psychosis, which clearly have an organic basis, there remains much obscurity regarding the causes of mental illness. A proportionately greater degree of progress has been made in understanding the psychoneuroses and allied personality disorders, but here, too, our knowledge remains incomplete. Without fuller knowledge of causes, the cure of some of the psychoses and psychoneuroses remains uncertain. Recent experimentation with various shock therapies has yielded favorable results on a symptomatic level in certain types of mental illness, but there still remains much to be learned.

Some of the impetus for the recent passage of the National Mental Health Act has sprung from the well-recognized need for research in the mental health field. Both prevention and treatment will of necessity be limited until fuller knowledge has been acquired. Research in this field is also one of the primary purposes of the Psychiatric Foundation, recently established under the sponsorship of the American Psychiatric Association and the American Neurological Association.

More and Better Facilities for the Treatment of the Ill

Admittedly, it is the part of wisdom to prevent illness, if possible, rather than to allow it to develop and then undertake treatment. But at the same time, from the point of view of the person who is ill, the demand for prompt and effective treatment has an urgency about it which is apt to be lacking even in well-considered plans for prevention. Sick people want treatment when they are sick, and feel that preventive plans can wait, if necessary. This emphasis has prevailed in medical education generally and in psychiatric education in particular. A humane and responsible society strives to make ample provision for the treatment of its citizens who are ill.

In the field of mental health it is doubtful if anything like adequate provisions for treatment have ever been made in any country at any time. There are a number of reasons for this. In the minds of many people shame and stigma are still attached to mental illness, though this attitude is less prevalent than it was. Because the mind is closely identified with the personality, there is a tendency to ascribe to the ill person responsibility for mental illness, with the result that the illness is charged with guilt and shame which in turn induce concealment and defensiveness. Then, too, because the causes of nervous and mental illnesses are multiple and complex, prejudicial attitudes have yielded much less to such scientific knowledge as we have.

Experience during the war and thus far in the transition period has revealed a most obvious need for more professional services in the field of mental health than are now available. The number of trained psychiatrists, psychiatric social workers, and clinical psychologists was not nearly large enough to meet the demands of the war period. For every psychiatrist which the Army was able to obtain through procurement and assignment, it had to train three general medical officers for psychiatric service.

There are in the United States 600,000 patients in hospitals for mental illness and it is estimated that at least 1,000,000 others are sick enough for hospital treatment. Moreover, there are an additional 8,000,000 people who should be receiving psychiatric guidance and treatment, although not requiring hospital care. It is believed that relatively small proportions of the last two groups are receiving any appreciable treatment.

As for the 600,000 who make up our psychiatric hospital population, it is a well-known fact that in most institutions the care is very inadequate. In most of them standards of care and treatment were reduced during the war period largely because of extreme personnel shortage. Except in very rare instances the care never has been adequate. Recent books such as *The Snake Pit*, and *They Walk In Darkness*, and such articles as "Our Mental Hospitals—A National

Disgrace" and "The Shame of the States—America's Bedlams" describe dramatically some of the grosser defects in our care of the mentally ill.[23] Apathy and stinginess on the part of the public which fails to provide proper funds, stereotype-mindedness on the part of administrators which militates against experimental research into the causes of mental illness and improved methods of treatment, the lack of sufficient numbers of trained physicians, psychiatric nurses, social workers, and ward attendants, have all contributed to inadequate standards of care. On the whole, service has tended to sink to the level of minimal requirements for chronic incurables, although it is a well-known fact that intensive individual treatment during the first few months of illness results in a much higher incidence of recovery than mass treatment which can supply little more than custodial care.

In the next chapters we shall point out the assistance that can be given by workers in various professions to persons suffering from mild psychoneuroses and aberrations of mood or involved in problems of social relationship. General physicians, social workers, clergymen, and other counselors can be of substantial service in relieving minor psychoneurotic disturbances provided they have obtained adequate orientation in mental hygiene and skill in the use of some of the simpler therapeutic tools.

Recruitment and Training of Personnel

The only hope, however, of securing anything like adequate treatment of the mentally and nervously ill is to recruit and train greatly increased numbers of psychiatrists and auxiliary personnel —psychiatric social workers, psychiatric nurses, clinical psychologists, occupational and recreational therapists, and others. Because mental and nervous illness involves the total personality, it is necessary to study each patient physically, socially, and emotionally. Such study is very time-consuming. Moreover, while much can be done through group therapy after the needs of each one have been ascertained through individual study, there are no known effective methods of psychotherapy for masses of people. Individual psychotherapy requires many personal interviews and psychotherapeutic sessions. For all these reasons, large numbers of professional personnel are needed.

It has been estimated, on a basis of what have been found to be reasonably adequate facilities for selected states and communities, that we would need in this country at least 10,000 additional psychiatrists,* a still larger number of psychiatric social workers, and at least half that number of clinical psychologists. Nearly all civilian psychiatric hospitals and clinics are grossly understaffed. The Veterans Administration requires large numbers of all three groups, and the rehabilitation needs of men rejected for or discharged from military service are extensive. It is estimated that an additional 3,000 psychiatrists and a comparable number of psychiatric social workers and psychologists are needed to care for the psychiatrically disabled in the veteran group alone, entirely apart from those in the general population. It is thus obvious that one of our most important tasks is to recruit men and women for work in these fields and provide more training opportunities at once.

Efforts are being made to recruit from present and forthcoming classes in medical schools large numbers to specialize in psychiatry. These efforts will help to meet the need for personnel four or five years ahead. It will not meet the immediate and pressing current demands.

Our only hope for additional physicians who are mature enough to be trained immediately in psychiatry is in the thousands of medical officers who were in the armed forces. Approximately 2,500 of these had brief orientation courses in psychiatry and also some valuable experience in the neuropsychiatric service. Others, assigned to medical and surgical services, expressed an interest in psychiatry. After their release from medical service several hundreds of these young medical officers applied for psychiatric train-

* See Appendix A for listing of various needs for psychiatrists and the bases of computation.

ing through the Psychiatric Personnel Service of the National Committee for Mental Hygiene and the American Psychiatric Association.

Unfortunately, there are insufficient numbers of training residencies. In 1946 there were in 155 institutions 758 assistant residencies and residencies approved by the Council on Medical Education and Hospitals of the American Medical Association and by the American Board of Psychiatry and Neurology.[24] Obviously we must increase the facilities for psychiatric education. University hospitals will carry their share. Some psychiatrists in private practice who have teaching skill will contribute part time if they are given an opportunity to affiliate with teaching centers.

The 32 NP hospitals of the Veterans Administration will offer opportunities for training when they are converted into modern teaching and research centers. Much progress in that direction has been made since the end of the war. In some instances teachers are imported, but more often training programs are focused in hospitals near established university teaching centers. The Veterans Administration's new mental hygiene clinics also provide training opportunities. Forty hospitals and clinics, with 39 medical schools cooperating, are now used as training centers. In these ways additional residencies have been made available. New facilities for teaching could also be provided by the establishment of a psychiatric service in general medical hospitals which do not have such service. There is considerable interest in such expansion at the present time.[25] If it could be speeded up, internists and psychiatrists jointly could provide valuable training in the methods of dealing with psychoneurotic and psychosomatic disorders. Some state hospitals are organized as good training centers. More of them could become teaching centers. This would automatically improve standards of care, for it is axiomatic that teaching and good medical practice go hand in hand.

Training for specialization in psychiatry is a rigorous discipline.[26] It must include inpatient and outpatient experience with psychoneurotic and psychotic conditions. Such training is always on-the-job training, during which the student psychiatrists treat patients under expert supervision. If such training could be provided through the outpatient clinics and hospitals of the Veterans Administration and through private and state psychiatric hospitals and established university clinics, thousands of veterans and other patients could be given immediate treatment which otherwise would be unavailable to them.

In the past we have failed to prepare the graduates of medical schools to function as psychiatrically oriented practitioners. We will continue to fail until every medical school recognizes psychiatry as a basic science and makes adequate provision for it in the curriculum. The teaching emphasis should be upon the recognition and management of the psychoneurotic and psychosomatic disorders, for these will constitute the bulk of the young graduate's medical practice. Effective teaching methods will increasingly utilize teaching films, supervised clinical work with patients, and seminar methods of teaching. It will also emphasize the use of auxiliary personnel (psychiatric social workers and clinical psychologists) and community services for the promotion of mental health.

To meet some of the demand for larger numbers of trained social workers, clinical psychologists, and psychiatric nurses, special efforts have been made to recruit for training in these fields men and women released from the armed forces who have had good educational background and who while in the service had had experience in working with people in classification work, instruction, medical corps, personal affairs, and hospital work. Professional schools have been flexible and fairly liberal in allowing credits for special training and experience in the armed forces.

Training for psychiatric social work has for many years been well standardized by the American Association of Psychiatric Social Workers* and advanced training in psychiatric nursing

* See Appendix B for outline of training requirements.

has been standardized by the National League of Nursing Education. The training of psychologists has too frequently failed to include work in psychiatric or mental hygiene clinics where students learn to work cooperatively with psychiatrists, social workers, and other specialized personnel. Recent proposals by a joint committee of the American Psychiatric Association and the American Psychological Association, if adopted, may help to correct this failure in the training of clinical psychologists.

There is need also for further in-service training of general practitioners, psychologists, social workers, and other auxiliary groups now at work, inasmuch as many people who have mental health problems seek help from these groups, especially in the many smaller communities where there are no stated psychiatric or mental hygiene clinics or hospitals.

As a rule, psychiatrically disabled people turn first to their family doctors, though the family doctor is often psychiatrically the least informed person to help them. An active program providing psychiatric orientation for practitioners of general medicine is urgently needed. The Commonwealth Fund conceived and organized an experimental course at the postgraduate level which was presented at the University of Minnesota in April, 1946, and which proved a success. Extensive planning went into the development of content and methods for such education of general practitioners and non-psychiatric specialists and the results are available for teaching groups.[27]

A similar program could be arranged for industrial and college physicians. In several states, more than half the practitioners who have been questioned by state medical societies as to graduate training needs have requested such orienting postgraduate courses in psychiatry. Thoroughgoing indoctrination of general practitioners to prepare them to be effective psychotherapists requires more training than can be offered in brief courses. To this end psychiatrists and internists might jointly carry major teaching responsibilities in medical and surgical outpatient clinics and wards. If every general hospital, whether connected with a university or not, had psychiatric teachers available for the education of practitioners, the number of physicians with a psychiatric orientation could be extensively increased.

In-service courses in mental hygiene and psychiatric social service will be of benefit to groups of social workers who are not fully trained in this specialty, including those engaged in administrative and group work, as well as case workers.

If academic psychologists without clinical experience who have worked exclusively in educational systems have opportunities to work in clinical set-ups as members of a professional team, their understanding of social and emotional problems and their skill in dealing with them will be greatly enhanced.

Clergymen, educators, and personnel men, foremen, and supervisors in business and industry will find in-service courses in mental hygiene helpful. Such courses would not attempt to make psychotherapists of these men, but could help them to do more effective counseling in their respective fields and aid them in directing the more seriously disturbed to places where more definitive treatment is available.

Effective Organization of Mental Health Services

As with other services needed by large numbers of people, there must be effective organization for mental hygiene services if maximal benefits are to be attained. Until the passage of the National Mental Health Act on June 3, 1946, such organization as was provided at the national level was distributed throughout several governmental agencies, namely, the United States Public Health Service, the Office of the Surgeon General of the Army, the Bureau of Medicine and Surgery of the Navy, and the Children's Bureau of the Department of Labor. The Bureau of Public Assistance of the Social Security Board and the Office of Vocational Rehabilitation of the Federal Security Agency have also had some interest in the field and have been authorized to pay for mental hygiene services, but not to administer any service directly. In none of them has there been an adequate relationship with state agencies nor has there been in many of them any consistent program of mental hygiene education, although the Children's Bureau has been fairly active in this field.

The recent passage of the National Mental Health Act and the appointment of the National Mental Health Council and a panel of consultants will unquestionably result in many improvements. This Act authorizes the construction and equipment of a hospital and laboratory buildings and facilities for a National Mental Health Institute to be erected in Bethesda, Maryland, in connection with the Naval Hospital there. It is to be operated by the United States Public Health Service as a center of research into the nature, causes, treatment, and prevention of mental diseases and also as a center for the advanced training of psychiatric and auxiliary personnel. It is planned to have the Institute in operation by 1950 or 1951. The Act also authorizes the appropriation of a large sum of money (approximately five million dollars for 1947–48) to provide grants-in-aid to public and private agencies for psychiatric research, for the training of psychiatrists, psychiatric social workers, clinical psychologists, and psychiatric nurses, and for the development of community clinics and resources throughout the states on a nation-wide basis. This is a significant step toward public awareness of the vast unsolved problems of national mental health and toward the assumption of public responsibility for meeting them.

Heretofore for every dollar spent to advance knowledge of the cause, diagnosis, and cure of mental disease, the American people have spent $100 to care for the known mentally ill. This new law should mark the beginning of the end of such a lopsided and expensive handling of the mental health problem since it provides for research not only at the National Mental Health Institute, but also through grants to public and private agencies for research in the field. It is hoped that much of the obscurity regarding the causes of mental disease may be removed in the course of not too many years and sufficient knowledge acquired to make preventive programs effective. Our universities, hospitals, and research laboratories now have before them unprecedented opportunities to throw further light on the cause and prevention of mental illness. Experimental research into methods of treatment will likely yield more satisfactory results in therapy.

The Mental Health Act will definitely speed up the recruitment and training of personnel so badly needed to staff our hospitals and clinics for the mentally or nervously ill. Since the Surgeon General is empowered to make grants to states, counties, health districts, and other political subdivisions of the state for the establishment and maintenance of mental health clinics, child guidance clinics, psychiatric social services, and services to veterans not provided for by the Veterans Administration, the new law will aid greatly in bringing much needed help to thousands of smaller communities throughout the country which heretofore have had no such facilities.

There is real concern and evidence of wise planning on the part of the council and the consultants of the United States Public Health Service to the end that there may be adequate integration of services provided by the various governmental agencies already mentioned. Through the stimulation of interest and aid to states in developing more adequate facilities, it will be possible for the various federal agencies to obtain more often the local services that are needed. The law does not insure that equally high standards of work will be maintained in all the governmental agencies interested in the field. Creation of a cabinet post with responsibility for health and welfare might help to further effective coordination.

Responsibility for the administration of the National Mental Health Act at the national level is vested in the Surgeon General of the United States Public Health Service, who has the assistance of the National Advisory Mental Health Council of six members. The Surgeon General and the Advisory Council have the full cooperation of organized professional groups represented in three major committees and of the National Committee for Mental Hygiene.

At the state level, there is still much to be desired. In quite a number of states each state hospital and each institution for the care of delinquent or feeble-minded children is almost a law unto itself with no direction from any division of state government, except a review of fiscal policies and budget by the division of government responsible for the construction of buildings and the expenditure of state funds. In many states, too, mental health services are concerned almost entirely with the care of the seriously ill and the feeble-minded. As has been pointed out, the large majority of both veterans and non-veterans suffering from neuropsychiatric disorders fall into the psychoneurotic rather than the psychotic group. For that reason, in developing mental hygiene facilities much more emphasis needs to be placed on psychiatric outpatient treatment and on social services in home communities. The provisions of the National Mental Health Act for grants-in-aid to states and communities should help greatly in this, but realistic planning and sound administration will have to be provided at the state and local levels.

The creation of a state division or bureau of mental health would help to maintain standards of hospital care and outpatient service. Such state agencies, if their staffs have the proper orientation and professional equipment, can also aid greatly in educating the people of the state along mental hygiene lines (see pages 399–402 for further discussion of mental health education).

Only about half the states have a state mental hygiene society and some of these do not have a professionally trained staff or executive. While good administration of the state governmental agency concerned with mental health can do much to maintain adequate standards of service, an informed and interested public is the best guarantee that services will be adequate. The development of understanding and interest is very largely dependent upon the work of voluntary agencies such as a state society for mental hygiene. The National Committee for Mental Hygiene has recently undertaken to bring more assistance to states in organizing such societies and developing balanced and adequate programs. This work would be speeded up by provision for additional field staff and the preparation of sound educational materials.

Communities having the best mental hygiene services are those in which consistent long-term planning has been done by all the major groups interested in the health and well-being of the citizens. In such communities mental health services are not isolated from other community interests or other needs of the people, but are undergirded by a mental hygiene emphasis in family living, schools, churches, industry, recreation, and general community welfare and are sustained by an active interest on the part of large numbers of the residents of the community. While national and state governments can do much to promote mental health, the whole job really gets done only through understanding and sound organization in the local community.

Communities should continuously evaluate the adequacy or inadequacy of their facilities for meeting the needs of people, and where unmet needs are found, take concerted action to increase and strengthen services. On the basis of experience during and since the war, many communities are finding it necessary to give further attention to a central information service, to physical and mental health, to family consultation and guidance, to vocational and educational guidance, and to plans for full, year-round employment and for adequate recreation for both children and adults.

REFERENCES

1. United States Bureau of the Census, Patients in mental institutions, Washington, Government Printing Office, 1944; and J.A.M.A. Hospital No., 1944.

2. Strecker, E. A.   Psychiatric education.   Ment. Hyg. 14:797–812, October 1930.

3. McLean, F. C. Psychiatry and general medicine. Ment. Hyg. 16:577–588, October 1932.

4. Salmond, P. H. Importance and value of psychiatric ward in public and private general hospitals. Dis. Nerv. System 5:233–236, August 1944.

5. Mittelmann, B., A. Weider, L. Brodman, D. Wechsler, and H. G. Wolff. Personality and psychosomatic disturbances in patients on medical and surgical wards; a survey of 450 admissions. Psychosom. Med. 7:220–223, July 1945.

6. Mental disease in selective service registrants. Washington, National Headquarters Selective Service, 1945.

7. United States Army, Office of Surgeon General, Technical Information Division. The physically disabled. Ann. Am. Acad. Polit. & Social Sc. 239:10–19, May 1945.

8. Child, I. L. Personal adjustment of the disabled veteran. Ann. Am. Acad. Polit. & Social Sc. 239:135–143, May 1945.

9. Mowrer, E. R., and H. R. Mowrer. The disabled veteran in the family. Ann. Am. Acad. Polit. & Social Sc. 239:150–159, May 1945.

10. Nathan, C. R. Service to amputees. The Family 25:363–369, February 1945.
Nathan, C. R. Service to plastic surgery cases. The Family 26:9–15, March 1945.
Nathan, C. R. Servicemen and tropical diseases. The Family 26:123–129, June 1945; 26:189–194, July 1945.

11. Deaver, G. G. Functional education in rehabilitation. In New York Academy of Medicine, Committee on Public Health Relations, Convalescence and rehabilitation, p. 89–94. New York, the Academy, 1944.

12. Raines, G. N., L. B. Hohman, and L. C. Kolb. Methods of recovery in combat fatigue and the influence of therapy. In Proceedings of The Association for Research in Nervous and Mental Disease 25:171–180, December 15, 1944.

13. Brill, N. Q., M. C. Tate, and W. C. Menninger. Enlisted men discharged from the Army because of psychoneuroses; a follow-up study. J.A.M.A. 128:633–637, June 30, 1945.

14. Ginsburg, S. W. The need and demand for psychiatric care among neuropsychiatric rejectees and dischargees, p. 3 and 5. New York City Committee on Mental Hygiene, 1945.

15. Preston, A., Jr. The mental hygiene unit in a WAC training center. Ment. Hyg. 30:368–380, July 1946.

16. Rusk, H. A. Rehabilitation. New York Times, March 17, 1946.

17. Olkon, D. M. Effect of war and army life contingencies on the behavior and breakdown of the inductee and soldier. Dis. Nerv. System 5:243–249, August 1944.

18. Kasanin, J. S. Personal communication. Based on research project, Neuroses of war wives.

19. Bossard, J. H. S. Family problems in wartime. Psychiatry 7:65–72, February 1944.

20. Levy, D. M. The war and family life; report for War Emergency Committee, 1944. Am. J. Orthopsychiat. 15:140–152, January 1945.

21. Stevenson, G. S. Civilian mental health in wartime. Dis. Nerv. System 6:173–178, June 1945.

22. Frank, L. K. Some postwar social trends which are of special interest to orthopsychiatry. Am. J. Orthopsychiat. 16:5–7, January 1947.

23. Ward, M. The snake pit. New York, Random House, 1946.

Philtine, E. C. They walk in darkness. New York, Liveright, 1945.

Maisel, A. Q. Our mental hospitals; a national disgrace. Life, May 6, 1946.

Deutsch, A. The shame of the states; America's bedlams. Reader's Scope, October 1946.

24. J.A.M.A., 131:1344, August 17, 1946.

25. Cunningham, J. M. The development of psychiatric service in the general hospital and its relation to the veteran. Am. J. Orthopsychiat. 15:463–471, July 1945.

26. Rennie, T. A. C. Needed: 10,000 psychiatrists. Ment. Hyg. 29:644–649, October 1945.

27. Smith, Geddes. Psychotherapy in general medicine; report of an experimental postgraduate course. New York, Commonwealth Fund, 1946.

Bauer, W., D. D. Bond, H. W. Brosin, D. W. Hastings, M. R. Kaufman, J. M. Murray, T. A. C. Rennie, J. Romano, H. G. Wolff. Teaching psychotherapeutic medicine; an experimental course for general physicians. Edited by H. L. Witmer with an introductory chapter by Geddes Smith. New York, Commonwealth Fund, 1947.

PART THREE
SOURCES OF HELP IN TREATMENT AND PREVENTION

VI

CONTRIBUTIONS OF THE PRACTICING PHYSICIAN

In February, 1945, a group of medical and psychiatric educators drawn from civilian and military life met at Hershey, Pennsylvania, to discuss the broad problem of psychiatric care for veterans. One outstanding fact emerged from those three days of discussion, namely, that the need is vastly beyond the limited number of psychiatrists available to meet it. It was agreed that for the treatment of minor psychiatric disturbances, both those directly related to war experiences and those in the population as a whole, it will be necessary to call upon the services of the 185,000 practicing doctors of America. Since most of these physicians have been poorly equipped by our usual educational procedures to comprehend or manage the problem, some training will have to be provided.[1] There have been many indications that practicing doctors want psychiatric orientation. In several states, half or more of the doctors questioned by the state medical societies as to their need for graduate education asserted their preference for additional training in psychiatric principles. Such training might well take the form of refresher courses like that organized by the Commonwealth Fund and presented at the University of Minnesota in 1946.[2] The results obtained were startlingly positive and indicated that general physicians and non-psychiatric specialists can in a relatively brief fashion be taught the simple and effective principles of the psychiatric understanding and management of everyday problems of medical practice.

NOTE: In the organization of this chapter, full credit is given to General William C. Menninger who has contributed the most concise and helpful statement for general medical men that we know.[3]

This brief chapter can provide little more than an introduction to such training. If it serves to stimulate interest, sympathy, and cooperation for the better medical care of veterans and other sick people, if it adds even a little to the reader's understanding of the psychoneurotic and psychosomatic responses and increases his appreciation of the patient as a living, dynamic person involved in a disease process, it will have done enough.

The physician's function is to treat people, not diseases. There are few diseases that do not have their emotional components, and this is often of first importance in the etiology, the course the disease may take, the length of convalescence, and recovery or chronicity. The old-time family doctor was uniquely successful in treating his patients because, though he had no knowledge of psychiatry, he knew them as people, their families, their backgrounds, their communities, and their day-by-day problems. With the increasing specialization of medicine and the growing preoccupation with particular areas of the human body, the person having the disease came to be more and more neglected. The specialty of psychiatry has brought into modern medicine a renewed emphasis on the importance of knowing the human being and has developed specific techniques and procedures of scientific validity for the understanding of the person. With knowledge of these principles the physician will be in a better position to practice what Dr. David P. Barr felicitously calls "comprehensive medicine." Could such an orientation be guaranteed to every young graduate, fewer unnecessary surgical operations would be performed, support and understanding would be available to more patients throughout their illness, and many people would be spared the process of running fruitlessly from one doctor to another in search of help which they do not find. The general physician is in the major position to help troubled and emotionally sick people. To this end it is of the first importance to attempt to elicit from every doctor his interest, sympathy, curiosity, and his desire to help sick people in the fullest sense.

War and the experience of military doctors have brought a re-newed awareness of this need and have revealed disturbing facts concerning the number of people who require such attention. Specific findings as to the incidence of psychiatric disorders have been presented in Chapters I and V. The physician should know that there is little fundamental difference between many of the neurotic responses to military life and those of the ordinary civilian. The chief difference is that in the military experience the precipitating stresses are greater and the dynamics are closer to the surface and more easily understood. The principles of treatment to be outlined here are the same for all neuroses, those of veterans and civilians alike.

In analyzing the failure of our past medical efforts certain difficulties can be offered in extenuation. For one reason or another, the psychiatrist has failed in the task of educating his colleagues and the general public. He has been too long isolated from the stream of general medicine. He has usually worked in specialized hospitals remote from general hospitals and has been unable to share his specific knowledge and techniques, too often beclouding his work with strange, incomprehensible language. He is frequently a poor internist, unable to combine the resources of internal medicine and psychiatry in his diagnostic evaluations. On the other hand, the internist has remained equally aloof from psychiatry. He frequently has ingrained attitudes of pessimism and nihilism toward it. He lacks the confidence to attempt the evaluation and treatment of emotional factors. He complains of the time involved in the process and claims that the techniques are intangible and non-scientific. Such objections are not valid. To be sure time is involved, but little more than in any really comprehensive physical work-up with its long delays in x-ray and laboratory studies. Psychiatric techniques are scientifically valid and although not measurable by the usual sensory perception methods of internal medicine, they are none the less based on sound principles of observation and evaluation and the pragmatic test of recovery.

Constructive Attitudes

Until the general physician's attitude toward psychotherapy becomes one of constructive optimism, little can be expected from him as a therapist. He must begin with the conviction that medicine deals not primarily with disease entities or organ pathology but with human beings reacting to various kinds of noxious stimuli. These may be chemical, bacteriological, or physical trauma or emotional unrest. Whatever the precipitating factor the end-result is the same: a sick human being. It is impossible to differentiate between "organic" and "functional"; every illness has both elements. Preeminently the physician still has to learn to recognize emotions in their many varieties and their total effect upon the person. His greatest effectiveness lies in taking a complete and proper history which gives due emphasis to the individual's emotional make-up and responses. He must learn how to establish an effective rapport or working relationship with his patient, and he will succeed in this in direct proportion to the degree of genuine interest he shows. A good relationship is facilitated by his sensitive and kindly inquiry into the patient's personal life, his respect for the facts he obtains thereby, his unfeigned desire to be helpful, his unspoken interest as evidenced by his undivided attention, his capacity for silence, his facial expression, smile, and gesture, and his mere willingness to take the time to listen. He must learn to recognize that everything the patient says and does is of importance, that the patient's reactions during the physical examination may be as important as his utterances in revealing sensitiveness and prevailing emotional attitudes. Of equal importance are the observation and evaluation of his own reactions toward the patient. Only thereby can he avoid those common pitfalls: telling the patient that there is nothing wrong with him or that his troubles are "imaginary" or immediately resorting to sedatives for relief when they are clearly not indicated. He may give too much attention to the physical examination, thereby heightening the patient's anxiety and implanting the impression that things are seriously at variance from the normal when they are not. He may waste time in protracted laboratory studies to no avail or, what is more important, he may let his own emotional responses color his evaluation and management. Unless he understands his own emotional life, he may err in the direction of too much sympathy, paternalism, and protectiveness, or the converse: indifference to the problem, abrupt dismissal of the patient, peremptoriness, show of annoyance, disdain, anger, scolding, or thinly disguised punitive behavior. Perhaps such self-analysis is asking too much of the general physician. He may be little inclined to study or analyze his own emotional responses toward his patient, although he would be a better physician if he did. It may be enough to ask that he learn to control his own emotional reactions to his patient. If his attitude is primarily disdain and annoyance toward nervous patients, he should not try to treat them.

Varieties of Conditions Encountered in Practice

The general physician need not be seriously concerned about psychiatric diagnostic terms. Diagnoses are at best convenient labels. They add little to the patient's understanding of himself. They often confuse and cloud the issue, and they are quite unimportant compared to the understanding of the facts and how they work. The diagnosis of psychoneurosis can badly frighten a patient who does not understand the meaning of the term and who has heard much about it in recent years, with all the unfortunate and frightening connotations that it so frequently and falsely conveys to the uninformed person. To tell him that he has a nervous illness or that he is emotionally sick is usually acceptable and does no harm to the facts or to the patient.

Certain common and frequent problems of an emotional nature present themselves daily to every experienced physician in his practice. Common sense has taught him to recognize the psychotic or grossly mentally disturbed individual. He knows that delirious reactions can result from fever, over-medication, alcohol. He has seen patients in postoperative states of excitement. He can easily recognize the seriously depressed individual with his suicidal preoccupations. With these problems he is relatively little concerned since they usually require the psychiatrist's attention. More commonly, however, he will encounter the patient with a well-defined organic illness who reacts with such strong emotion to it that convalescence is delayed, symptoms are protracted, and there is little or no response to the usual medical regime. Second, he will encounter individuals whose disease picture represents a combination of physical and emotional problems (such conditions as peptic ulcer, colitis, hypertension, asthma, and so forth). Here he needs to know whether the patient's emotional state is the fundamental cause, aggravates, explains fluctuations, or determines the entire course of the disorder. These disturbances fall under the heading of that much misused term "psychosomatic" illness, an area of medicine which requires the joint cooperation of internist and psychiatrist. There is growing evidence that many of these states begin first with emotional unrest and that protracted periods of emotional disturbance may ultimately lead to permanent and irreversible organic changes. Third, he will come to recognize a group of patients whose genuine physical complaints are primarily expressive of emotional disorders: the fatigue states and the insistent bodily complaints which the ordinary techniques of medical examination are inadequate to explain. Fourth, there will be those patients whose complaints are predominantly psychic in nature. These individuals put to the foreground their symptomatology of anxiety, fear, obsessive thoughts, and compulsive actions. In all these groups, some patients may spontaneously recognize the role of their emotional disturbances in the cause, or particularly in the fluctuation, of their symptoms. They will have partial insight. The general physician may be as yet little acquainted with a fifth group of patients, those who present the interesting phenomenon of repeated accidents, and who represent a special kind of personality make-up. The industrial physician recognizes this group, for he knows that the majority of accidents occur repeatedly among a small group of workers. The surgeon, the gynecologist, the genitourinary and other specialists will recognize the particular problems of individuals who do not respond to repeated manipulations, who get persistently worse in spite of or because of them, who may be rendered chronically disabled unless techniques other than physical manipulation are employed. There are patients who seek and crave operations, others who seem almost addicted to genital, pelvic, and cystoscopic procedures. Finally, every physician must learn to recognize the depressed patient with his characteristic sadness, insomnia, weight loss, gloomy outlook on life, and risk of suicide.

Essential Orientation for Psychotherapy

What, other than recognition, can the general physician do about these disorders? First, he must become convinced that these states are never conscious or feigned or deliberate, that they are beyond the average patient's capacity to resolve, that the true causes are largely unconscious or unknown to the patient, and that they are always indicative of emotional conflict within the person. The simplest example is anxiety. We are all familiar with normal anxiety responses, because we have all experienced them: the dry throat, the trembling hands, the tightening of the chest, the nausea, the diarrhea, the polyuria. The entire organism is involved in anxiety responses; we have learned to study the cardiovascular changes, the increased leucocyte count, the metabolic and chemical imbalance accompanying anxiety. States of anxiety instead of being transient may become protracted, chronic, sweepingly disabling, and may arise whenever external stress or threat is present or whenever the threat derives from unrecognized conflicts within. Anxiety may be considered a natural defense mechanism of the human being which is called into play whenever the person is threatened. Many of the phenomena of psychiatry can be understood as the person's attempt to handle this anxiety. The patient may experience it directly with all its attendant physical discomforts. He may attempt to protect himself from its pain by the development of physical complaints. He may deny it and escape from it by substituting hysterical symptoms to which characteristically he is emotionally indifferent. He may project it upon others as blame and suspicion; or he may rationalize it to himself by all kinds of thinly disguised and false explanations. None of these mechanisms is deliberate. Anxiety in essence, then, represents the attempt of the organism to achieve some kind of balance within itself. The degree of anxiety a person can tolerate or the point at which he reaches his dilemma of sickness depends in part upon his constitutional stability and capacity to bear stress, upon the severity of the noxious stimuli or events of his life, and upon the degree and stress of his internal conflicts. It is important for the physician to recognize also that the organism can be similarly thrown off balance by anger, rage, resentment, fear, jealousy, and suspicion. The physician will be most effective, therefore, in treating psychoneurotic conditions when he learns to recognize and deal with the vast range of emotional responses of which people are capable.

The mere recognition of these facts, although helpful, is not enough. In the treatment of psychoneurotic patients, the physician needs to know that hospitalization is rarely an adequate solution; that it may make the condition worse by providing too much attention, by putting a premium upon illness as a mode of reaction, by recourse to bed rest with its attendant increased preoccupations. These patients are best treated as ambulatory patients in repeated visits to the physician's office. Such visits can be brief; half an hour may suffice if the patient is not merely permitted to rehearse symptoms but is obliged to search into causes. Similarly the physician should know that like most surgery the effects are best when therapy is begun promptly and as early in the illness as possible. His main tool will be language through conversation. He must recognize that he will play a vital and significant role in which he will find the patient thrusts upon him all kinds of emotions and feelings, most of which are not related directly to him, but represent the transfer to him of feelings, attitudes, and emotional responses that have their origin in the patient's earlier life. He must expect the positive emotions of respect and admiration, but he must be equally prepared to accept the negative and hostile feelings which the patient may have toward him. He must not be threatened or misled by the patient's anger, resentment, criticism, or dislike. Some such feelings will inevitably appear as a phase in treatment.

His therapy begins with his very first contact with the patient, is maintained throughout the physical procedures, and hinges preeminently upon the process of history-taking. The cornerstone of psychotherapy lies in the patient-physician relationship. It is not amiss to recall that historically the physician or healer was once a priest. Sick people will turn to the physician with some of the old belief in his magical power to cure. Thus he is invested with attributes that become powerful therapeutic tools. The patient himself is frightened, insecure, and dependent. A strong dependency on the physician usually develops quickly. In taking the history, the physician begins with the patient's complaint, more often than not offered on a somatic level. He should not take the first utterance of the patient as the chief complaint, for this often merely disguises the patient's fundamental problem. The history begins the process of the interview. Numerous treatises have been written on the technique of the interview, all of which stress the importance of permitting the patient free, complete, and spontaneous expression of his problems and needs. An interview is not the same as social conversation. It is a process specially devised to permit the patient to express anxieties and uncertainties, fully and without reservation, to the physician, who will not interfere or hamper the spontaneity by injecting his own personality or his own convictions into the situation. In essence it is sensitive, objective, understanding, non-interfering listening.

The physician's next task is to understand the origin and chrono-
logical development of the complaint and its relation to the full activities of his patient's contemporary life, with particular searching
for evidences of dissatisfaction, conflict, or anxiety relating to contemporary financial, occupational, marital, familial, social, religious, and sexual tangles. Very soon he will see that the onset of
the symptoms frequently coincides with a period of particular
emotional stress or a disturbing contemporary event in the patient's
life. Now he has come to the "present illness" to which the step-by-
step account of the appearance and development of the main complaint in its total personality setting has led him.

With veterans, the major scrutiny should be given to the military experiences for the fullest understanding of the present illness. Often enough, however, it will be seen that life in the armed
forces only exaggerated symptoms that were in existence before.
In that case, the real present illness will date from civilian life. In
Chapter III the common emotional events that cause or have a
bearing on the veteran's present illness have already been enumerated. The general physician should keep them in mind for evaluation as he seeks to understand the present illness in cases of war-
related neuroses.

Getting the Personal History

A brief experience with psychiatric or psychosomatic illness soon
makes it evident that contemporary difficulties have their inevitable precursors in the earlier life period of the individual; indeed,
they are commonly only repetitions of earlier and more basic patterns of adjustment or maladjustment. When the material emerges
spontaneously a rigid history review may not be necessary. For
the physician's own assurance of completeness, and sometimes for
the orderly accumulation of material, it is well to pursue a planned
review. This constitutes the personal history. The patient is told
that for the physician's fullest understanding of the current diffi-

culties, certain early biographic material must be elicited. One begins then with the record of the patient's birth and any untoward events associated with it; the outstanding data of the infancy and childhood period; evidence of early instability in the form of nightmares, sleepwalking, enuresis, and other so-called neuropathic traits. The outstanding facts are then elicited from the school record—performance and extent of education; the work record in terms of actual job successes, failures, and reasons for change; the family status; the place of the patient in the sibling group. The marital history and status are obtained chronologically with particular emphasis on the adjustment to husband or wife, the relations to or worries about children, the general satisfactoriness or unsatisfactoriness of the sexual adjustment. It is well not to force confessions about sexual orientation during the first interview but to await the development of full confidence before eliciting the details of what is the most sensitive area of most patients' functioning. The general religious, racial, and social adaptation as it relates to friends and community is surveyed for particular evidence of difficulties or failure of adjustment. The degree and extent of use of tobacco, alcohol, medication, and drugs must be obtained.

A brief review of the family history is necessary with particular attention to the incidence of similar complaints among family members and to the incidence of nervous, emotional, or psychotic difficulties. The description spontaneously given by the patient of his outstanding traits of personality make-up gives interesting leads as to undue emotional lability, dependency, conscientiousness, meticulousness, anticipatory anxieties, resentments, and hostility feelings.

When the review has been completed, the physician will have a preliminary over-all view of the person and his major life problems. He should be able to formulate to himself his impressions as to the patient's general level of intelligence, emotional maturity or immaturity, the degree of his innate stability, and the major stresses having a bearing on his present adjustment. If, on the other hand, the facts do not fall together into a picture that makes sense to him, the physician has every reason to ask for psychiatric consultation in order that the meaning and interpretation may be clarified and his course of procedure outlined. He is accustomed to refer unclear problems to other medical specialties for evaluation. The psychiatrist can serve the same function of consultant. In one or a few visits the psychiatric consultant may be able to orient the internist to the problem so that he can carry on unaided. This is the case with patients who have simple problems. Others have more complex problems that require psychiatric evaluation and treatment. For still others, therapy is best carried out jointly by internist and psychiatrist. The treatment of involved neurotic reactions should be turned over to the psychiatrist.

Having ascertained the facts, what specifically can the general physician hope to do about them? He may decide upon one of two procedures: to help the patient rid himself of his crippling emotional reactions or to help him deal with them constructively and perhaps to wall them in. This he can do in two main ways: by helping to modify the unbearable situations of life, or by attempting to modify the patient so he can better tolerate the unbearable situation. Both procedures are included in what is called psychotherapy. Let us examine them in more detail.

Working with Environmental Stresses

The physician may have found that the patient is faced with very real difficulties in his contemporary life. When these can be changed or alleviated, they should be. This may involve talking with members of the family to give them understanding of the illness; to relieve their anxiety about the sick person; to give them confidence in the therapist's attempt to cure the illness; to clarify the problem of the tangled emotional relations with husband, wife, or parents; to minimize the tendency on the part of relatives to be overindulgent or oversevere; to act as marital and family counselor;

to help with problems of emancipation; or to counsel in the sexual problems of husband and wife to the end that both have satisfaction. Today fourth-year medical students in some schools are discovering how enlightening a visit to the home of their patients may be in revealing attitudes, tensions, and socio-economic factors that bear upon the illness. A brief history from a close relative may throw additional and revealing light upon the patient's problem.

Much can be done, too, by analyzing and attempting to correct unhappy, stressful work and school situations. Employers need to have psychological interpretation of their employees' difficulties and increasing numbers are seeking it. They usually welcome help in arranging work assignments and in understanding the workers' problems and needs. Much can often be accomplished by a change to better and more appropriate work or school placement. If the physician is in doubt of what to advise, he can often get professional help through employment counselors. It should be remembered that overwork is more often the symptom than the cause of a neurosis, although overwork at uncongenial tasks may aggravate the condition.

Where economic and social privations are extreme, the physician can usually get help through the various social agencies in his community. He needs to remember that every human being functions best within a framework of balanced work, play, and relaxation. Attention to simple needs can bring much relief, such as regular exercise, vacations, rest, time for relaxation, the necessity of ending each day of work with a mind closed to the task until the next morning. He may prescribe play: a movie, a social evening, or bowling, if need be. Many a patient has found in a sustained hobby an abiding relief from tension and daily strain. It is better than sedatives. Activity is important; bed rest and unearned vacations accomplish little for the psychoneurotic. Specific principles of relaxation can be taught the patient: self-induced muscular relaxation; vigorous exercise of a non-competitive variety; prolonged warm tubs, showers, massage, steam baths. Sedation may be temporarily used for emergency situations. The hygiene of sleep habits can be inculcated.

In brief, where obvious, unbearable stresses exist in the actual contemporary life, they should be alleviated when feasible and practical. Suggestions are in order, but it is well to avoid arbitrary regulation of the patient's life. The wise course is to help the patient come to his own decisions and choices regarding major or critical changes in his usual routine and to adhere to this stand no matter how much the patient pleads for the physician's authoritative decisions.

Relieving Inner Tensions

Situational relief of the kind described, while important, may be unrealizable or only partially effective. Far more important is the effort to help the patient achieve inner security, freedom from anxiety, and an enhanced capacity to meet the reality stresses. For this the "talking therapy" or psychotherapy in its more specific sense is required. The aim of this is to have the patient talk out his troubles, get verbal catharsis or release, get his problems "off his chest," so that he may gain greater understanding of his emotional life and difficulties, free himself from his crippling anxiety, and manage himself more wisely. In the process, the physician will listen more than he will talk. This can hardly be stressed too much. He must learn how to sit and just listen, and he must forego the pleasure of hearing his own voice in order that his patient may freely have the time and opportunity to say what he thinks and feels. He will invite full expression, and he will note whether talking brings genuine relief or merely upsets the patient. By observation of the patient's response he will know how far he can go and what topics to discuss. His task is not to dig out confessions, or to force premature discussion of sexual experiences, or to delve into unconscious motivations. It is rather to create an atmosphere of trust and confidence wherein the patient will spontaneously bring into the discussion his sensitive, anxiety-laden experiences, memories, and phantasies. As the history unfolds, he will recognize that contemporary problems almost always have their prototype in earlier patterns of feelings, habits, and difficulties, particularly as they relate to childhood developments, the powerful family constellations, and the prevailing habits of response to family members. It is surprising indeed how quickly and how spontaneously the contemporary difficulties give way to a discussion of the early life with heavy emphasis on the feelings and emotions experienced toward parents and brothers and sisters. As the patient comes to recognize that he is transposing early feeling tones and traumatic emotions to contemporary people and situations, there may come a degree of insight that brings automatic relief from the present distress. More important is the healing that comes automatically through the talking and sharing with the understanding physician.

Further Techniques

Some degree of explanation to the patient of these mechanisms may be needed. Similarly, explanations of the nature of his symptoms and how they are expressive of emotions may have to be given. The patient has to be taught these simple and to us self-evident, psychosomatic relations. They can be taught him by simple analogies: the somatic responses to talking in public or to taking an examination; and he must then be brought to see the relation of his symptoms to the emotions he has been discussing. This is easier if he can be shown that increase in discomfort commonly occurs when he is in a situation of particular stress. This process is what is meant by the technical term "explanation."

Hand in hand with explanation goes reassurance. Here the physician's authoritativeness and the patient's confidence are of prime importance. The physician needs to know exactly what the physical findings actually are. He himself must perform the necessary physical examinations. The findings of some previous physician will not suffice. The patient wants the reassurance of his therapist's examination and findings. Such reassurance may be necessary repeatedly if the patient is frightened, but it should not be overdone lest it defeat itself by false and hearty optimism. It is more effective when offered sparingly and thoughtfully than frequently and glibly. Properly used, it is a powerful and necessary tool, for it is the voice of authority and protectiveness. The physician should not promise too much, lest he lose face when the promised results do not occur. Once the physical status is settled, it should not be reopened unless for new somatic indications, for it may raise doubts of the physician's competence or certainty and undo all that has been accomplished.

The technique of reassurance may require added persuasion: persuasion that the physician is right, that the patient must relinquish his problem to him, and that the symptom must be given up. If the secondary gain of illness is great, that is, if the patient enjoys his illness, profits by the attention, sympathy, or love it causes, or finds it financially profitable in insurance or compensation, the physician may need to use strong suggestion or direction, or even implied command. Frequently, too, the kindly ignoring of the actual symptom is indicated. Suggestion must also be recognized as a powerful weapon. Any medicine is more effective if it is given with confidence and assurance that it will work. "I feel confident it will help you" may bring remarkable improvement. It should be borne in mind, however, that suggestion, which is apt to be short-lived in its effect, is only a temporary measure to carry over while more effective psychotherapy is being pursued.

The physician's increasing knowledge of his patient will inevitably show him what are the patient's special psychological needs and limitations and will indicate the direction of the reeducational processes. He will see how the personality is poorly balanced; how too much conscientiousness cripples performance; how excessive guilt feelings lead to insecurity and inadequacy; how foreboding anticipation cripples adventuresomeness; how habits of shyness, inarticulateness, distrust, exclusive self-preoccupation, and lack of concern for others handicap social relations and friendships; how life-long attitudes of submission or aggression, temper or withdrawal, interfere with the fullest realization of the patient's potentialities.

Strength and courage and new direction will come to the patient mainly in proportion to what he can express and share with the physician. Haunting memories lose their stigma, and fears and anxieties are relieved when they are talked out freely. The long-haunting worry about masturbation disappears when it is understood as a developmental phase in every normal person's life. Similarly the emotional intensity of other anxieties is reduced if not eliminated through discussion.

In performing this therapeutic function, the physician may be little able to formulate or follow the steps in the process, or to determine whether he has been using techniques of explanation, reassurance, persuasion, suggestion, or reeducation. Few psychiatrists and fewer patients can give logical verbalization to what has happened during the relationship and therapy. The pragmatic test of relief is what really matters.

War has heightened our appreciation of the amount of help and understanding that can be obtained from allied disciplines. The physician should inform himself of the excellent contributions made by the clinical psychologist and the social worker since both are available in many communities and they are ready to add their skills to his study. In the field of psychology, extensive tests have been devised and proved to be of value in determining the kind, degree, and severity of neurotic disability. Such tests as the Cornell neurotic index, the Rorschach test, the Murray Thematic Apperception test for the determination of personality profiles, and so forth. A great variety of intelligence and aptitude tests are available for the better placement of individuals at work or in school.

The social worker is especially trained in the understanding of individual and family relationships and community problems and resources. The history he obtains of the patient will take the physician far in the understanding of the essential personality with which he is dealing. The social worker is also ready to help in finding community resources for recreation, exercise, companionship, housing, special training, and employment and in advising in regard to their use. These major contributions have long been left out of the curriculum of medical schools. Slowly and fumblingly the average doctor stumbles across their usefulness. He would do well to learn to use the full range of social work possibilities in his community.

Skill in therapy comes from experience. Experience involves continued study. A helpful literature for medical practitioners is beginning to accrue. A list of books for further reading appears at the end of this chapter. The journal, *Psychosomatic Medicine,* is also recommended.

It is hoped that this simplified presentation will give physicians fuller appreciation of the fact that patients are improved by appropriate attention to their emotional life. Nothing said so briefly will make the physician a psychotherapist, but it may stimulate his desire to know more about the techniques. If the doctor has achieved an attitude of tolerance toward these disabled people he will already have gained much. If he has been encouraged to look for the emotional attitudes and responses, even though they are not always evident or immediate, he is on the right track.

The question often arises, "Can the general physician afford to take the amount of time necessary for this kind of medical practice?" There are valid reasons for an affirmative answer. If the physician does not allow his patients the amount of time they need to give an adequate history, the result may be an inadequate diagnosis which often leads to prolonged, misdirected, and unsuccessful treatment. The result is that the patient does not get well and seeks another doctor. Furthermore, experience has shown that patients will go to the doctor who knows how to offer understanding, sympathy, and interest in addition to a prescription or physical treatment. There are no patients so grateful as those who have been relieved of their anxiety. The financial aspect of the question is not so easy to answer. Some physicians report that patients are willing to pay somewhat larger fees when they understand that they are being given more time than the usual brief visit. Many patients are quick to understand that an adequate history may lead to fewer visits so that the net cost to them in the end is rather less than if they are kept coming back for repeated physical procedures. Experience shows that the time and expense involved in repeated laboratory studies and x-rays can often be saved for more constructive purposes.

Most physicians get their real satisfaction in the practice of medicine from being able to help people in trouble. By and large the doctors who do the most for their patients get the most out of their practice, in both personal and financial rewards. The approach to the emotions brings the development of a close and enduring relationship with patients. This means an increased interest in medicine and in human problems. It means less wear and tear on the doctor's emotional life. The results become more satisfying and more deeply gratifying. Actually, almost all doctors in practice deal to some extent with emotional and personality factors. The real question, therefore, is not whether they should practice this kind of medicine, but rather whether they will practice medicine badly or well.

Some of the 25 physicians who took the course in Minnesota were interviewed six months later. They uniformly reported a heightened zest in the practice of medicine, the rich rewards of more effective results, a lack of frustration in dealing with chronic problems, and a personal ease and relaxation in practice which they had never previously known. These gains, aside from any monetary considerations, speak strongly in favor of this approach to medical practice.

The Importance of the Nurse in Medical and
Psychiatric Practice

Traditionally, and by training and experience, the nurse's function is closely related to the physician's. Her position calls for new definition and greater appreciation, if nurses are to be retained and recruited in larger numbers as valued members of the therapeutic team.

No member of the medical profession has a greater opportunity for good mental hygiene work than the nurse. Whether working in a hospital, in a home, or in community or public health service, she spends long hours in intimate relationship with sick people, which gives her unusual opportunities to practice mental hygiene principles and to teach others the basic facts of sound emotional health. In the hospital care of psychiatric patients, the nurse plays a most significant role, since it is she who observes the day-by-day behavior, is responsible for the twenty-four-hour care and protection of emotionally sick people, and in large part creates the atmosphere of understanding, supportiveness, gentleness, and psychiatric insight which is most conducive to recovery.

To carry out her various roles more effectively, two major developments are needed. The first is a complete reorientation in our traditional thinking about the nurse's function; the second demands better and fuller educational opportunities in psychiatric principles for all nurses. There was a long time when medical men considered the nurse as a relatively impersonal agent for carrying out medical recommendations and procedures. Modern educators recognize that the nurse plays a leading part in all therapy, that her relationship with the patient is of profound importance in the recovery process, and that the nurse-doctor relationship needs new definition. Just as every medical student today is being better trained in psychiatric principles, so a new kind of nursing education must be developed which will sensitize every nurse during her training period to the principles of personality growth and needs. At graduation she should have some knowledge of normal personality growth and development, mental hygiene, and some awareness of her own personality make-up as it enters into the therapeutic relationship. This training is fully as necessary for nurses planning to work in medicine, surgery, obstetrics, pediatrics, and other specialty fields as in the more specific area of graduate psychiatric nursing.

Such orientation should begin early in the nurse's training, and should not be limited only to the period of affiliation with some psychiatric service, which usually occurs in the third year of student training. Thus equipped, the graduating nurse should not only be more fully aware of herself and her emotional reactions to other individuals as patients, but should have skill in therapeutic interpersonal relationships, in the fundamentals of psychopathology, and in the hour-by-hour therapeutic management of sick people. She should be able intelligently to handle the more common psychiatric and emotional problems displayed by the general medical patient. She will have acquired an appreciation of the patient as an individual, be able to recognize psychiatric symptoms as they appear, and have some skill in managing them. As a result, she will find her task more stimulating, and will increase the worth and value of her own professional status. This kind of training is long overdue, and should be vigorously promoted.

Graduate training programs for psychiatric nursing have been far better planned, but all too few training centers exist, and there are inadequate training opportunities for mature, intelligent nurses who wish to specialize in psychiatric nursing. A valuable report by the Subcommittee on Psychiatric Nursing of the National League of Nursing Education clearly outlines the content and methodology of such training.*

Aside from her role as therapist, the nurse has an extremely important role to fill in public education of individuals and groups and in preventive mental hygiene. The real importance of this role

* An Advanced Course in Psychiatric Nursing, prepared by Subcommittee on Psychiatric Nursing of the Special Committee on Postgraduate Clinical Nursing Courses, published by National League of Nursing Education, 1945.

has long been overlooked. Its potentialities for the vigorous promotion of mental hygiene are tremendous.

REFERENCES

1. National Committee for Mental Hygiene. Medicine and the neuroses. New York, the Committee, 1945.

2. See page 159 and item 27, page 166.

3. Menninger, W. C. Neuropsychiatry for general medical officer. War Department Technical Bulletin, Med. 94. Washington, September 21, 1944.

FOR FURTHER READING

Binger, C. The doctor's job. New York, Norton, 1945.

Dicks, R. L. The ministry of listening. New York, Federal Council of the Churches of Christ in America, 1944.

Dunbar, H. F. Emotions and bodily changes. New York, Columbia University Press, 1935.

Hamman, L. The relationship of psychiatry to internal medicine. Ment. Hyg. 23: 177–179, April 1939.

Levine, M. Psychotherapy in medical practice. New York, Macmillan, 1943.

Menninger, K. A. The human mind. 2d ed. New York, Knopf, 1937.

Preston, G. H. Psychiatry for the curious. New York, Farrar & Rinehart, 1940.

Rennie, T. A. C. Relation of psychiatry to internal medicine. Bull. Johns Hopkins Hosp. 65:265–282, September 1939.

Weiss, E., and O. S. English. Psychosomatic medicine. Philadelphia, Saunders, 1943.

Whitehorn, J. C. Guide to interviewing and clinical personality study. Arch. Neurol. & Psychiat. 52:197–216, September 1944.

VII

CONTRIBUTIONS OF SOCIAL WORKERS

SOCIAL workers have a significant role to play, both in giving services to people who need help with family or other problems in adjustment, and in planning more adequate provisions for meeting human needs and preventing mental and social distress. For several reasons social work is not well understood by the general public. A majority of doctors, ministers, lawyers, and teachers are not well acquainted with the social worker's function nor do they appreciate the training and experience that go into the making of a social worker. The lay person knows even less of the social worker's function unless he happens to have been aided by such a worker in the solution of some problem. Our main concern here is to give a realistic picture of the contributions which social workers can make in the treatment of people with psychiatric, health, family and other social problems and in the broader phases of social research and social planning. A brief account of the development of social work as a profession seems to be needed to dispel some of the common misconceptions and bring out the current emphases in the profession.

As a profession social work is relatively new, the first professional school of social work having been organized in 1898. Compared with the professions of medicine, ministry, and law it is very young. The oldest grandparents have known at least one doctor, one minister, and one lawyer. Members of these professions have been subjects of conversation in every family for generations. Except perhaps for brief contact during the worst of the economic depression a majority of families have not had first-hand contact with professionally trained social workers.

Human distress is, of course, as old as the race and various provisions have been made from time to time to alleviate it. In agrarian societies quite often farmers were forbidden to glean the crops too closely. The law required that enough scattered grain be left so that the poor could glean it as a means of obtaining food. Begging has been a practice in all cultures and nations. It was only in fairly modern times that communities began to take more definite steps to alleviate the most severe forms of human suffering. Hostels were established to provide shelter and, with the development of the medical sciences, hospitals for the care of the sick. The English Poor Laws gave the government some responsibility for providing basic necessities, but in effect poverty was held to be a moral offense and often compulsory labor was made a condition for receipt of food. There was no recognition of the fact that those engaged in alleviating human distress needed any special kind of training or particular skill.

In the United States from the earliest date government's responsibility for the relief of distress was recognized. In New York, for instance, when Peter Minuet landed in 1626 and purchased Manhattan Island from the Indians, he immediately appointed *kranken bezoeckers* to care for the sick and when the government was taken over by the English in 1664 the church wardens were given power to raise taxes for the relief of the poor and the English system of poorhouses and workhouses was later developed.

It was not until after the Civil War that charity organizations, family societies, and children's societies were organized to relieve the multiple family, child, and other social problems that developed in the aftermath of the Civil War and concurrently with the rapidly increasing industrialization and urbanization which then occurred. The first charity organization society was formed in Buffalo in 1877 followed in a short time by similar organizations in most of the major American cities. Behind this organized effort was a recognition of the fact that, in congested areas particularly, there are people who need assistance in earning a living, maintaining a happy family life, taking care of orphaned children, and problems of a similar nature. These organizations in the early days depended largely upon volunteers. Some of them became "permanent volunteers," but as a rule they had no special training to equip them for this work. Naturally, those who were doing the work more or less permanently learned much, but such learning was not well systematized. It was out of a sense of need to systematize that knowledge and to make it available in advance to those who would be undertaking such work that the New York School of Philanthropy was set up as a one-year graduate course in 1898. Fifteen years later it was extended to a two-year graduate course. At the present time the United States has about fifty recognized schools of social work giving professional training for all divisions of the field.

During the many years when well-meaning people were endeavoring to relieve human distress without professional training for their task, certain concepts grew up which still plague the profession to some extent. In those early days the untrained social worker was often regarded as a "Lady Bountiful" who went about dispensing food, clothing, and other necessities. She made the decision as to who would receive her aid. While the charge was not always justified, it appeared to onlookers that she gave or withheld on the basis of her own standards of conduct and personal likes and dislikes, and that, notwithstanding her sympathy and sorrow for the needy, she really looked down upon the recipients of her bounty and enjoyed her superiority. Seldom did she take steps to prevent problems and to help her clients find ways of living comfortably by their own efforts.

In order to conserve resources and to avoid being subjected to the fraudulent appeals of those who posed as needy and looked upon the social worker's help as an easy mode of existence, it became customary to make some investigation before dispensing money or the things needed for living. It was hardly to be expected that untrained people would invariably be tactful or altogether effective in their efforts to determine who was "worthy" and who was "unworthy." Their unskilled methods of investigation led to

the popular conception—which was a favorite subject for carica-
ture by playwrights—of the social worker as a long-nosed snooper
into other people's business. Instead of the round and jolly Lady
Bountiful the social worker came to be thought of as a thin and
austere judge of other people's morals who seemed more interested
in withholding than in giving service, or who imposed her own
standards on people in ways that made it impossible for them to
have any choice in the matter and restricted their liberties. Negative attitudes resulting from the mistakes of those who performed
social work tasks in the pre-professional era became rather firmly
fixed. Fifty years of professional social work has not succeeded
fully in breaking down those early public prejudices. Many people
who have had no first-hand experience with modern, professionally
trained social workers still assume that they combine the characteristics of snooper and Lady Bountiful rather than those of the social scientist and a friendly, democratic, and objective counselor.

Social work developed as a profession largely because of the increasing awareness that human life is extremely complex and that
to help people with their problems of human relationships requires
much knowledge of all phases of daily living. Social work, therefore, attempted what might seem like a contradiction in terms. It
has always specialized in the complexity of life and the significance
of life's many interrelationships rather than in some part of life or
some particular relationship. Its wide scope has often caused misunderstanding. It seemed to the doctor and biologist and chemist
that the social worker could not possibly be scientific and encompass so much. Pretty much the same was true of the economist, the
sociologist, the anthropologist, and others who pursued their studies of particular phases of organized life. Notwithstanding criticisms and misunderstanding, social work has consistently stuck to
its knitting and, whether the pattern of what one must know and
do fitted that of any other profession or not, it has kept its focus on
life's complexity and the significance of its many interrelationships.
How true this is will be effectively borne out by even a cursory

comparison of the curriculum of a standard school of social work and that of a medical, law, engineering, or theological school. Invariably one finds courses on different cultures, anthropology, family life, child development, health problems, mental hygiene, psychopathology, labor relations, case work methods, group work, administration, social insurance, and other fields. This range of topics seems too wide for anyone to encompass, but it is no wider than the range of problems which confront the social worker engaged in his task. In a typical month's work the trained social worker draws from his knowledge in all these fields, and his knowledge must be well integrated so that he can use it practically in solving community problems and aiding his clients to work out better adjustments.

In the course of their professional activities social workers, particularly case workers who are concerned mostly with individuals and families, relate themselves to a succession of other professional groups. They consult with physicians about the social and health aspects of their clients' problems. They go to schools in the interest of children in the families they serve. In other cases cooperation with a psychiatrist is required. Or it may be a government administrator or a private employer whose cooperation must be enlisted.

These groups, busy with their own jobs, are likely to see the role of the social worker only in relation to their own specialty. In the brief time usually available, it is difficult for the social worker to explain sufficiently what he does and why, to give an adequate interpretation of his function. Also, the social worker's need for information that will throw light on his clients' problems sometimes gives the false impression that he is primarily concerned with assembling social data, but in reality he is interested in this only as a means of understanding a client's needs, never as an end in itself.

In one other regard the social worker has been in a rather difficult position in our society. He works at the focal spot of socioeconomic breakdown. If he limits his work to handing out money or goods to relieve dire needs, he is in danger of developing dependency in his clients and failing to solve the problem on any permanent basis. If he tries to help the client to understand himself better with a view to improving his attitudes and relationships, including those that affect his employment, this may seem like a futile attempt to help the client to feel better on an empty stomach. If he attacks the problem on a community- or nation-wide basis in the interest of full employment, social insurance, or other means of improving the socio-economic status of people, he is likely to be charged by the self-appointed defenders of the status quo with being a starry-eyed dreamer or with promoting subversive ideologies. All too often when an economic problem has been the focal point of his attention, the social worker has been damned if he took emergency action and damned again if he took the long view and attempted to correct the basic causes of socio-economic difficulties.

Out of this background social work slowly emerged as a profession which has developed (1) a body of knowledge and a social philosophy which can be taught, and (2) methods of working with people, the principles of which can be set forth in classroom instruction and the skillful use of which can be taught in field work practice under the supervision of experienced workers. Half of the two-year training period is devoted to field work practice.

Social work is carried on in many kinds of organizational set-up, as in hospitals, outpatient clinics, schools, courts, churches, family service agencies, public welfare departments, councils of social agencies, children's agencies, recreational agencies, and, to a small but growing extent, in labor and industrial organizations.[1] The point of focus and the emphasis are determined somewhat by the organizational set-up, and the particular type of social work that is undertaken. Most case work services, for example, focus on the individual or the family and on the bearing which psychological factors, economic needs, health, job, and other environmental factors have on the person's or family's problems and adjustment. Psychiatric social workers and medical social workers most often work in hospitals and clinics and are concerned with medical and sociopsychiatric problems. Social workers trained in group work function in recreation, adult education, and social action. Others in increasing numbers are engaged in social research and in community-wide planning of social services.

The What and How of Social Case Work

Social case workers hold a number of profound convictions in common with members of other professions, notably psychiatry. (1) Individual persons have great worth regardless of the presence or absence of economic assets. (2) All behavior has real and adequate causes. Each person is what he was born with plus all that has happened to him in his total experience. The influences which impinge upon the individual from the time of his birth are numerous and intricate and proper understanding of the individual is possible only through a knowledge of the individual's history and of the many social and community forces which have left their imprint on him. (3) Personal attitudes are extremely significant both for the satisfaction of the individual and as a determinant of the number and quality of his relationships to others. The behavior of the individual is constantly being determined in part by the environment in which he lives and in part by inner feelings and personal attitudes. (4) People have a marked capacity for adjustment. With fuller knowledge of the demands of the environment and with increased insight into their own feelings and purposes, the direction of their lives can be substantially altered and their personal efficiency and happiness can be increased.

The social case worker who is equipped with such a philosophy and has acquired skill in case work methods is able to bring practical assistance to people who are distressed with emotional and social problems.[2] It is difficult to describe in brief and simple terms just what the social case work method is. The method is essentially interviewing. But the trained case worker brings to the interview a quality of understanding that makes it quite different from ordinary talking and listening. People who have been interviewed by social case workers find it hard to describe what happened in the interview except to say that they like to be talked with "in that way" and that in the course of the conversation they gained insight into themselves, came to understand some of the reasons for their problems, and got at least some inklings of the way out of their difficulties.

The case worker engages in several kinds of activity which in toto comprise the case work method. (1) He listens and he talks. But usually he listens much more than he talks. Because each individual differs from every other, the case worker must do much listening before he can understand the person before him well enough to be helpful. (2) Throughout the interviews he observes the hesitancies and uncertainties and the moods and emotions of the client, often expressed in guarded and subtle ways. He takes mental note of the issues and incidents that are charged with anxiety or other strong emotion and awaits or creates opportunities to bring these into fuller discussion. (3) In his listening, questioning, observing, and commenting he focuses on the here-and-now of problems that are of concern to the client, and also tries to trace problems to their roots. He notes the person's hopes and major goals, both those which he is achieving satisfactorily and those in the pursuit of which he is being frustrated. (4) He accepts the person as he finds him, without blame for failures and errors, for he appreciates the latter's efforts and the barriers that he has encountered. He maintains a feeling of warmth in his relationship, thinking and feeling with the client without robbing him of any responsibility for managing his own life. (5) He brings to the client his own wider perspective, born of professional training and experience with many other people's problems in adjustment. He asks only questions which he thinks may lead the client to bring out and appraise crucial facts that may help him to achieve better perspective. (6) He deals gently and reassuringly with the client as he discusses his conflicts and when the client is unable because of some resentment, hatred, or fear to make an appropriate decision, the case worker helps to objectify these inner forces. He does this particularly through the development of confidence which makes it possible for the client to talk out his feelings without fear of being judged or condemned, and by tactful questions that give some promise of helping the client to understand himself and to clarify some of the intricacies of his past and present relationships. Often, in the course of the interviews, the client's anxiety is drained off and his feelings of hostility and guilt are lessened to the extent that he is freed from the blinding and thwarting effects of these emotions and sees for the first time psychological connections of which he formerly had been totally unaware. Long-forgotten and emotionally charged incidents are recalled with a characteristic comment, "I never thought of this before, but I see now how much I have been influenced by it." (7) He offers to the client information regarding resources through which health services, recreation, companionship, employment, and so on, may be obtained and, as the client is interested, discusses with him ways of using these resources most helpfully. In contradistinction to the psychiatrist who undertakes to relieve the patient's intrapsychic conflicts and thus to remove his symptoms, the social worker strives to remove or reduce the stresses and conflicts caused by the environment and to help the client find and use the potentially constructive factors in his situation so that he can channel his life anew, obtain more genuine satisfactions, and pursue his goals with greater success. By virtue of his professional training, his greater mobility in the community, and his numerous contacts with social and health agencies and other community resources, he is well fitted to help people utilize constructive environmental forces.

PSYCHIATRIC SOCIAL WORK*

In the field of mental hygiene, psychiatric social workers have much to offer people who are in emotional distress, for their work

* See Appendix B for outline of training requirements.

is carried on "in direct and responsible relations with psychiatry and is practiced in hospitals, clinics or other psychiatric auspices the essential purpose of which is to serve people with mental or emotional disturbances."[3] In an increasing proportion of psychiatric hospitals and in virtually all community mental hygiene clinics individual social studies are made routinely as a requisite and integral feature of diagnosis, and social case work comprises an essential part of treatment.

Many psychiatric social workers are connected with hospitals. Especially in military hospitals they have natural, brief, and repeated contacts with patients on wards, and give many incidental services, such as increasing patients' comfort, answering questions which they are much concerned about at the moment, giving information to their families, and getting information in return, and aiding patients to get especially desired forms of recreation. The extension of this pattern to many civilian hospitals would improve their service, particularly if they are not staffed with psychiatrists in sufficient numbers.

Another major function is to interpret to the patient's family the meaning of his illness, give such reassurance as is justified by the physician's prognosis, and enlist the interest and cooperation of the family in the patient's treatment.[4] Families and others who have known the patient have adjusted themselves to the kind of person they knew when he was well and they feel estranged and lost when the personality of the patient changes, as it may do in recovery from psychiatric disorders. The patient, in turn, notices this and often becomes more miserable. To prevent misunderstandings, the social worker interprets the changes and helps both the patient and the members of his family to reconstruct their relationships on a mutually satisfactory basis. Before the patient is discharged, the social worker considers the family's readiness for this step, and may arrange for a trial visit. He discusses with the family in some detail ways in which the members can be of the greatest help to the patient when he returns home. To those who are ready for work further assistance is given, appropriate work being sought and the patient's needs being interpreted to the employer so that maximum work success may be assured.[5]

Because of the unavailability of a sufficient number of workers, the lack of civil service classification for psychiatric social workers in various states, and the fact that the training of some psychiatric administrators did not take sufficiently into account the social aspects of illness and treatment, many agencies and institutions serving patients with psychiatric disorders have made only minimal use of psychiatric social workers. Many psychiatric hospitals could improve their service by making more careful study of the social background and current social situation of patients. Such study is needed both in diagnosis and in treatment and in reference to policies of admission and discharge. Felix reports that it has been estimated that 20 per cent of patients admitted to psychiatric hospitals could be discharged after a few weeks of treatment if social workers were available to make proper provision for their post-discharge care.[6] There is need for more use of psychiatric social workers not only in state hospital systems, but also in some of our best private hospitals and clinics affiliated with medical schools, especially those which draw their patients from wide geographical areas.

A recent study made in New York State illustrates the value of paying adequate attention to the social aspects of mental illness and its treatment. This project involved study of 207 dementia praecox patients who had received intensive psychiatric social service both during their stay at the hospital and after release; whereas a carefully matched control group of 207 patients received only the regular state hospital social supervision (an amount which greatly exceeds that available in a number of state hospitals). One of the social worker's most frequent tasks in working with the former group was to make clear to the family the nature of mental illness, to aid them in eliminating feelings of disgrace, guilt, and self-accusation, and thus to prepare in advance a more favorable atmosphere for the return of the patient. With the release of family tension thus achieved, the fuller recovery of patients was expedited.

More than 70 per cent of the patients receiving such psychiatric social service did at least as well in the outside world after their illness as they had done before, as against 51.1 per cent in the control group. Relapse and return to the hospital occurred in only half as many patients in the group served as in the control group and the patients who had psychiatric social service spent less time in the hospital when they did return. Human values accruing from the reduction of suffering and the increase of happiness and hope cannot be shown in figures, but it was calculated in the study that 14,674 days of hospital care were saved, amounting to a cash saving of over $15,000 after costs of the study had been deducted. If such service were equally effective with all discharged patients, it would mean greater health and happiness for many thousands and an annual saving of at least $7,000,000 in the care of the mentally ill throughout the nation.[7]

The function of the psychiatric social worker in outpatient psychiatric and mental hygiene clinics is somewhat different. He is usually the first staff member to see the new patients. He alleviates some of the anxiety and tension which many people have when they first come to a clinic. He notes their reactions to other patients and to the doctor, answers their questions about the clinic, explains the procedures involved in study and treatment, and determines in each case whether the person is eligible for clinic service. Patients who appear without appointment, often quite disturbed, are seen as soon as possible and reassuringly advised regarding next steps in what may appear to be an emergency. In receiving and advising new patients, the trained social worker observes the varied manifestations of psychiatric disorders, is sensitive to the needs of different personalities, and uses skill in handling psychiatric problems safely until appropriate treatment can be instituted.

In most community clinics the psychiatric social workers conduct the initial history-taking interview. This is often a new step for the patient and he may not be ready to take it. If he has ever been hospitalized he may be afraid that he will be hospitalized again. It has been the prevailing experience in the veterans' rehabilitation clinic, of which one of the authors was the director, to see men come in nervous, upset, and unable to look at one directly but go out reassured after good social work interviews. Even the dishonorably discharged, the homosexuals, and other men with deep guilt feelings who expected to be ostracized and punished, developed favorable attitudes toward the clinic and returned ready and eager to see the psychiatrist. In no instance among more than 700 patients were the psychiatrists' later contacts with patients endangered by the social workers' initial interviews. Patients developed trust in the clinic and not just in the social worker or physician. Increasingly it is the practice to limit the initial history to as much selected, psychiatrically significant data as can be obtained in one interview. Fuller information is sought in some instances when symptoms or background information suggest the possibility of psychopathic personality, hysteria, convulsive seizure, or other pathologies the diagnosis of which is based to a larger extent on history.

There is definite economy in the psychiatric social worker's role in the clinic. He not only supplies the psychiatrist with essential social data but develops favorable attitudes in those who are to be seen by the psychiatrist. There is further economy in directing toward appropriate community resources those patients who cannot be accepted for clinic treatment. Many are referred to physicians for private treatment, others to clinics better equipped to give the specific treatment required, and still others to family or children's agencies equipped to handle the particular problems presented.

The role of the psychiatric social worker in treatment cannot be rigidly defined for it varies with the type of clinic, the viewpoint and methodology of the psychiatrist, and the therapeutic under-standing and skill of the social worker. In some instances, following the recommendation of the psychiatrist or internist, the social worker handles medical aspects such as reassuring a patient that an electroencephalogram will not hurt him or that the metabolism test taken before breakfast is an unusual kind of performance but one that he will survive safely. In most cases he works with the family of the patient—mother, father, mate, or sweetheart—to increase their understanding of the needs of the patient and to help them develop favorable attitudes toward the patient. He may also work with the employer and others with whom the patient comes in contact.

Again, the role of the social worker varies with the different skills of psychiatry. In working with a psychoanalyst he may help pa-tients adjust to obvious reality situations so that their analyses may proceed more smoothly. When the psychiatrist uses a supportive or educational type of treatment, the social worker applies his knowledge of the patient and his needs to social case work with him. With a knowledge of the diagnosis arrived at in a conference of the clinic team, he analyzes the dynamic forces at work and aids the patient in getting reality satisfactions. As Elizabeth Healy Ross puts it:

Psychiatric social workers usually serve both the psychiatrist and the patient, providing social data, reports and observations on the one hand, and maintaining a social service relation to patients on the other. The case work consists of assisting the patient to come to terms with his illness or emotional upset and to utilize the relation with the case worker to mobilize what desire and capacity he has to do something about getting better. Out of that purposeful relation the patient is aided to make some use of his own, the hospital's or clinic's, his family's and the community's resources. . . . As psychiatric social workers, we've been trained, as few other professions have, to value and utilize the give and take, hitching and hauling of interpersonal relations. We've learned to work with worried, grouchy, garrulous, irresponsible, subdued or deeply baffled people—all sorts of people with every sort of trouble. . . .

Skilled use of interpersonal relations to help people deal with their individual and social difficulties is really the content and core of our job.[8]

The psychiatrist's and social worker's services must, of course, be integrated. As the pendulum swings, the patient is more in need sometimes of the social worker and sometimes of the doctor. During periods of intensive treatment by the psychiatrist, the role of the social worker is relatively unimportant. At other times, when an undecided patient is confronted with the necessity of making a decision, such as going to a state hospital, he may return again and again to the social worker over a long period of time to discuss his fears. For example, one very sick young man who definitely needed hospitalization refused to see the physician because he was afraid that he would be "locked up" again. The social worker who had interviewed him initially saw him frequently through a period of seven months before he was willing to enter a psychiatric hospital. In another instance, through continued planning and control of environmental factors, a depressed patient was aided over a period of months until his depression had lifted enough for him to undergo outpatient psychiatric treatment. After that he was very seldom seen by the social worker.

In most child guidance clinics, the social worker participates actively in treatment in nearly all cases. During the eleven years of experience in such a clinic by one of the authors, the social workers gave some service on every case treated by the psychiatrist. In some clinics it is the policy for the psychiatrist to treat the child and for the social worker to treat parents and others with whom the child is associated. In other clinics, it is the policy for the psychiatrist to treat the more disturbed, whether parent or child, and for the social worker to treat the less disturbed member of the family. In any case, the psychiatric social worker must be able to deal with transference phenomena and be able to bring constructive environmental forces to bear upon the life of both child and parent. In dealing with the mental hygiene problems of most very young children and of some older children whose symptoms have not become firmly fixed and are caused primarily by environmental pressures, the social worker often carries on the entire treatment.

Besides contributing to the study and treatment of patients receiving psychiatric service, psychiatric social workers bring help to large numbers of people who are not receiving such service. Within community clinics particularly, they interview many people who are not seen by the psychiatrist. Among these people are many who, upon initial interview by the social worker, are found to have problems of a social nature which require social case work rather than psychiatric treatment. When selection is well made this kind of service proves very satisfactory and the psychiatrist's time is freed for intensive work with those who have neurotic or other illness. In one large child guidance clinic where many children having primary behavior disorders, unfocused emotional problems, school difficulties, or very early neurotic symptoms have received only social case work treatment, the percentage of children who have shown satisfactory improvement at the time of follow-up has been as high as that shown by children with more serious problems who had received full clinical study and treatment. This has been true consistently over a period of fifteen years. In some clinics the number of people served in this way is considerable, amounting in some instances to as much as 50 per cent of the referrals. At the New York Hospital Rehabilitation Clinic, nearly 600 of the 1,300 veterans who applied were handled only by the social worker, and in the Child Guidance Bureau of the New York City schools 500 or more children are served each year through the social workers' assistance to parents and teachers.

Recognizing the great need for extension of mental health services and the dearth of trained psychiatrists for such work, Felix has raised the question whether psychiatric social workers can do "independent duty" by treating persons with psychiatric problems who are too remote from established clinics and private psychiatrists.[6] If he means strictly independent duty with no provision whatever for consultation with psychiatrists even in extremely ill and involved cases, the answer is "No." But if even minimal consultation were available and fully trained and widely experienced social workers of proven skill in psychiatric social work treatment were selected, the answer might be "Yes." Some past experience suggests that this might be practicable notwithstanding the fact that psychiatric social work has heretofore been carried on "in direct and responsible relation with psychiatry." Experienced psychiatric social workers have for a long time given services to many individuals who were not being treated by psychiatrists. In those child guidance clinics where the social workers invariably work with the parents and the psychiatrists with the children, this has often meant that the social workers were actually carrying the treatment of the persons whose illnesses or neurotic patterns had become the more fixed. During the war in some of the military mental hygiene units and hospitals, military and Red Cross psychiatric social workers were given substantial responsibility for the treatment of patients both individually and in groups. There is evidence in both military and civilian agencies that the psychiatric social work treatment carried on by some of the well-trained and experienced workers—with minimal psychiatric consultation—was effective in reducing the symptoms and improving the social adjustment of persons who had suffered psychoneurotic breakdown. As Lowrey states:

With regard to therapy by the social worker, I can see no reason why the psychiatric [social] worker should not do psychotherapy under proper conditions. These chiefly involve such supervision as may be necessary in view of the problems presented and the worker's experience level. The sum total of orthopsychiatric experience validates this judgment. There are many social workers who do what seems to me a highly superior job in psychotherapy.[9]

During the war years numbers of psychiatric social workers have served, too, in organizations such as the Travelers Aid Society and veterans' information and service centers, where the usual clinical team could not be used and where contacts invariably were of a short-term nature. As Ethel Ginsburg has observed, "It has been gratifying to watch psychiatric social work come out of the clinic and make its contribution to so vital a war agency (Veterans Service Center). Those of us who have been close to the work of the center are convinced that this is only a first step. What has been learned about the application of psychiatric social work techniques to brief service contacts will serve as a base for further study and development."[10]

In the light of such experience, it seems to the authors that well-trained, experienced psychiatric social workers might give a large amount of independent service if psychiatric consultation is available when needed, and that mental health services can be substantially extended in this way if enough social workers can be trained. There clearly is a trend in this country toward more selective use of all members of the clinic team, with an increasing tendency to use the psychiatrist for diagnostic examination, consultation with staff and psychiatric treatment, and to use the social worker for the treatment of persons whose tensions relate to social and environmental pressures and to less profound intrapsychic conflicts.

Many psychiatric social workers, after having had professional training and substantial experience in psychiatric clinics or hospitals, have been employed in supervisory capacities in family and children's agencies, public assistance programs, veterans' information centers, schools, courts, and other types of organization. In these capacities they are able to bring their skill to many people outside the clientele of strictly psychiatric agencies.

Psychiatric social workers are also active in interpreting the clinic's work and needs to the community and in enlisting the cooperation of various community groups. In some places the psychiatrists interpret the clinic experience to medical groups and invite their cooperation and the psychologists do the same with the administrative and teaching staffs of the schools. The social workers, however, usually serve as the chief interpreters to parents, social agencies, and miscellaneous community groups in bringing about more effective community organization.

With the increasing demand by the public for orientation in mental hygiene, it is expected that psychiatric social workers will be participating increasingly in such education. Such efforts should help to remove some of the sense of stigma that has attached to psychiatric problems, should better acquaint people with available services, and should result in the earlier discovery of those needing such services, thus helping to prevent the development of some of the more serious problems.

MEDICAL SOCIAL WORK

Like psychiatric social work, medical social work is carried on both within the hospital and in outpatient clinics and other health and rehabilitation agencies in the community. The chief difference between this and psychiatric social work is that physical illnesses and disabilities constitute the patients' major problems.

In hospitals and clinics most of the medical social worker's time is occupied with assembling and interpreting social data for the use of the patient's physician, explaining the social significance of handicaps both to the patient and his family, and arranging for convalescent care, recreation, and social service in accordance with the patient's needs and social interests. There are, of course, real values in the casual contacts and the incidental services given along with the performance of these main functions. The social worker often does a major service just by listening to patients' accounts of their experiences, hopes, and fears and by fully accepting and respecting them as real persons notwithstanding their handicaps.[11]

The specific service which a medical social worker gives depends partly upon whether he is working in a hospital or in the community, and partly on the nature of his client's illness or disability. For example:

In dealing with any of the tropical diseases, the social worker serving in the military hospital can be of great help to the patients by clarifying, under the supervision of the medical officer, the medical misconceptions they may have concerning the nature of their illness, by reducing anxieties they may have about other matters, and by rearousing and supporting their desire to recover. The social worker in the community can relieve many of the fears of the families of these men and can foster public understanding through the dissemination of accurate knowledge.[12]

While the primary point of focus is the patient's recovery from his present illness, the medical social worker is also interested in his long-term problems and his total adjustment, as Cynthia Rice Nathan points out in her concluding discussions of plastic surgery and amputee cases:

The social worker is also concerned with the patient's personal problems which may have been with him over a period of time and which the injury may have intensified. Dormant feelings of physical inadequacy, of structural difference, feelings of guilt, may all be brought to consciousness by the new injury. In addition to this, the man who sees the social worker on his ward daily, and learns to know her through the variety of little requests she can fulfill, is freer to take his problems to her. She, too, has learned to know each patient through his waking day, and she has observed his social relationships; often he brings a problem to her. She knows, too, that he will probably remain in the hospital for about a year, during which time case work may help him. And so case work, though in a military setting, need not be short-contact; the initial contact need not be planned and worried over, or even consciously sought by the patient, but may come about as a natural course of events in the hospital life of the patient.[13]

The Red Cross social worker who has followed the men at the amputation center since their admission talks seriously with them about the problems that still remain unsolved. She helps them to execute their claims for government pension, talks over again their decision regarding their chosen vocation, helps them to understand all the government benefits to which they are entitled, listens to plans for marriage or for children, says good-by at last, letting them know that there is a Red Cross worker in the chapter back home to whom they can always turn.[14]

In agencies concerned with vocational guidance and rehabilitation the emphasis is somewhat different. Evelyn Horton describes the characteristic needs of physically handicapped persons in this regard and indicates the medical social worker's function in meeting these needs:

Clarification of the medical situation with the physician or clinic in order to obtain necessary data as a basis for vocational recommendations; interpretation to the individual of what he needs to know about his physical condition and limitations; obtaining the cooperation and participation of the physician in the vocational plan; arrangements for medical and psychiatric care; help to the individual in obtaining an understanding and acceptance of his physical conditions and its limitations, together with an acceptance of the vocational recommendations; motivation of the individual toward an understanding of emotional factors that may play a complicating role in his use of his potentialities; understanding of the family's attitude toward the individual and interpretation to them of the vocational recommendations, especially when they are a dynamic force in influencing vocational plans, medical care, or his emotional adjustment; and coordination of thinking and planning regarding vocational recommendations with the social agencies serving the individual, the worker in some cases acting as a liaison person between the vocational guidance clinic and the agency.[15]

OTHER SOCIAL CASE WORK SERVICES TO INDIVIDUALS AND FAMILIES

Many kinds of assistance are brought to individuals and families by social case workers in family and children's agencies. Sometimes it is a matter of relieving economic hardship; sometimes it is helping a husband and his wife to work out a better adjustment. Again, it is helping parents to get on a good working basis with their children.[16] In the interest of family stability and personality growth, problems of health, employment, recreation, and child care may likewise require basic case work services, the philosophy and method of which are well described in social work sources.[17]

Some Broader Issues

The wants and needs of people are much broader than the services which social workers have ordinarily been able to give. Max Lerner, philosopher and columnist, has well stated the broader and deeper needs of veterans, needs which are surely shared by millions of civilians:

They want, first, an America in which the machines are not idle, in which their own skills are not left unused—an America great enough to use the techniques at its disposal for full production and employment.

Secondly, they want a world without war—a world which, having willed the ends of peace, is able to will the means also, even though those means include international force. They want a world in which this will have been made the last war.

And thirdly, they want a sense of belonging to something bigger than themselves, inklings of which they have begun to find in the Army. They want an America and a world in which they can thrust down their roots, in which they can feel wanted and used, for which they can have a fighting faith.[18]

In the face of wants as broad and deep as these, social workers are obliged to adapt their goals and methods. The needs of men who entered the armed forces from all walks of life and who are returning to equally diverse situations and the needs of rank-and-file citizens everywhere cannot be met within the usual framework of social agencies. As was to be expected, a certain moving out and broadening of scope is taking place in all branches of social work. During the war years, many case workers, for example, played new and challenging roles which related their work more intimately to lay groups. More than 10,000 social workers aided selective service boards by making dependency investigations and compiling social, health, and work histories of registrants for the use of psychiatric examiners in evaluating registrants for military fitness. Others participated in civilian defense activities, worked as counselors in industrial plants and labor unions. As individual needs have become mass needs social workers have had (1) to become part of the democratic forces striving for improved social conditions; (2) to deal cooperatively with people who are active instead of passive about their conditions; and (3) to develop the skill of short-time interviewing in order to meet numerous and immediate problems. In many of the larger communities social workers, particularly those who have had training and experience in community organization, have played leading roles in the establishment of veterans' information and service centers and in other efforts to bring sound planning and coordination not only to the social and health agencies but to the work of all community groups, such as schools, business and industry, churches, and veterans' organizations.

There is already evidence that this large volume of social work carried on during the war in many settings, civilian and military, and the adjustments which are being made in giving service to veterans and their families, is resulting both in a better understanding of social work and in greater demands for it. This view is held by several observers.[19, 20] Two of them state:

Social workers in the Army who have been permitted to practice their profession as part of their military duties are participating in a rare opportunity—that of bringing the practice of social work to a cross-section of the general population not usually reached in civilian life. It has extended the frontiers of social case-work beyond the services established for, and usually identified with, the ill, the underprivileged, and the delinquent elements of our country. It is reflective of the trend in social work toward services to private paying clients, and to industrial and labor organizations. It represents a service to individuals who, by the very nature of their stake in participation in securing help, will demand that more responsibility be assumed by social workers in response to more active participation on the part of the client. In this stimulus is to be found the vitality of the future of the profession.

In work with individuals who have met a reality far more demanding than that in which human personality should reasonably be expected to carry on under peace-time circumstances, the resilience and strength of human personality have been demonstrated. In the recovery of neuro-psychiatric battle casualties there is ample evidence to warrant profound respect for the reservoirs of personality resources that individuals are able to call upon. In recognition of this, social workers will further refine their techniques to increase the participation of their clients as they are able to assume new responsibilities. This presupposes an increased skill in understanding the client, and will eventually determine the degree to which social case work achieves the goal of aiding in maturity of action.[19]

As the current emphasis in practice shifts there will be corresponding changes in training. In the judgment of Menninger:

It is to be expected that far more mental hygiene content and psychopathology will be included in the training of all social workers, and that the demand for well qualified psychiatric social workers will be far in excess of the supply. Only by intelligent planning can we begin to meet this need. Such planning should include a program of recruitment, a resurvey of training methods and the provision for increased opportunities for training and a national certification program. It is to be hoped that the national leaders of this field will develop such plans and effect their execution on a local basis, a state basis, and a national basis.[21]

There are still other broad and very important implications for social work if the profounder needs of veterans and other citizens are to be met. In fact, these needs cannot be met by social workers alone, nor can they be supplied by dealing with people in special groups. The whole of our society is involved, and the problems ahead, such as international order, full employment and production, and personal and national health and security, will take the combined thinking and concerted action of all socially minded citizens who are ready to insist that the democracy for which our veterans fought shall bring to them, and to all the people, opportunities for the fulfillment of their basic needs.

This is no new emphasis in social work. In fact, from its birth at the turn of the twentieth century it has been concerned with "cause," or social goal, as well as "function."[22] At times the profession has been so busy defining and developing its varied functions that it has been relatively inactive as a cause. In recent years, however, there has been a resurgence of interest in getting at the roots of social pathology and in organizing community forces to prevent, as far as possible, the development of the more serious individual and social problems. A few of the larger family service agencies and an increasing number of councils for social planning now maintain both research and public relations staffs. There are committees on social action in most chapters of the five professional social work associations.* There is increasing awareness among social workers that, while they cannot neglect service to individuals, they must become constructors and not mere patchers-up if the whole challenge of human needs is to be met; they must become "interpreters of the community to itself—the bridge between the community's needs and the potentialities it has for meeting them."[23]

Leonard Mayo, who has had long and varied experience in social work practice and education, after making a penetrating analysis of what social work has done and is doing, suggests some adaptations which the profession will have to make in shifting from a therapeutic to a preventive emphasis:

As agencies we must look critically at our policies and structure as we enter the public health phase of social work when prevention, rehabilitation, and action on broad issues are at the fore. Most of our agencies were organized to treat the ill, not to prevent illness. As a result, they are not yet streamlined to take action on, nor a real part in the solution of, those problems which create the ills they seek to alleviate.

The genius of social work's being is that of bringing together diverse groups in a common search and action for the common good. . . . In this important respect we differ from most groups in the community— we seek not only to gain the long-range goals of social and economic betterment but, in so doing, to reconcile differences, cement common interests, replace strife with understanding, and give warm and under-

* American Association of Social Workers, American Association of Medical Social Workers, American Association of Psychiatric Social Workers, American Association of Group Workers, National Association of School Social Workers.

standing leadership in lifting the whole level of community life. . . . The lessons of the past need careful application at no other point quite so much as in relation to the crucial question as to how social work with its knowledge of human suffering and its vision of prevention and rehabilitation can be fully effective in the building of a new and healthy society.[23]

REFERENCES

1. Social Work Year Book, 1945. New York, Russell Sage Foundation, 1945. (Note: Contains articles on all phases of social work, under 75 titles.)

2. Towle, C. Social case work in modern society. Social Service Rev. 20:165–179, June 1946.

3. French, L. M. Psychiatric social work. New York, Commonwealth Fund, 1929.

4. Stern, E. M. Mental illness; a guide for the family. New York, Commonwealth Fund, 1943.

5. Crutcher, H. B. The function of the psychiatric social worker in a mental hospital. News-Letter Am. Assoc. Psychiatric Social Workers 12:3–11, Summer 1942.

6. Felix, R. M. Factors in the development of a national mental program. Paper read at the National Conference of Social Work, May 1946.

7. Field, M. Psychiatric social work with insulin-treated patients. Utica, New York, State Hospital Press, 1945.

8. Ross, E. H. Social work's responsibility for veterans. Read at the National Conference of Social Work, May 1946. Available in mimeograph through: American Association of Psychiatric Social Workers, 1790 Broadway, New York City.

9. Lowrey, L. G. Training principles in the use of social service. Am. J. Orthopsychiat. 16:418–426, July 1946.

10. Ginsburg, E. L. The psychiatric social worker in a veterans' service center. News-Letter Am. Assoc. Psychiatric Social Workers 16:33–39, Autumn 1946.

11. Mayer, L. These will come back. Survey Midmonthly 81:137–139, May 1945.

12. Nathan, C. R. Servicemen and tropical diseases. The Family 26:189–194, July 1945.

13. Nathan, C. R. Social service to plastic surgery cases. The Family 26:9–15, March 1945.

14. Nathan, C. R. Service to amputees. The Family 25:363–369, February 1945.

15. Horton, E. Discussion; rehabilitation and medical social work. Social Service Rev. 17:328–334, September 1943.

16. Nathan, C. R.   Servicemen face discharge with hope and fear.   The Family 26: 91–97, May 1945.

Rabinoff, R. M.   While their men are away.   Survey Midmonthly 81:110–113, April 1945.

Thomas, D. V.   The veteran as seen in a private family agency.   The Family 26: 203–208, October 1945.

17. Garrett, A. M.   Interviewing; its principles and methods.   New York, Family Welfare Association of America, 1942.

Hamilton, G.   Theory and practice of social case work.   New York, Columbia University Press, 1940.

Reynolds, B.   Learning and teaching in the practice of social work.   New York, Farrar & Rinehart, 1943.

Robinson, V. P.   A changing psychology in social case work.   Chapel Hill, N. C., University of North Carolina Press, 1930.

18. Lerner, M.   A nation worthy of heroes.   In Proceedings, National Conference of Social Work, 1944, p. 22.   New York, Columbia University Press, 1944.

19. Greving, F. T., and M. J. Rockmore.   Psychiatric case-work as a military service. Ment. Hyg. 29:435–506, July 1945.

20. Hofstein, S.   The impact of family forces on the soldier as met by the military social worker.   Ment. Hyg. 29:385–394, July 1945.

Tobias, I.   A psychiatric social worker overseas.   New York, Family Welfare Association of America, 1945.

21. Menninger, W. C.   Psychiatric social work in the army and its implications for civilian social work.   In Proceedings, National Conference of Social Work, 1945, p. 85–92.   New York, Columbia University Press, 1945.

22. Lee, P. R.   Social work as cause and function.   New York, Columbia University Press, 1937.

23. Mayo, L. W.   The future for social work.   In Proceedings, National Conference of Social Work, 1944, p. 25–34.   New York, Columbia University Press, 1944.

VIII

CONTRIBUTIONS OF THE PSYCHOLOGIST

What is a psychologist? How does he differ from a psychiatrist? These are not infrequent questions asked by non-professional people. Both psychologist and psychiatrist may call themselves "doctor," although the former is a Ph.D. and the latter is always an M.D. Both may undertake to help emotionally sick or distressed people. What therapeutic role is the psychologist equipped to play by virtue of his non-medical training and experience?

As has been noted in previous chapters, war experience re-affirmed the importance and therapeutic effectiveness of the clinical team regularly composed of psychiatrist, psychiatric social worker, and clinical psychologist. The psychologist has a recognized contribution to make in research, testing, and diagnosis of emotional and mental disorders, a contribution which is growing in importance in spite of the controversy which surrounds the precise role he should play in clinical therapeutic work. Many psychologists in the armed services were assigned tasks of major responsibility in intellectual and personality evaluation, choice of personnel, and diagnostic testing, and in actual therapeutic work with patients, usually but not always under the supervision of, or in collaboration with, the psychiatrist. Many of the therapeutic opportunities were made possible by the dearth of psychiatrists and the urgent demand for treatment services. With the return to civilian life the psychologist has found less freedom and opportunity for the continuation of his treatment role, although in many clinics and community agencies, the need for therapy is so great that he finds himself forced into some kind of therapeutic work. Yet today lack of understanding as to his function exists, as well as a widely prevailing reluctance to accept him as a therapist.

Nevertheless, it can be well argued that whenever a psychologist works with a human being, even in the simple situation of administering an intelligence test, he is inevitably drawn into a relationship in which therapeutic potentialities exist and are served even though at a limited level. The exact role that the psychologist can and does play in psychiatric therapy remains ill defined. There is much controversy on both sides, but heated discussions give little opportunity to clarify the precise status of the profession.

Some of the difficulty stems from a lack of knowledge on the part of many people, including some physicians and psychiatrists, of the training and preparation that go into the making of a psychologist. On the other hand, training for *clinical* psychology has remained at best a haphazard procedure and there is as yet no standardized training process or indeed much agreement among training schools as to what should constitute the preparation for so important a function. The psychiatrist with his clinical knowledge of emotionally sick people is the only one who can contribute to certain phases of the psychologist's training. Some experience in clinics or hospitals is imperative if he is to understand the emotionally sick individual. But there are few psychiatrists with teaching skill available and most of these are overburdened with responsibilities for training more psychiatrists. Thus, a practical bottleneck exists, and no ready solution is in sight.

Who shall be designated as a *clinical* psychologist and how does he differ from other psychologists? Clarification may best be found through the scrutiny of the historical development of modern psychology and the growing complexity and specialization within psychology as a separate branch of science. Like psychiatry the science of psychology as a formally organized body of knowledge was a creation of the nineteenth century. In the early part of that century the study of behavior was still designated as "mental philosophy" but the term "psychology" was also used quite freely. It was the intention of many of the psychologists of the time to make psychology a science based on observation and experiments like the physical sciences, although concern with the mind-body problem at the end of the century pushed much of American psychology into philosophy.

In spite of this, however, the experimental psychological approach to behavior developed rapidly during the last two decades of the nineteenth century. The first formal research laboratory in psychology was established in 1879 in Leipzig by Wilhelm Wundt, and G. Stanley Hall organized the first American psychological laboratory at Johns Hopkins in 1883, a few years after William James began demonstrating psychological experiments in his classroom at Harvard. American psychologists almost immediately introduced practice experiments and animal-learning experimentation as well as the general study of comparative psychology.

Early in the present century interest in mental and behavioral development became manifest and institutes for child study and the study of developmental psychology began to be established. Many of the present child study and guidance clinics were instituted by psychologists during the first thirty years of the twentieth century.

Interest in psychological testing has been characteristic of American psychology throughout its history. In the early days during which the first psychological clinic was established in 1897 in the University of Pennsylvania, interest centered primarily on the evaluation of memory, association, reaction speed, and similar behavior. Later, individual intelligence tests, based on the Binet test but with modifications and adaptations, were introduced, and group tests and performance and achievement tests were constructed and widely used, particularly after the impetus given to intelligence testing by the first World War.

In the period immediately following World War II, interest in the "total personality" became ascendant and led to the psychological evaluation of motivation, social adjustment, attitudes, and personality traits in addition to the testing of intellectual abilities. The study of the person was extended by the use of the interview and by the personal history. Such a wide range of interests and diverse avenues of development led inevitably to the founding of particular "schools" which from time to time in the past tended to dominate the psychological scene.

Modern Schools of Psychology

In the modern scientific period of psychology it was Wundt who established psychology as a separate science. His first work was concerned with sense perceptions and the meanings attached to sensations. His chief problem was the analysis of mental processes into conscious elements. Mach (1885) stressed the importance of conscious experiences by declaring that everything in the world exists simply as "complexes of sensations."

STRUCTURAL PSYCHOLOGY

Titchener (1898) adhered closely to the teachings of Wundt. He declared that the greatest need in psychology was the study of conscious *elements* rather than of mental functions. Psychology should restrict itself to a description of the structure of the mind in a manner similar to that in which the science of anatomy describes the structure of the body. He regarded sensations, images, and feelings as conscious elements which are the simplest units of analysis. These possess inseparable but variable "attributes." For Titchener, the subject matter of psychology is consciousness, consciousness of experience as dependent on the experiencing organism. The psychology of Titchener played a major role in the development of American psychology.

William James (1890) described mental life as a biological function of adjustment between impressions made upon the body by the outer world and the reactions of the body to it. He said that mental activity is always accompanied by bodily change and shows a dependence upon bodily conditions, such as the effect of a person's age upon his ability to remember. James combined the teachings of

Wundt with his own biological descriptions, thereby producing a comprehensive system into which many kinds of scientific observations were readily integrated. James analyzed the consciousness of the "self." He showed that it is a complex experience built up from many aspects of life. As early as 1875 James introduced a certain amount of experimental demonstration into his lectures on psychology at Harvard. His characterization of mental activity as a process of biological adaptation was widely accepted by American students. In his treatment of the emotions, James developed the theory that is probably his most famous single contribution to psychology. This is the conception known as the James-Lange theory of emotions. James became convinced that emotion is nothing but the feeling of bodily activity that is reflexly aroused by certain exciting situations. Lange, studying specifically the circulatory system, came to the conclusion that feelings of vasomotor changes constitute the essentials of emotion. The two men announced the theory independently and almost simultaneously.

FUNCTIONAL PSYCHOLOGY

In functionalism, American psychology made its first definite and organized stand against domination by the schools of Titchener or Wundt. Functionalism was concerned primarily with activities—with mental processes not merely as contents but as operations. Its first exponents, Dewey and Angell, were interested in studying these processes in their natural setting and from the standpoint of their utility. Taking their cue from Darwin and regarding mental processes as useful to a living organism in the business of adapting itself to its environment, their approach from the first was distinctly biological. Functionalism, frankly joining hands with common sense, was from the first interested in utilities. Dewey and Angell were not ambitious to found a new school. But, partly because their statements openly sanctioned heresies and partly because Titchener definitely excommunicated it, functionalism became a definite school. Functionalism came to be associated with the kind of psychology that was developing at the University of Chicago. In 1902 Dewey himself became director of the School of Education in the University of Chicago, taking the opportunity to put into practice the principles both of his philosophy and his psychology. Angell was head of the department of psychology, and made the department one of the strongest in the country. Carr carried on the work after Angell left. Nevertheless, functionalism does not at present stand out in American psychology as a distinct school and system. It did so only in its beginning, when it had the conspicuousness of a new movement. In functionalism, American psychology passed through a phase of its development in which it brought together and organized many tendencies already in existence, utilizing them so successfully that they passed into general practice.

BEHAVIORISM

Watson (1913) declared that the method of introspection is a detriment to psychology. Introspection yields nothing but the description of consciousness and furnishes no means of verifying the description. The terminology of introspection is not like that in which scientific facts are stated and consequently no direct relations can be drawn between introspective data and scientific facts. Watson therefore claimed that the elimination of states of consciousness as proper objects of investigation in themselves removes the barrier which has long existed between psychology and the other sciences. Thus Watson's proclamation of "behaviorism" is a proclamation of method. He regarded behavior as consisting of a series of connected or "chained" reflexes. He held that the process of thinking is "a form of general bodily activity which can be described without any reference to subjective imagery." Watson's most valuable contribution to psychology was his work on infant behavior. From his observations of newborn infants at the Johns Hopkins University, he presented an exact account of the behavior of the newborn. He strongly emphasized the predominance of diffuse activity in the earliest period and the scarcity of coordinated behavior. His findings thus tended to discredit the lengthy classifications of instincts compiled by the early students of psychology. However, so one-sided an approach to the complicated phenomena of human behavior was inevitably doomed to failure.

DYNAMIC PSYCHOLOGY

As interpreted by Woodworth (1918), dynamic psychology is a modest, matter-of-fact, unaggressive system, first formally presented in a series of lectures which when published made an unpretentious volume of barely more than two hundred pages. Unlike most systems this psychology is not grounded on a protest; it does not derive its motive power from what it is against. Its tolerance is derived not from the lack of a definite and distinguishing point of view but from the fact that it discerns in the many activities included in psychology a common interest and aim. The object of this common interest and aim Woodworth designates by the phrase, "the workings of the mind." Having discovered that psychology has followed a constant course in the past and believing that it has accomplished and is accomplishing results of scientific value, Woodworth tried to make explicit the principles that have guided psychology all along. These are described as the psychology of cause and effect. Woodworth regularly utilizes such concepts as stimulus and response, facilitation, inhibition, and integration. His psychology is very definitely a psychology of reactions. There are three main points which he believes must always be considered when one uses the terms of stimulus-response connections. The first is that the stimulus is not the cause of the response, but only part of the cause. The structure of the organism, its stores of energy, the activities going forward, its general condition—all these are involved in determining the response. A second point is that no stimulus-response reaction can be considered as an isolated, discrete event. No reaction occurs in an organism in which there is no other activity in progress. His third point is that the reaction-arc is a divisible unit. The reaction is not independent of its surroundings and its internal unity is not absolute. It can be broken in the middle. In spite of the dangers lurking in its application, Woodworth believes that the stimulus-response concept, when taken with the proper precautions, is the most useful tool psychology can employ for analyzing its material.

GESTALT PSYCHOLOGY

Wertheimer, with Kohler and Koffka, proposed a more complete synthesis between psychological factors than had yet been attempted in any previous view. They considered that the properties of consciousness are created out of the relations which arise between physical and physiological events. The properties thus evolved are unitary and indivisible, and are not merely the sum of the properties of the individual causes. They are simply "forms" or "configurations" (the German term is *Gestalt*). This Gestalt theory has been called the relativity theory of psychology. It is at odds with the traditional atomistic analyses of the mind which had isolated the sensory elements of consciousness and the reflexes of behavior; it is also opposed to separate mental forces such as association and attention. For distinct elements and forces in experience, the concept of unitary wholes is substituted. Koffka asserted that the earliest experiences of childhood are especially general and "configurative" in character, because the first perceptual responses are made to complex situations such as the distinction of "a friendly from an unfriendly countenance." Kohler, who was closely associated with Koffka in the leadership of the school of Gestalt psychology, found many illustrations of the Gestalt principle in the behavior of the higher apes. In mental terms he labeled the animal's performance as "insight" and proposed that the factor of "insight," the sudden comprehension of correct relations, should replace the older explanation of learning as trial-and-error behavior with gradual increments of improvement.

An extension of Gestalt principles into the understanding and description of the personality was accomplished by Kurt Lewin in what he calls topological psychology. Using certain concepts from the mathematical science of topology and applying the concept of vectors to psychology, Lewin has constructed a psychological system which takes into account both the conscious and unconscious characteristics of a person, his momentary state and his psychological or behavioral environment.

Under the impact of the genius of Freud with his brilliant elucidation of the role of unconscious dynamic factors in the motivation of human behavior, psychology as well as psychiatry drew heavily upon his principles in their move to interpret human behavior in terms that were truly dynamic, biographical, and closer to demonstrated facts as revealed through the searching analysis of adults and the objective observation of infant and child behavior. Thus psychology increasingly concerned itself with personality, less in terms of description and testing than as a search for motivation and dynamic principles. In this search, the whole range of human behavior, normal as well as abnormal, became legitimately the concern of both psychologist and psychiatrist.

As was inevitable in so widespread a historical development, training in psychology became a heterogeneous experience, and widely divergent points of view and emphases still characterize the many departments of psychology in our universities. There is, therefore, a remarkable lack of uniformity in the background and experience of contemporary individual psychologists. In some universities the emphasis has been entirely theoretical and limited largely to such topics as sense perception, reflexes, and introspection, or, where the predominant emphasis has been experimental, to animal psychology. In others, educational psychology with special attention to methods of learning applied to various fields has occupied major attention. Again, the orientation has been toward industrial psychology and vocational guidance. In still other schools research has been the predominant theme and practicability has scarcely been considered. Krugman has reported that "the head of the graduate psychology department of one of our largest universities actually has said that it is not the business of a graduate school in a university to teach anything that has anything to do with the practical application of knowledge." This is, as Krugman observes, a typical attitude in our higher institutions of learning.[1] However, increasing emphasis has been placed on psychometrics and the current trend is toward real clinical psychology.

This variability is perhaps even more striking in the preparation of the considerable number of psychologists who have been attracted to the clinical task of helping normal and maladjusted personalities meet the demands of their environment by other than somatic means. Because their interest is primarily in work with people both for understanding and help, the term clinical psychology has come increasingly into use.

The Function of the Clinical Psychologist

Notwithstanding the diversity of training, clinical psychologists as a rule have been thoroughly trained in the administration and interpretation of intelligence, aptitude, educational, and certain other tests. But this training, while thorough in reference to testing skills, has usually been rather academic in its general framework and has failed to give psychologists sufficient knowledge of the social and emotional factors in human behavior which supply much of its drive and motivation. Until very recently almost no university in the country provided anything like adequate training in clinical methods which would really equip a graduate who had specialized in psychology to function as a member of the usual clinic team of psychiatrist, psychologist, and social worker. However, as increasing numbers of psychologists obtained positions in hospitals and in child guidance, mental hygiene, or psychiatric clinics, they learned to adapt their methods to the demands of the clinic and have given the other members of the clinic team a larger appreciation of the range and significance of intellectual deviations and of other diagnostic values accruing from the proper administration of tests. They in turn have learned much from the psychiatrists and social workers and have thereby developed a more dynamic psychology, rooted in the emotional and social needs of people as well as in the learning or thinking process.

Two further influences have served to increase the clinical psychologist's potential contribution to the study and treatment of people with mental, emotional, and social problems. The Rorschach test, which was developed in Europe as a psychiatric tool and was used there almost exclusively by psychiatrists, has been taken over in America extensively by the psychologists. Most advances in the adaptation and use of this test, the Thematic Apperception test and other tests of a projective nature have been made by psychologists, among them, Beck, Klopfer, Murray, and others.[2]

Throughout World War II, many psychologists were forced out of the academic world by the demand for therapy. In spite of their long insistence on psychology as an exact science of mental phenomena reducible to predictable laws, and on research as the highest achievement, they were pushed into the area of treatment. Not only did the armed forces need and use many psychologists in testing and classification, but there was also great need for clinical study and treatment of men who were adjusting poorly or showing signs of mental or emotional breakdown. Consequently, many psychologists whose training and experience in some cases had been limited to psychometrics were set to work with psychiatrists and psychiatric social workers on clinical teams under psychiatric direction. Because of the shortage of psychiatrists to carry on treatment, a considerable number of clinical psychologists were given responsibility in therapy as well as in clinical study. Most of those who had had extensive clinical experience proved effective in this role. Many whose previous work had been limited to psychometrics left the Army after four or five years of clinical experience with a more dynamic point of view and better equipped to use clinical methods.

About a quarter of the time of military psychologists was given to some form of guidance and therapy, chiefly to individual therapy, but also to counseling and to group psychotherapy. These therapeutic efforts were carried on under the direct supervision of the psychiatrist. Many psychologists were utilized in the reeducation of aphasic and physically handicapped patients. In spite of their participation in therapy, the majority of the military psychologists indicated that their major interest lay in diagnostic work and in clinical research.[3] However, the demand for therapy in civilian life is so great that it is likely that an increasing number of clinical psychologists will be enticed or forced by circumstances into the therapeutic role.

The traditional training of the psychologist today fits him only in part for this function. It generally begins in undergraduate college and continues into graduate school. It includes, or may include, introductory, abnormal, and experimental psychology; psychology of learning, memory, and motivation; the administration of objective tests of intelligence, aptitude and other traits; the use of projective techniques such as the Rorschach test; mental hygiene; statistics; theory of interviewing; counseling. Practical experience may be given in vocational, educational, industrial, and clinical testing and independent research. The real deficit, however, is that supervised internships of various lengths in psychiatric clinics or hospitals, which should be mandatory, are rarely provided and those that are provided are apt to involve the application of diagnostic methods rather than therapeutic techniques and skills. Frequently courses in related fields such as human biology, physiology, cultural anthropology, and sociology are required. Occasionally clinical psychologists consider a personal psychoanalysis important in their education but this is not emphasized as frequently as in social work or psychiatric training. There has been as yet no consistent curriculum devised for training in clinical psychology and its aim has not been focused specifically on helping human beings who need aid.

The major trend thus far has been away from the therapeutic role. Today psychologists are writing advertising, choosing personnel, counseling normal individuals on vocational and marital matters, investigating public opinion, figuring social trends, determining principles of proper education, analyzing administrative organizations, devising methods for preventing fatigue and safety hazards, etc. An extensive listing of psychological functions and jobs has been recorded by Shartle.[4] Among these multiple functions can be listed: teaching psychology; counseling college students; testing and remedial work in public schools; clinical work in court, agency, feebleminded institute, child guidance clinic, psychiatric hospital, juvenile correctional institution, penal institution, court, general hospital; rehabilitation of physically handicapped; personnel and consulting work in industry; employment interviewing and counseling; serving as vocational adviser and member of clinic team in private, state, and federal hospitals and clinics. More and more, training for clinical psychology must recognize the need for specific training in therapeutic principles, which is possible only through the careful personal supervision by a psychiatrist of individual work with patients. Thus if the clinical psychologist is to function in this area, more internship or apprenticeship training must be provided.

There are approximately 1,000 clinical psychologists engaged in practice in this country. Since there are no set standards of training for the clinical psychologist, he himself must largely decide on what his own training should be. Of all the clinical psychologists in the United States, approximately 17 per cent have no more than a bachelor's degree, 46 per cent a master's degree, and about 37 per cent, the Ph.D.[5] Clinical psychologists have tended to operate independently and without strong organizational support in spite of the formation of the Psychological Corporation in 1921, and in 1937 of the Association for Applied Psychology (1941 membership over 600). The *Journal of Applied Psychology* was founded in 1915. Psychologists as a whole have shown increasing interest in the application of their science. As a group, clinical psychologists probably spend and prefer to spend most of their time in the analysis and manipulation of problems of relatively simple order. Few of them have shown an interest in the psychoses. Probably the majority refer involved psychoneurotic problems to the psychiatrist.

The clinical psychologist has a role to play as a psychotherapist. To this extent he appears to encroach upon the territory of the psychiatrist and he frequently meets strong opposition from the psychiatric profession. He has often had to work in areas avoided or ignored by the psychiatrist because of lack of time or interest. Where he has made his way in situations which are commonly the interest of the psychiatrist, he has done so largely on the basis of his personality and individual ability, and his work has been under the supervision of psychiatrists. It is recognized, however, that some psychologists function as psychotherapists with no guidance or direction from the psychiatrist. This has been consistently deplored by the medical profession and raises the pertinent question whether the psychologist should function at all as a therapist except in an organized psychiatric treatment structure.

Thoughtful members of the psychological profession who have long been concerned about the inconsistency and variability of their training for the clinical function and who sincerely desire to join hands with the psychiatrists to further a common aim of psychotherapy, have made sincere efforts to bring a standardization into their training programs and to seek and enlist the cooperation of the psychiatric profession. To this end a joint committee appointed by the American Psychiatric Association and the American Psychological Association has recently met and formulated a tentative program for joint training and responsibility. The main features of the program are likely to lead to some such recommendations as the following:

1. That there should be some form of certification for clinical psychologists.
2. That there should be joint training of clinical psychologists and of

psychiatrists in the same teaching hospitals and that internships should be available for students from the allied disciplines, since each has much to contribute to the training and experience of the other.

3. That a better balance should be worked out between formal didactic and theoretical instruction on the one hand, and apprenticeship training on the other hand, both for the clinical psychologist and for the psychiatrist.

4. That there should be careful selection of personnel for this type of training.

5. That the team principle should be adhered to, both in hospital and in extramural practice, for diagnosis, research, and therapy.

6. That administrative leadership should vary in different types of community services.

7. That plans should be worked out between the two disciplines for exchange of material for publication in scientific journals, for courses, lectureships, professorships, and internships, to assure intensive future cooperation.

It may be objected that these general principles open the door to lay psychotherapy (psychotherapy by others than those with a medical degree) and fail to define the training, the limits of therapeutic responsibility and activity, and the conditions by which control of lay therapeutics and diagnostic activities can be insured. The attitude of the physician toward these objections often depends upon the type of experience he has had with psychologists. However, most medical men would probably agree that:

1. The position of the clinical psychologist is unassailable in research, in psychological testing, and in all forms of selective procedure.

2. There is an inevitable trend toward some kind of therapeutic work by psychologists.

3. The shortage in personnel trained in psychotherapeutic techniques will never be met by physicians alone, nor can all community needs be met by physicians only, since their services command too high a price to meet all individual or community needs.

4. There are too few psychiatrists to undertake the clinical training of psychologists, as a group; their services are necessarily limited to

training a few psychologists who would then have to take over the burden of training the clinical psychologists.

5. Training for clinical psychotherapy need not be as long as the medical training of the psychiatrist. Details of what content might go into a course leading to a Doctorate in Medical Psychology or a Doctorate in Psychotherapy need thorough discussion and exploration.

6. Valuable cross fertilization for medical education, both for medical faculties and student bodies, could result from the presence of an active group of medically minded clinical psychotherapists and clinical psychologists.

7. Certification of clinical psychologists by scientific societies is an ultimate goal, but would be dangerous until basic scientific, practical, organizational, and curricular plans are worked out.*

Contribution of the Psychologist to Diagnosis, Treatment, and Research

Well-trained clinical psychologists make very valuable contributions in the mental hygiene field in several ways. The findings from tests used in measuring verbal and non-verbal intelligence, educational achievements, aptitudes, interests, and personality factors, and the psychologist's description of the patient's behavior during the test situation, including his manner of attack in different types of mental functions, his spontaneous comments, and the content of his responses and attitudes, yield much that is of diagnostic value in understanding the patient and his problems. The range, extent and value of diagnostic testing are fully described in a number of books including two large volumes by Rappaport and others.[6] A brief summary statement by Krugman may serve to indicate some of the problems studied and tools used:

The various deterioration indices, for example, developed in recent years are nothing more than fragments of intelligence tests in which the different elements show different rates of loss when mental functions

* An American Board of Examiners in Professional Psychology was incorporated by the American Psychological Association as a separate organization in 1946.

deteriorate. . . . Wide discrepancies between verbal and performance tests frequently characteristic of those with cortical involvements constitute another example of diagnostic value. Still others are: the measurement of aptitude and interests and their relation to personality, to motivations, drives and emotional values; the measurement of basic abilities such as reading, writing, speech, number concepts, artistic abilities and manual dexterity and the discrepancies between these abilities and actual function or failure to function at capacity. Reading disabilities in particular . . . require different approaches and treatment depending upon the type of disability. Much depends upon whether we are dealing with a generalized educational disability or a speech reading disability; whether the special disability is due to cortical anomalies, such as cortical word blindness, strephosymbolia, the various aphasic conditions, and the like, which can be uncovered in the careful psychological examination. Indications may be for neurological study, the aphasic status, or the electroencephalographic study. The same is true of speech and motor disturbances. The psychiatrist and psychologist are both involved.[1]

In terms of the number of people served, psychologists obviously have made their greatest diagnostic and therapeutic contribution in the educational and vocational fields. Long before the movement for the establishment of child guidance clinics got under way, many psychologists were employed in school systems for intelligence, educational, and aptitude testing with a view to the proper grading of children. The mental hygiene value of such work is obvious, for the children who are continuously exposed to instruction that is beyond their grasp are almost sure to develop marked feelings of inferiority, manifested by withdrawal tendencies or compensatory symptoms. The same is true of children who struggle along with unknown specific subject disabilities. Grading below the student's ability ordinarily leads to waste of time and poor application to learning tasks. Aptitude testing and vocational guidance have had similar value in insuring vocational training appropriate to abilities and interests, and placement in work for which one is fitted.

The major contribution of clinical psychologists engaged in clinical work, whether in schools, community clinics, hospitals, child care institutions, courts, correctional institutions or other types of agency, continues to be in the educational and vocational fields. As a rule the psychologist is better informed on schools and vocations than are other members of the clinic staff, and is thereby better equipped for educational and vocational guidance. Being also more skilled in corrective work in the educational field, he usually carries responsibility for treatment of persons with problems in this field. As Krugman indicates:

Problems of school adjustment or maladjustment, choice of school or course, vocational opportunities, resources for special types like the mentally retarded, the gifted, those with special abilities or disabilities, the disturbed, the delinquent, those with physical or sensory defects, and many others, are usually turned over to the psychologist when psychologists and psychiatrists work together, although joint efforts may not be necessary. In the main, the psychologist is the educational specialist of the clinic team. . . . Reading and other educational disabilities, speech disturbances, some types of motor disturbances, and emotional disturbances which are not too deeply rooted and can be alleviated by supportive methods, are some types that are usually treated by the psychologist, occasionally with concomitant psychotherapy by the psychiatrist.[1]

In addition to treatment of children with educational or speech problems, psychologists in some children's clinics have carried on play therapy as a means of releasing pent-up emotion and improving social adjustment. In recent years psychologists have also engaged more and more in group therapy. Their experience in administering group tests and in teaching groups of children with or without emotional or behavior problems has helped them to develop skill in group activities designed for therapeutic purposes. Some of this work has involved an extension of play therapy to groups of children. During the war psychologists, under psychiatric direction, engaged in group therapy with men who had suffered combat fatigue or other emotional or psychiatric problems. For this work, of course, knowledge of motivating forces and of mental hygiene principles as well as skill in discussion is required. Counseling that is essentially therapeutic is also carried on to some extent in industrial and other non-clinical set-ups.[7]

Research is another area in which the clinical psychologist contributes substantially. As a rule the professional education of the psychologist has included more training in research than has that of either the psychiatrist or social worker. Trained as he is in the use of statistics and of the objective approach both in research and in diagnosis, he offers a valuable corrective to any tendency to trust unduly to subjective judgments in clinical work, and research is particularly needed in the psychological and psychiatric fields.

A statement prepared by the National Council on Rehabilitation on the psychologist's role in the process of rehabilitation will serve to present in summary form the contributions of the psychologist in that field. Functions naturally will differ from this somewhat in fields other than rehabilitation, in some of which treatment constitutes a larger part of the work. The functions of the psychologist are:

1. To administer and interpret tests (or questionnaires) designed to measure the intelligence, aptitudes, abilities, interests, and personality traits of the disabled individual in order to secure information which may be helpful in selecting a vocational objective or in planning a program of re-education. (The psychologist who has been trained in vocational guidance may also serve as vocational counselor.)

2. To assist the essentially "normal" individual in solving his personal, social, and vocational problems so that his adjustment will become more satisfying or more socially acceptable.

3. To refer to the psychiatrist all individuals showing symptoms that deviate from those of the "normal" individuals, and to render assistance in carrying out the program of psychiatric therapy planned and supervised by the psychiatrist.

4. To present the significance of the psychological findings to the professional personnel involved in the rehabilitation program for the disabled individual.

5. To conduct research related to the above functions, as, for example:

a) To refine and improve instruments now used in measuring aptitudes, abilities, and interests.

b) To improve existing techniques used in determining personality traits and characteristics.

c) To evaluate the effectiveness of psychological procedures developed to measure intelligence, aptitude, personality, and degree of personal and social adjustment.[8]

REFERENCES

In the preparation of this chapter, the authors acknowledge their appreciation to Dr. L. C. Hutchins and Dr. James G. Miller for orientation in the historical development of psychology and in defining the education of psychologists, to Dr. Nathaniel Warner and Dr. Edward Stainbrook for general advice and criticism.

1. Krugman, M. The psychologist's contribution to the training of psychiatrists. Am. J. Orthopsychiat. 16:440–444, July 1946.

2. Beck, S. J. Rorschach tests: I. Basic processes; II. A variety of personality pictures. New York, Grune & Stratton, 1945.

   Klopfer, B., and D. Kelley. The Rorschach technique. Yonkers-on-Hudson, N. Y., World Book Co., 1942.

   Murray, H. A. Explorations in personality. New York, Oxford University Press, 1938.

3. Hutt, M. L., and E. O. Milton. The duties performed by clinical psychologists in army medical installations. Bull. Military Clinical Psychologists 1:115–117, 1946.

4. Shartle, C. L. Occupations in psychology. Am. Psychologist 1:559, December 1946.

5. Darley, J. C. Survey report to the Committee on Professional Employment, American Association for Applied Psychology, Washington, D. C., November 1939. Quoted in How is psychology used in clinical practice? by C. R. Rogers, in Psychology in use, edited by J. S. Gray, p. 114–167. New York, American Book Co., 1941.

6. Louttit, C. M. Clinical psychology. New York, Harper, 1936.

   Rappaport, D., and others. Diagnostic psychiatric testing, vols. I and II. Chicago, Year Book Publishers, 1945 and 1946.

   Wechsler, D. The measurement of adult intelligence. Baltimore, Ohio, Wood & Co., 1939.

   Wells, F. I., and J. Reusch. Mental examiners' handbook: I, Verbal; II, Pictorial. New York, Psychological Corporation, 1942.

7. Cantor, N. Employee counseling; a new viewpoint in industrial psychology. New York, McGraw-Hill, 1945.

Rogers, C. R.   Counseling and psychotherapy.   Boston, Houghton Mifflin, 1942.

Rogers, C. R., and J. L. Wallen.   Counseling with returned servicemen.   New York, McGraw-Hill, 1946.

8. National Council on Rehabilitation.   Report of the Committee on the Processes of Rehabilitation, second revision, December 1945.   New York, the Council, 1945.

IX

PASTORAL COUNSELING AND CHURCH LIFE

Dr. RICHARD C. CABOT, for many years professor of social ethics at Harvard Medical School and eminent leader in medical and social work education, was responsible for the statement that the minister could be doing 75 per cent of the healing work of the physician and could do some of it better than the physician if he knew his business. Such was his estimate of ministers' opportunities for mental hygiene service. He recommended that to equip them for this work all divinity students should be required to work one year under supervision in a general hospital or social case work agency. Considering that there are 140,000 ministers of all faiths in the United States, the potential contributions of ministers to mental health are obviously large. The crucial problem is that of converting potentialities into actual accomplishments speedily enough to meet the current and expected demands. Psychotherapy must be left primarily to the psychiatrists, but in terms of preventing mental and nervous illness and building positive mental health, adequately trained ministers can render valuable service.

Supervised clinical training in hospitals and agencies was initiated in 1923 and to date approximately 2,000 clergymen and theological students have had a significant period of internship.[*] Larger numbers have attended extension courses in mental health offered by theological schools, and the literature for ministers has been growing in volume and in quality. The schools have been reviewing their curricula, and in 1941 Hiltner estimated that 18 of the 90 schools in the country had on their faculties men who had been trained to teach pastoral work through separate clinical study

[*] Such training has been promoted especially by the Council for the Clinical Training of Theological Students, New York, and the Institute of Pastoral Care, Massachusetts General Hospital, Boston.

as well as general pastoral experience.[1] Wartime experience has greatly increased both the sense of need for such training on the part of the clergy and the opportunities to secure it. Chaplains in the armed forces found that from 50 to 75 per cent of their time had to be devoted to pastoral counseling. Some of these nearly 10,000 chaplains had been trained for this work but many had not. A small amount of training was provided by official chaplain courses, and this was supplemented substantially by counseling seminars conducted by competent leaders at large military posts.* These were intensive, three-to-five-day courses attended by Protestant chaplains and any others who wished to participate and later by civilian clergy and by professional personnel of the USO. Seminars were held in almost every state, with the heaviest concentration in the states where the clergy had paid least attention to this subject. Total attendance was about 1,500 chaplains and 3,500 civilian clergy. Literature on counseling prepared from the point of view of the clergy was widely distributed to chaplains and other clergy working with military personnel.[2]

This, of course, does not mean that all of the clergymen who received additional training during the war period are fully equipped for mental hygiene work, but it does mean that both interest and knowledge increased considerably during the war. Further impetus to counseling was given in the preparation made by churches and clergy to receive returning servicemen. The churches in nearly every sizable city held one or more conferences to discuss their responsibility and opportunity in aiding returning men, and counseling was a major subject in all of them. Moreover, certain denominations are planning to employ well-qualified persons from the mental hygiene field to develop a program of education and counseling service to increase the psychological effectiveness of the ministers' work.

* Originally conducted by the Committee on Religion and Health of the Federal Council of the Churches of Christ in America and later with the assistance of the Army and Navy Department of the YMCA.

Assets and Liabilities of the Minister in Mental Hygiene Work

By virtue of their position and function, ministers have particular advantages in mental hygiene work; but on the other hand, certain emphases in their traditional training offer difficulties which they have to surmount before they can be effective in this field.

One great asset that a minister has is the attitude of trustfulness toward the profession which generally prevails, and this is reinforced if the individual pastor has proven to be an understanding, tolerant, and helpful person. Not all people are willing to confide in him and not all pastors are sufficiently trustworthy to merit such confidence. But many people are quite as ready to confide in their pastor as in their physician or any other professional person. When people talk to the minister they are apt to tell him about their troubles, to reveal their thoughts and feelings, and to discuss some of the social and moral issues which have to be considered if they are to achieve a better adjustment, for they know he is interested in their personal happiness and their relationships with others as well as in their spiritual problems.

Again, the pastor has some advantage for mental hygiene work in the very fact that he is a minister of religion. In view of religion's concern with personal and social goals and with ultimate and time-tested values, the minister is in a position to help people develop a sound philosophy of life and to strengthen their sense of security. As Pollock has stated:

Underlying the reactions of the healthy-minded person is a philosophy of life, or a general attitude of mind that gives assurance that the world as a whole is well ordered; that people in general are striving to be considerate, just and honest; that regardless of the evils and imperfections of human society, truth and right will ultimately prevail.[3]

The minister who combines with such an attitude, an understanding mind, warmth of personality, and a dynamic faith is in a position to allay many of the fears and anxieties with which well-meaning persons are often afflicted. Doubtless the inordinate emphasis on sin in some churches has increased the guilt feelings of some people, perhaps to the point of driving them into psychoneurosis or even into mental illness. But on the other hand, congregational worship, the confessional, and pastoral services have doubtless brought to many assurance of forgiveness and a reality-rooted sense of rightness and well-being.[4]

Again the minister has an advantage in that he deals with people as individuals in a total situation, for almost all phases of human experience belong to his province. If he keeps close to his parishioners he knows their economic status and their unfulfilled strivings for comfort, independence, or superiority. He knows their personal reactions to illness, to family tensions, and to the moral hazards in the community. He sees how each individual is meeting life or evading it. He believes in the inherent worth and sacredness of personality, but he sees also that men are scattered all along the scale of social adjustment and that his task is to help them move further up the scale. The gossip monger, the social climber, the offensively righteous pillar of the church, the flamboyant youthful rebel, the faithful worker, and the veritable saints in his midst, all these are members of his flock. Seeing thus the manifold strivings, frustrations, and achievements of many different kinds of people, he learns to consider each in his or her total situation. This is a great advantage, for all of life is significant for mental health.

The minister has many and close associations with the family as a unit. His part in marriages, baptisms, and funerals together with his pastoral visits and his educational work with the children give him easy access to families and multiple opportunities to be helpful. He sees at first hand the interplay of the several personalities in the home and is in a position to observe beneath the social disguise the conflicts which are active in family life, including those which if not arrested may destroy mental or emotional balance. The minister is less likely than anyone else to be regarded as an intruder in family matters. Constructive suggestions offered by him are likely to be given favorable consideration.

Conversely, the minister's training and, in some instances, the motives which led him to choose his profession place before him certain psychological hurdles. He has been taught to have definite beliefs and convictions and to impart them to others. Doubtless the minister's secure sense of values is as great a source of strength to the confused and troubled as the formulations of faith of his particular church, but he cannot expect everyone to hold the same beliefs, for beliefs and convictions have always been influenced by previous life experiences.[5] Particularly in his counseling function he must hold his personal convictions sufficiently in abeyance to avoid blaming or condemning his counselees. If he is appreciative of the present circumstances and past influences in the lives of those he counsels, he can retain all his convictions and give them reassurance. If he attempts to impose his convictions on them, he is almost certain to induce or increase in them a sense of guilt.

Theological training, particularly if it has not been supplemented by discipline in the psychological and social sciences, is likely to give the minister the illusion that he has all the answers. In counseling, however, he must start with the assumption that he knows little and has much to find out. He brings to the counseling room only his understanding of people, some sense of what to look for, and a quality of trustfulness which induces confidence. He must avoid the tendency to fit people into fixed patterns, and learn to recognize and be tolerant of all kinds of human variations. He has been taught to talk, not to listen; and in his counseling efforts his parishioners are likely to invite him to advise much too soon and often. Therefore, he must be doubly fortified against his own characteristic professional habit and the tempting requests of his counselees.

The minister must supplement his religious beliefs and theological formulations by the knowledge and use of psychological processes and learn to make use of psychological methods. Virtue is not confined to the religious experience; it is part of everyday feelings and attitudes. The sense of guilt must be talked out until it loses its power and shame. In the counseling relation, grace and forgiveness must be actually experienced if absolution pronounced by the minister is to be truly effective. The pastor as counselor, by his receptive listening and his obvious and full acceptance of his counselees as persons, will permit the free expression of hostility, fear, or shame and will thus aid in the abreaction of unhealthy emotions. And, of course, the minister must learn to keep confidences inviolate. Parishioners hesitate to seek a pastor's counsel until they are well assured that their confessions and confidences will never be used as illustrations in sermon or other public address, even when the situation is so disguised that there is no danger of identifying the individual concerned. The pastor who offends even once is likely to have few further opportunities to counsel on intimate problems.

Problems and Methods in Pastoral Counseling

Almost every kind of personal or family problem is likely to be brought to the minister whose understanding and poise inspire confidence. One of the authors was engaged on a part-time basis over a two-year period in counseling in a church organization where referrals were received from thirty or more ministers. The following were the more frequent types of problem: (1) marital difficulties; (2) behavior disorders of children and problems of parent-child relationship; (3) emotional instability, especially in young adults, middle-aged men, women at the menopause; (4) problem love affairs—one-sided, uncertain, unduly protracted, regretted, or disappointing; (5) adolescent conflicts; (6) need for information and guidance regarding education, social health, and mental hygiene. Of less frequent occurrence, contrary to what ministers and church members might expect, were religious or moral doubt, distress over wrong-doing, and depression following the death of relatives.

Since the end of the war many veterans and their families have consulted their pastors about problems of readjustment. Some men were wrestling with problems of a moral or spiritual nature; they had feelings of guilt over violations of their standards of conduct or they had been taking stock of their faith and wanted their pastor's help in thinking it through. Others sought help in planning their future. Still others wanted marital counsel or assistance in re-establishing their relationships with their children after long separation. Those who had not been altogether secure in their family relations before the war were more likely to need counsel when they returned, but others had problems arising from long separation[6] or wounds, injuries, or other handicaps.

Pastoral counseling in regard to some of these problems requires all the wisdom and grace the minister can muster. There is no easy answer to the family whose young sons have been killed in the war or whose children have met with fatal accident. Neither is it easy to counsel wisely the lad who has lost both legs or the man whose wife wants a divorce so that she can marry another. In such situations the minister who has had a sound orientation in the science of human behavior and is familiar with the complex causes of emotional conflicts is the one most likely to be effective in counseling, for the most valuable spiritual guidance is that which is combined with a thoroughgoing knowledge of human motivation. To counsel and advise wisely, particularly those who have psychiatric difficulties, a minister needs to know the basic principles of mental hygiene. Intuition and sympathy are not enough. A genuine understanding of people, ability to listen, and a dynamic faith comprise the most essential equipment for pastoral counseling.*

A few illustrations of pastoral counseling with veterans will serve to illustrate how much some of them have needed opportunities to talk things out and how significant the pastor's sharing of faith and friendship may be. Such help is needed particularly by

* The methods used in pastoral counseling are different from those used by other counselors only in so far as the method is influenced by the minister's particular functions. (See Chapter XI for discussion of interviewing and counseling methods.)

those who have been so severely wounded that they have but a short time to live or have to go through a long period of medical treatment and convalescence.

CASE 21. *Mortally wounded.*

This man is dying from severe wounds. His family lives in a distant state. The pastor's chief role has been that of friend; and when the boy has raised questions he and the pastor have frankly discussed the meaning of life, death, and immortality. He has lost all bitterness and all anxiety about himself and in fact has a great spirit. When he has expressed concern about his parents the counselor has sought to give reassurance and later reinforced this with facts learned through correspondence with them.

CASE 22. *Severely burned and disfigured. Plastic surgery operations with long convalescence.*

This young sergeant suffered extensive burns a few months before the end of the war in Europe. His commanding officer, two other officers, and he were inspecting a German film which had been brought to company headquarters. It exploded in their faces, causing third degree burns in all four men, especially about the head, face, and hands. The sergeant's ears were burned off in the explosion, and his left hand was so severely burned that it was thought it would have to be amputated, but it was finally saved. Eyeglasses saved his eyesight. The best of medical care was provided and graftings were performed by the best plastic surgeons in the world. Skin from his legs and back was successfully grafted on his face and hands and strips of flesh where his ears used to be. In spite of this excellent care, the sergeant's face is still badly disfigured.

The pastor had talked frequently both with the sergeant and with his wife, who have been married over a year and had enjoyed a honeymoon of two weeks just before the sergeant was shipped overseas. It has been difficult for the wife to understand why her handsome husband should have to be so terribly mutilated. The young man himself was always a most exemplary churchman, but his new cross of suffering has been hard to bear. In the early interviews, both were inclined to interpret this misfortune as personal, unjustified, and inexplicable punishment, and they were bitter and resentful. By affording repeated opportunity for them to express their feelings and by helping them to focus attention on what was left, rather than what was lost, the pastor helped both of them to gain new perspective and to endure courageously the period of treatment, which will probably last for a year and a half. They are able to take a less personal view of the war, and have sublimated much of their grief by their interest in helping to build the peace. This man's disfigurement means less, and his personality and comradeship have come to mean more to his young wife. Together they are eagerly looking forward to having a home of their own as soon as he is discharged from the hospital.

Many men who saw combat had the problem of getting rid of their tension, or, as Rusk has put it, "getting down from condition red."[7] To talk it out with someone who is understanding and does not condemn is usually more effective than to think, soliloquize, or act it out. The pastor who listens well can do these men a real service.

CASE 23. *Cooling off by drinking and swearing.*
This man entered the service at the age of 38. He did not receive a furlough before being sent abroad. For 27 months he sweated it out in the Pacific. His pastor had written to him regularly, but received only one letter from him during those months. Two days after discharge, he came to the pastor's study very much under the influence of liquor. After the pastor had greeted him and welcomed him home again, the man began to speak in profane language. (Before his period of service he had drunk very little and his pastor had never seen him intoxicated and had never heard him swear.) The pastor allowed him to talk without making any reference either to his language or to the fact that he had been drinking. After talking and swearing for an hour, he said, "Pastor, you're a real Joe, you haven't given me hell for what I have said or for drinking." The pastor agreed that he had not, nor did he intend to censor him. The man then insisted on seeing the pastor's wife, although he had not known her very well before his entrance into the Army. In talking to her, he did not change his language. She gave him her attention without censure by word or look. Finally, he asked if he might go into the church. The pastor took him to the sanctuary, where he went immediately to the altar alone and stood with bowed head for a few minutes. Then with tears in his eyes he returned to the rear of the church, took the pastor's arm and said, "You and this church have been good to me. You can count on me."
The pastor reports that he has seen this veteran a number of times

since then. He is not altogether regular in church attendance, but he has never again been under the influence of liquor. Apparently he got from the pastor what he most needed—a chance to cool off and not be condemned for it. The pastor rightly observes that many more men will need that same chance.

The problems of many men relate not so much to what happened to them during the war as to their relationships within the family group. Again, it is sometimes the family members, rather than the man, who are concerned and take the initiative in seeking counsel.

CASE 24. *Parental solicitude and complaints.*
The parents of a man of 22 who had recently returned from overseas duty with both a nervous condition and tuberculosis came to the pastor with the complaint that they believed the food and medical care received in a veterans' hospital in an adjacent state were totally inadequate. Their son was subsequently moved to a veterans' hospital in the local community and was finally discharged to his home. Both the father and the mother were oversolicitous and protective. The pastor gave them opportunity to talk their problems over periodically and in the course of these discussions they saw things more objectively. They were given information regarding resources and possibilities of help for their son. Through questioning they were helped to see the possible danger of too great solicitude on their part. When the young man returned home, at first he did little but sit on a darkened porch. But his parents now realized the wisdom of giving him small responsibilities. He accepted these and carried them out quite well. The earlier discussions with the parents had helped them over their own despair to a more hopeful outlook. The young man began to look increasingly toward a worth-while future. He became interested in the boys' work in the church and later decided to return to school to complete his education.

CASE 25. *Anger, bitterness, and shame over wife's infidelity.*
This father of three children returned from the armed forces to find that his wife had become pregnant by another man in the community. On the first day of his return he sought the minister's counsel. Although the situation was naturally tense, the minister was able to interpret the pressures of the time and the wife's conduct in such a way that this veteran gave up thoughts of doing actual physical damage to

the offending neighbor and decided to remain with his wife and family. While this incident had been a severe blow to him, he was obviously fond of his wife and children, so that return to his family seemed the wise thing all around. The counselor's role was primarily that of listener, not only at the time of the initial interview but on many subsequent occasions when this veteran "blew off steam," thus easing the tension and enabling him to return again to normal pursuits. By his very presence and approval, the pastor also served to mitigate this husband's sense of shame and disgrace.

CASE 26. *Father-child adjustment.*

This young man entered the Army three months before his son was born and after a short period of training was sent to the Pacific theater of war. His wife lived at home with her father. After her child was born she talked to the pastor several times in anticipation of the father's home-coming, whenever it might be. The pastor discussed with her ways and means of keeping the father informed concerning the growth and development of his son. The child was two years old when his father returned from the Pacific and came home for a thirty-day furlough. Things went smoothly for two or three days, then the tensions increased.

The child had learned to go to his grandfather when he wanted help or companionship, and the grandfather had quite effectively taken the place of the father. The man went to see his pastor about the problem. He wanted to know how he could win the boy. Further tension was added because his wife, although she had been cautioned about this, wanted to go out "to make up for the many nights alone," whereas her husband wanted to stay at home and spend his time with the child. The pastor first talked with the young father, pointing out how natural it was for the boy to go to his grandfather and to become attached to him. It was noted that children require some time to get acquainted with a new person and that the father would have to be patient with both the child and his wife. He also came to appreciate the naturalness of his wife's desire for a more active social life, and a compromise was made. He took his wife out considerably more, and she in turn helped by persuading the grandfather to yield his position gradually in favor of the father. Decided improvement in the situation occurred during the thirty-day furlough, as was evident in a visit which the entire family made to the pastor's study before the man returned to camp. Tension between him and his wife had disappeared, and while the child was still a bit shy with his father, they clearly were making progress in getting acquainted.

Wife and child returned with the man to his camp, and together they were happily looking forward to his discharge.

It may be noted that family relationships figured largely in these cases of veterans' problems. In normal times family problems are equally prominent in pastoral counseling. Some of them arise in connection with marriage, birth, or other crises in family life, but in others, the onset is more insidious as the following case illustrates:

CASE 27. *Marital difficulties arising from social and emotional maturing of husband.*

This couple had been married for nine years. Their relationships had been mutually satisfactory with the wife playing a somewhat dominant role. She was a bright girl who had gone to college in spite of her parents' strong conviction that girls do not need higher education. Following her graduation she obtained a business position in which she was very efficient and received several promotions. After marriage she was equally efficient as household manager and handled the family budget entirely.

The husband had grown up in a home where dependence was fostered. His mother, who was the dominant parent, had given him an unusual degree of care and attention, had managed his finances, and more or less controlled his schedule but did it with such consideration that he had never rebelled against it. After his marriage it was quite acceptable to him for his wife to play a similar role. His work involved a great deal of travel and many contacts in the homes of well-educated and financially independent men. In the course of several years of such experience he matured a great deal and it became increasingly clear to him that he enjoyed much less freedom and carried less family responsibility than most of his business associates. For example, they had no hesitancy in inviting him to their homes without giving their wives advance notice, whereas every time he had attempted it his wife offered serious objections. He was increasingly irked by having so small a part in family finances. "I felt regulated and controlled within an inch of my life and I didn't like it," was the way he put it.

The situation became so obnoxious to him that at the end of a business trip of several months' duration he decided not to return home and notified his wife by mail. This news was a severe blow to her for, notwithstanding her husband's occasional protests, she had not fully appreciated the strength of his feeling nor the extent to which he had matured.

The pastor, who in this instance had had substantial training in social work and counseling methods, interviewed the wife twice and the husband once. It was a matter of retracing with each of them their own social and psychological growth and discovering why an adjustment that had formerly been satisfactory had ceased to be so. Fortunately, the wife's habit of domination was not so fixed that she could not change. Once she discovered the extent to which she had dominated her husband, and traced the development of his attitudes during the years he was growing up under parental domination, she was able to give her husband the freedom and initiative which he had come to crave; and in the light of her new understanding she was able to do this without feeling too guilty about her former domination. In fact she came out of the experience with a far more mature and cooperative attitude. When the man saw the reason for his wife's pattern, it no longer was a personal offense to him and during the period of a few months' separation he discovered how much she meant to him, notwithstanding their recent differences. Their mutual affection and their desire to help each other to be happy were of course the chief assets. Pastoral counseling merely gave both of them a chance to ventilate their negative feelings, to discover the reasons both for their former adjustment and their recent difficulties, and to consider a way of life in keeping with their greater maturity.

The minister has other opportunities for strengthening family life and releasing family tensions through his pastoral visits to the homes of people where he sees the peculiar love and ego needs of the several members of the family. These visits put him in a particularly favorable position to discuss and deal constructively with problems while they are in a formative stage. The pastor may be somewhat handicapped in his efforts to bring about better relationships because he may not always be accepted as having professional skill in dealing with family adjustments; yet he may accomplish much if he is patient and is not disturbed when his suggestions are rejected.

The scepticism of his ability that some parishioners feel will merely be their way of defending themselves against the necessity of facing unpleasant facts and making difficult changes. In regard to childhood jealousies, temper tantrums, and other problems of "discipline," a pastor can usually get the desired cooperation from the adults because children with these difficulties make trouble for the parents. Overdependence and problems involving insecure or antagonistic parents are very difficult because the parents often do not want any change and, of course, one cannot help them until they do. The same is frequently true of marital difficulties. Sometimes, however, one can help the better adjusted members of the family to gain insight into the maladjusted person's problems and get them to adopt suggestions which relieve the tension somewhat. Of course, here the pastor must have their complete confidence or he will probably do more harm than good. He must truly be "as wise as a serpent and as harmless as a dove."

In less acute problems and where there is a respectful and receptive attitude toward the pastor, he can often drop bits of diagnostic information and friendly counsel, sometimes half jokingly. If uttered with good humor such comments "register" without the sting that comes from being "put on the spot." Here is a father who was jealous of the attentions boys were beginning to pay to his oldest daughter with whom he had previously been very chummy. Being sensitive to criticism, he could not have stood a full explanation of the situation; but a few remarks of mixed truth and humor, which sometimes favored him and sometimes his daughter, helped somewhat in enabling him to let the girl grow up. He caught the idea of what the pastor thought about it and adopted a more mature attitude, partly because he felt what the pastor said was true and partly because the pastor had not been "preachy" about it or had not told him that he was wrong. Had the pastor said, "I think you should do thus and so," the father would probably have advised him "to stick to religion." The pastor who has acquired the mental hygiene point of view and has trained himself to listen and see, to live and let live, can by seemingly casual suggestions effect better relationships within a family group.

THE CONFESSIONAL IN RELATION TO PASTORAL COUNSELING

Confession assumes various forms. Quite commonly people confess to friends, relatives, and other sympathetic individuals mistakes or other behavior about which they are somewhat ashamed. In such confessions they usually protect themselves by withholding information about behavior which is charged with more profound guilt.

Confession as used by the psychiatrist is sometimes a difficult tool. Premature confession can be disturbing and destructive to some patients. The psychiatrist knows that it is often better to postpone or delay confession until the patient is able to handle the guilt feelings associated with or released by it. It requires great psychiatric skill to know when confession as such will be truly helpful and not devastating to the self-esteem and pride of the patient.

The confessional of the Catholic church, in which violations of the Ten Commandments are confessed, automatically carries with it the concept of repentance and forgiveness of sins. As stated by Moore,* who is both a priest and psychiatrist: "The mental hygiene value of the confessional derives from the fact that the penitent has a consciousness that his sins are forgiven when he leaves the confessional. Without this consciousness there would be very little mental hygiene value in the confessional." In this respect the Catholic confessional is different from confession in psychotherapy wherein the psychiatrist is not concerned with the moral or ethical values per se but only in giving interpretation and insight into the motivation of behavior. Because of the church's educational emphasis on the value of confession and the absolute sanctity and inviolateness of the confessional, free and ready use of it is made by most Catholic parishioners.

Some people who have a pathological degree of guilt seek to use the confessional of the Catholic church in reference to minor infractions of moral principle and for counsel on other types of prob-

* Moore, Thomas V., personal communication.

lems. Such parishioners are advised to consult a priest at the rectory regarding problems which do not properly belong in the confessional. In pastoral counseling on such problems the viewpoints and methods already discussed are applicable. Readiness to consult a priest may be enhanced by the fact that priests are celibate and do not live in a family group to whom it might be tempting to reveal confidences. Psychiatrists have found that priests are often very helpful in counseling Catholic patients whose problems involve strong guilt over attitudes or practices which they believe to be condemned by the church. With the cooperation of the priest, guilt is relieved without loss of faith or surrender of principle.

In the attempt to alleviate mental and emotional disabilities, the aims of psychiatry and those of religion are identical. This common task was well formulated by a group of psychiatrists as follows:

For centuries, religion and medicine have been closely related. Psychiatry as a branch of medicine has been so closely related to religion that at times the two were almost inseparable. As science developed, however, medicine and religion assumed distinctive roles in society, but they continue to share the common aim of human betterment. This also holds true for that method of psychiatry known as psychoanalysis.

We, as members of the Group for the Advancement of Psychiatry believe in the dignity and the integrity of the individual. We believe that a major goal of treatment is the progressive attainment of social responsibility. We recognize as of crucial significance, the influence of the home upon the individual and the importance of ethical training in the home. We also recognize the important role religion can play in bringing about an improved emotional and moral state.

The methods of psychiatry aim to help patients achieve health in their emotional lives so that they may live in harmony with society and with its standards. We believe that there is no conflict between psychiatry and religion. In the practice of his profession, the competent psychiatrist will therefore always be guided by this belief.*

* Statement passed by the entire membership of the Group for the Advancement of Psychiatry, July, 1947.

Visiting the sick affords a special opportunity for mental hygiene work. During illness fears and apprehensions which otherwise might have remained unknown tend to rise to the surface, although they may be quite as significant in seasons of relative health.[8] Then, too, the sickness itself is often as much mental as physical, the physical condition being greatly aggravated because of mental anxiety and emotional conflict. Even the worst fears lose some of their power when they are talked out. "The ministry of listening" is often a real service and contributes substantially to the sick person's sense of security.[9] The pastor's genuine personal interest, plus the use of appropriate comment, reading, and prayer may do much to strengthen the spirit of those who are ill and give them a "slant toward health."[10, 11] As Rice has pointed out:

Guilt and hostility, as well as doubt and fear, often are present in the minds of patients. Illness is always frustrating, and that brings hostility, which patients pour out and we absorb. Draining it off is a valuable therapeutic agent. Typical was a man who was overanxious about the operation he was to undergo. He was vituperative about the hospital, and accused his family of railroading him. He was rebellious and antagonistic to the nurses, but when he started talking to me all this abated, and he switched to a guilty feeling of having mistreated his wife. When he got it all out of his system, he felt better, was relaxed and slept well. He then faced the operation as a means to help him, not as punishment for sin, which is a common reaction.[12]

In any parish there are likely to be some adults whose personalities are poorly integrated and who show certain peculiarities. The pastor who has just begun to study psychology and mental hygiene is apt to overemphasize minor symptoms and conclude that most of his parishioners have psychological problems. He should guard against being so "case-minded" that he fails to treat people as normal persons. On the other hand, he can render real service to those who have developed a psychoneurosis or incipient psychosis by encouraging them to seek the help of a specialist or the protection of a hospital. It may require the wisdom of Solomon and the patience of Job to get them to undertake treatment, but a few successes in thus averting more serious illnesses are ample reward for much effort. Lowrey's *Psychiatry for Social Workers*[13] will be found helpful in differentiating various illnesses and making proper referrals.

Group Fellowship and Attitude Education

Pastoral counseling and other services to individuals often need to be supplemented by opportunities for group fellowship. For example, in the case of patients who remain at home during psychiatric treatment, the minister can play a supporting role in collaboration with the physician and also, through the organizations of the parish, can supply opportunities for patients who are well on the way to recovery to achieve social satisfactions and acquire social status by affiliating themselves with some parish group and taking part in its activities. This is particularly important for those who have recovered from a mental illness. Their minister and their fellow members must show them that they are welcome and acceptable by giving them ample opportunity to participate actively in parish life. It is the friendliness with which they are welcomed after they return to the church and the dynamic quality of the church's life that really count.[14] This is especially true of veterans who have suffered psychiatric disability, the wounded, and those whose nervous stability has been weakened by their participation in the war. Recent comment of a chaplain serving in a military hospital is much to the point:

Often the glad hand of welcome home becomes the cold shoulder to the discharged veteran of a few months. His sense of continuity has been worn thin enough—the once familiar places and faces have an air of unutterable strangeness about them. Unless the glad welcome of church and community develops into a continuing interest and concern, the ex-soldier suffering from war neurosis is likely to jump to the conclusion that it is all a sham and retreat much deeper into his self-created shell. Numerous cases of the first festive welcome and consequent inconsiderateness of the communities back home are coming to us each day. The church and its pastors, above all others, can make this a continuing effort, a repeated effort. Perhaps at first the ex-fighter will seem to rebuff all friendly advances—we see this happen at early stages of treatment almost constantly. He is suspicious of everyone and everything. But we have no right to stop with the first rebuff. It may be but his crudely invented mechanism to see if we ring true—to see if we have the continuing interest for which he longs.[15]

Church fellowship can be equally helpful to men who come out of the war with problems of personal conscience. Many who through training in home, school, or church had come to believe in the sacredness of human life were thrown into severe conflict in the armed forces, where national and group sanctions required them to kill. Others have felt guilty over the death of friends, and still others have pangs of conscience over marital infidelity or changes in personal habits. Both those who suffered wounds of the spirit and those who came back with psychiatric disabilities have strong feelings of difference and apartness and very much need to acquire again the sense of belonging to a group. When their fellow members of the church group show sustained personal interest in them and treat them with real respect, they can the more quickly accept themselves. It is then an easy step to more active participation in the church's work and fellowship which helps further to give them purpose and direction.

Because soldiers are men of action rather than of words, the average healthy veteran wants to do something more than listen to a sermon and take part in congregational worship. Many of them have developed leadership and acquired a breadth of knowledge and a variety of skills which enable them to contribute more to the life of the parish than they could before the military experience. They should be offered opportunities in line with their interests and abilities—singing in a quartet, teaching a class, leading a boys' group, or coaching a team.

In all work with groups, special attention may have to be given to certain individuals who have difficulty in group relationships in order to insure that the group experience is a positive one and that they get maximum benefit from it. We may illustrate with a boy in his upper 'teens, who was undersized and had formerly been very shy. His older brother had always been the idol of the family, his older sister was decidedly attractive, and his younger sister was much petted because of a chronic heart condition. He had always been made to do the menial tasks about the home and was never praised as the others were. He thus came to have a strong inferiority feeling. He frequently did "most unreasonable" things to get more recognition at the society meetings, and he joined every society to which he could get elected just because of this need. He had little sense of his limitations but, on the other hand, he did with vigor the unimportant and menial tasks as well as the more significant ones. As property man for a play he was excellent. His habit of thrusting himself into conversations made him obnoxious to many people, but became less offensive to them after they realized how hard he worked and how many things he got done. Observing the boy's emotional needs, the leader of the group frequently appointed him to serve on committees which involved few persons and a good deal of work. He did this, not to "use" the boy, but to help him meet his need. When the boy got into conflict, he came to the leader about the matter and was gradually helped to see his problem and make a better adjustment to the group.

While such services to individuals afford the minister many opportunities to contribute to the mental health of those who have personal problems and special individual needs, some of his most constructive work in mental health can be done through his educational influence on people's attitudes. For instance, the minister can do much to change the general attitude of sentimentality toward the physically crippled and of fear and suspicion toward the mentally ill. In the pulpit, in addresses to parish and community groups, and in his pastoral visits he can make it clear that the crippled want and need to be treated as normal people; that mental and nervous illnesses are real illnesses for which the sick person is no more responsible than for a cold or fever; that many nervous ailments are curable and that some people have become stronger in mind after treatment than they ever were before.

All church bodies should tackle these problems aggressively in cooperation with other groups working toward the same end. As Hiltner has pointed out:

> These attitudes are a part of our general culture. They cause harm, make many difficulties worse and need improvement at any time. It becomes more important now than ever to change such attitudes since we have many newly crippled and a large number of cases of mental illness as our heritage from the war. It is a difficult task, for when we deal with attitudes which are deeply imbedded in our general culture we do not have a controlled environment like a rest home in which we can keep our hands on the situation. The church may do much to create islands of understanding, of fellowship, of spiritual resources and help. But we shall fail in the task if we do not go on to do whatever can be done in altering some of the basic attitudes of our culture which are un-Christian.[16]

Another area in which the church has extreme opportunity to deal with unfavorable attitudes and resentments which are shared by many servicemen and civilians has been described so well by Booth that quotation in full seems in order:

> There is one problem in relation to at least a large number of the returning service personnel which may be overlooked because it is shared by so many at home. On the surface it appears to be a mere lack of interest in peace aims, and in particular in peace aims for Europe.
>
> The attitude of the American soldiers, at least in Europe, has been described consistently as one of indifference regarding the peace aims. Though the fact is recognized, the basic cause of it is rarely considered. Nearly every American who originally emigrated from Europe did so under a sense of frustration strong enough to overcome the many forces

which usually hold man to his family and to his native soil. There have been many positive results from this break with the past: the emphasis on progress and movement, eyes fixed on the possibilities of the future, and others which have become nearly synonyms for American spirit. But in spite of the American achievements a deep undercurrent of resentment has persisted as a subconscious tradition.

Now it is the second time in twenty-five years that Americans have been drawn to fight in Europe. It is small wonder that finally, in the attitude of many, the underlying resentment has become a dominant factor. They tend to feel they are fighting a war for people whose values they or their ancestors rejected—whose adherence to the old culture and to old ways has caused all the trouble. No matter how unaware the individual American soldier may be of this meaning, it shows itself in the mass spirit of indifference toward peace aims.

When the soldier returns home, the problem may be more acute. To find a positive meaning for sacrifices made is essential for the emotional health of everybody. If the soldier's only feeling about Europe is one of resentment, that will not only cloud his view of Europe but also his view of the problems of America. Europe will be for him the past which must be rejected; America, the promise of a future as different as possible from what the "past" represents. Past and future will be unable to meet in his mind. If this happens, it will be the returning service man who may lead the nation into isolationist blindness.

The Christian churches are the holders of the only spiritual values which, in any considerable measure, Americans have continued to share with Europeans. This unique position should allow the churches to do much to heal the old wounds of resentment which persist in the American attitude toward Europe, and which may be even stronger among the returning service personnel. By its very understanding of this situation, the church may be of immense value not only to the emotional health of the service men as they return, but also the cause of peace itself.[16]

Although the war accentuated certain unfavorable attitudes, it helped to give us a new sense of the value of group morale which evolves in the process of learning and acting together. While in the armed forces men had a strong sense of their unit solidarity.

The chief reward for the loss of their individual freedom was their loyalty to one another and the united strength which they had as a unit. In civilian life they equally welcome opportunities to get together in groups where they can discuss matters of common interest and carry on worth-while activities.[17] To provide such opportunities is fully in line with the concept of the church as "the fellowship of believers." Active and meaningful participation in the worship, educational programs, and organizational activities of a church can contribute substantially to the morale and social well-being of its participating members.

Mental Hygiene and Preaching

Ministers in America have always used the Bible as their great authority. The Bible also contains the fundamental principles of mental hygiene, as many psychiatrists acknowledge. The most cherished and best remembered passages reveal how largely the writers of the Bible were concerned with people's inner life, with motives and difficulties, with psychological health and happiness.

"Keep thy heart with all diligence, for out of it are the issues of life. . . . The good man out of the good treasure of his heart bringeth forth good things, and the evil man out of the evil treasure of his heart bringeth forth evil things. . . . Out of the heart proceed evil thoughts, fornications, thefts, murders, adulteries, covetings, wickedness, deceit, lasciviousness, an evil eye, railing, pride, foolishness. . . . As a man thinketh, so is he. . . . Sufficient unto the day is the evil thereof. . . . With what measure ye mete shall it be measured to you again." All these verses—and the Beatitudes might well be added—are statements of unquestioned psychological fact. Again look at a few of Jesus' exhortations: "Let your yea be yea and your nay nay. . . . Be not anxious therefore for the morrow. . . . Do not your righteousness before men to be seen of them. . . . Make friends with thine enemy whilst thou art on the way with him. . . . Judge not that ye be not judged. . . . Love your enemies and do good to them that hate you and pray for them who despitefully use you."

Anyone, whether preacher, pastor, social worker, or psychiatrist, who has had intimate contact with people, knows that for those who live in fear and uncertainty, those who are restless without constant approval, those who need to bolster their self-esteem by criticizing others, and those whose love has turned to hate, these exhortations wisely suggest the only real solutions of their problems and the genuine healing for their troubled spirits.[2, 18] If the preacher does not advance the mental and spiritual health of his people, it is no fault of his heritage.

Notwithstanding the prominence of mental hygiene principles in the Bible, the efficacy of preaching is often questioned on the ground that listening to sermons is substituted for socialized conduct. This charge is very probably warranted in some cases, yet insecure persons who use a sermon only to convince themselves of a virtue they do not really possess may by that very fact and the security which it gives become more stable and socialized than if they had not gone to church at all.

Preaching may, however, do much more than this. If the preacher has acquired a thorough understanding of personality development and habitually sees people as individuals with distinctly personal histories, if he accepts their present habits and characteristics in the light of their earlier conditioning experience, he can develop a manner and method in preaching which give people the feeling that they are understood. The rich mental hygiene texts of the Bible then gradually appear as statements of profound insight into the way our minds and feelings work. The principles involved are more readily accepted because of the attachment many people have to the Bible. If the preacher will talk in terms of everyday feelings, attitudes, habits and aspirations, commonplace life situations, and familiar Biblical scenes and sayings rather than in technical formulations of a theological or psychological nature, he can accomplish a great deal to help his people to better understanding of themselves and better adjustment to each other. The following incidents testify to this. A woman, with evident joy in her face, tells her pastor that through his sermons and his way of "taking no account of evil" she had gained insight into her previous inability to forgive certain people, and that she has recently been setting things right, with surprising satisfaction to herself and her one-time enemies. A man invites his pastor to his home to tell him that through the recent series of sermons dealing with home life he has discovered his own inherently selfish streak and the reason for it in his own childhood experience. There is real advantage in people's making such discoveries and adjustments themselves without having been treated as "cases." It preserves their independence and enhances their self-respect.

THE WORTH OF WORSHIP

The very persistence of the custom of worship indicates that there is mental hygiene value in it, although worship programs have not usually been devised with this in mind. They have been built up on the basis of a particular theology or the liturgical usage of some historic period rather than on psychological laws and principles. They are effective, of course, to the degree that they observe psychological laws (devisedly or accidentally) and fit the particular emotional needs of the worshippers. If the worship meets their feeling needs and leaves them less in conflict and more secure, they hold to it. If it offends their aesthetic taste or intellectual integrity or if it moves in a system of thought and feeling that is unfamiliar, people naturally turn away from it, for they find in it no real value for themselves.

Most of the worship services in wide use today and the theologies on which they are based were developed in an age when most people were decidedly dependent, both economically and politically, and when the monastic ideal was strong. Because of this, most worship services posit for the worshipper a relation of extreme dependence, an excessive sense of sin, and an inordinate otherworldliness. This kind of worship service has value for some people. It gives an emotional lift and a sense of righteousness and hope to many who are overdependent, who have acquired a strong sense of guilt, or who have been frustrated and broken in spirit by the hardships of life.

There is, however, a large group of independent, self-reliant, and socially-minded people who respond to a worship service that posits a more liberal theology, gives a larger place to personal worth and purposiveness, and is motivated by zeal for the kingdom of God in terms of social righteousness. In worship of this kind they find themselves continuous with something beyond themselves and lose the extreme individualism which is a real danger today. Participation in worship services that are conducive to a deeper respect for the creative aspects of reality adds to the social zeal and the spiritual vigor of this very worth-while class of people.

The principle of worship is sound, for it builds on the well-nigh universal need of people to add up and find meaning in their total experience, and on the equally inclusive tendency to aspire to values which are yet unachieved but are within the range of possibilities. Worship, when its form and content serve the real needs of worshippers, can fortify their minds and strengthen their spirits. It can, by enhancing both their sense of personal worth and of social solidarity, equip people for sustained work and social action. (Etymologically, *worship* and *work* spring from the same root.) In fact, worship has no other purpose, for as the Hebrew Prophet Micah stated 2,700 years ago: "What doth the Lord require of thee but to do justly, to love mercy and to walk humbly with thy God."* The very word religion means "binding together"; and when religion is at its best it binds together past, present, and future, the individual, the social group, and the cosmos with a single purpose into a unified whole.

---

* This statement which is engraved on the column dedicated to religion in the Library of Congress was chosen by the late Dr. Charles W. Eliot as the one which best expresses the meaning of religion.

Religion and Present-Day Needs

The church, if currently true to its heritage of concern for all of life, must take into account our wartime experience and the large social problems which now confront us and gear its message and work accordingly. Returned servicemen are interested in what the church has to say about God, about human life, and particularly about how human lives—their own and others—can be made more meaningful and secure. Impressed with the multiple confusions in the world, they want to add things up and develop a sound and effective working philosophy. Religion as basic truth and as an integrating force interests them. Petty purposes, empty formalities, and minor sectarian differences do not. As Bell has stated: "It has come home forcibly to many of them that for freedom to be worth a man's life laid down, it must be not only freedom from oppression, but also and even more, freedom from triviality."[19]

The message of the church must be sincere and honest. As one chaplain has put it, "The returned veterans are too wise in fundamental spiritual realities to accept vague generalities. Good will and talk of good feeling, the veterans will tell you, is pure nonsense."[20] One of the reasons for this has been well stated by another chaplain:

Some returning soldiers will be skeptical and cynical. Too many promises will have been made to them which will never be kept. They will have little sympathy for the hypocrisy and sham which democracies have a tendency to use. It is here where the Church can do the most good. To preach fearlessly and honestly against such hypocrisy is the Church's supreme task. No mere mouthing of pious platitudes will suffice. Some deep thinking by ministers and the Church about life and God will have to be done. These men will have seen life at its worst. They will have to be made to feel that their suffering wasn't futile. This suffering will have to be placed against God and His plan for the world, because these men will not be interested in "flag-waving" or insincere patriotism.[21]

Honesty and zeal for social justice seem to be the keynotes sounded by men who have expressed their convictions. One denomination asked many army and navy men what suggestions they had for preaching to returning servicemen. The following are a few of their answers:

Unless the pastors carefully (and prayerfully) restudy the techniques and content of many of their sermons, I greatly fear they will have a terrific fight to hold the attendance of returning servicemen. They will attend the services for the first two weeks after they return, and after that they will drop out—let the pastors streamline their messages, stripping them of non-essentials. These men have become accustomed to fifteen-minute sermons by their Chaplains, and therefore they have had to deal with a realistic gospel only. Our Chaplains confine their messages to just what God had said to them, and then they quit. . . . Yes, we want sermons when we return, but let them challenge our loyalty to the changeless Christ and His Code, in this day of moral breakdown— I'd like to know the one, two or three of Jesus' World Order. It is so vague in all of our minds that no one can get enthused about it. Sermons should present this so logically as to capture our imagination as have the Nazis captured the German people. . . . Sermons that will challenge us to the great causes of humanity, such as industry, labor, housing, government and world peace. . . . This war was caused by economic and political blocs. Let all preachers sound a call for Christian leadership in the areas of life where the trouble lies, including economics, politics, etc.[22]

The war has given veterans, and in fact many others, some tough lessons in the problems of social relationships. They know the world can't be kept safe merely by keeping it static. They are likely to be interested in the church to the degree to which they find it interested in developing a better order of things. They are likely to pass it by if it is interested merely in the perpetuation of itself and maintenance of the status quo. Many a man feels as a certain marine did, who, in no uncertain terms, voiced his resentment at advertisers' inferences that servicemen want to return to exactly the same conditions which they left.

"I'm sick of fancy advertisements telling everybody that I, as a member of the armed services, don't want any improvements in America! Since when has my country been afraid to grow? Too many of us guys have seen houses on our street that should have been ditched long ago. I'm fighting for a lot of things—freedom, democracy, my family—but also for some fresh new homes instead of some crates built by a phony contractor in 1906. If getting those houses built means tethering a few boys down to twenty-five thousand a year, it's O.K. with me."

When asked, "Why are you so burned up about the ads—who cares?" he answered with vigor:

"I care. You'd be surprised how many people think the writers of such ads know how we're thinking. Besides, those ads are so self-righteous; they spread on the idealism too thick. One of them even started with 'Onward Christian Soldiers' being taught to a bunch of nice kids in a school room. I'm no saint, but I have enough Christianity in my bones to resent a good hymn being used to sell the American people—and us soldiers—the idea that we as a people are afraid of change. My religion stands for change, lots of it, where it's needed. Now.

"My Bible wasn't different from anyone else's, and it gave me a religion of people who wanted to get up and go places, to fix what was obviously wrong in the setup around them and get men and women to have a little faith that God doesn't expect them simply to hang on with their teeth. . . . Didn't Moses go into Pharaoh's brickyards in Egypt and lead the Jews to freedom from their oppressors? Didn't Amos lead off with his right and attack the black markets, loan sharks, and bribe-taking priests? My Christianity has taught me that the answer is always *Yes* to the question, 'Am I my brother's keeper?' "[23]

Servicemen with earnest convictions and civilians who think and care about other people know that being our brother's keeper means stepping out of the world of the Bible and out of modern church buildings into homes, streets, factories, and stores. They know it means fighting prejudices in high places and in low; creating work opportunities for all; removing trade barriers and supplying basic materials to people who lack them; and taking up the cudgels for the "have not's" in all parts of the world, with the sure knowledge that many of the "have's" entrenched in high places will oppose such efforts, whatever their religious professions may be. They know, too, that it means constant hard work in local communities the world over, as well as in international conferences, to build a world organization that will both win and hold the peace. They share this cogent conviction of Sumner Welles:

> During the fatal decades which elapsed after the close of the first World War, the people of the United States time and again joined in initiations to outlaw war on paper. From any tangible or potential contribution of their own toward an international attempt to channel the elementary forces of mankind into the ways of construction rather than of destruction they studiously refrained. We cannot afford to concentrate our attention purely upon questions of political and military security and overlook the economic problems which will confront us when the victory is gained. To do so would be fatal. No political and security structure of international organization could stand for long if economic relations between nations were characterized, as they were after the last war, by thrusts and counter-thrusts of such economic weapons as high tariffs, restrictive quotas, embargoes and discriminations. The nations in the world organization of the future must be economic friends, cooperating in that basic field of human relations, as well as political friends. Political cooperation and economic isolation simply will not mix.[24]

It is not to be expected that every returning serviceman will be challenged by the mighty tasks which confront the church, but to catch the attention and hold the loyalty of those who are challenged, the church must be ready to bring together her veteran members who have won the war and her civilian members who see clearly their peacetime obligations, in a united effort to win and maintain the peace and build a healthier social order. Joined thus in a common purpose they will achieve the kind of team spirit and loyalty which were the soldiers' mainstay in military service and which can make our American people "the salt of the earth." The eager pursuit of such a worth-while purpose which is shared with others is one of the surest ways to achieve and maintain mental health.

REFERENCES

1. Hiltner, S., and others. Clinical pastoral training. New York, Federal Council of the Churches of Christ in America, 1945.

2. Hiltner, S. Religion and pastoral counseling. Am. J. Orthopsychiat. 17:21–26, January 1947.

3. Pollock, H. M. Security and mental health. Ment. Hyg. Leaflet no. 10, issued by New York State Department of Mental Hygiene, Albany, New York.

4. Hiltner, S. Religion and health. New York, Macmillan, 1943.

5. Woodward, L. E. Relations of religious training and life patterns to the adult religious life. New York, Teachers College Bureau of Publications, 1932.

6. Thomas, D. V. The veteran as seen in a private family agency. The Family 26:203–208, October 1945.

7. Rusk, H. A. The journey down from condition red. New York Times Magazine, July 29, 1945.

8. Hiltner, S. The case for the clergy as ministers to health. Mod. Hosp. 60:75–76, May 1943.

9. Dicks, R. L. The ministry of listening. New York, Federal Council of the Churches of Christ in America, 1944.

10. Holman, C. T. The religion of a healthy mind. New York, Round Table Press, 1940.
Wise, C. A. Religion in illness and health. New York, Harper, 1942.

11. Cabot, R. C., and R. L. Dicks. Art of ministering to the sick, p. 12–13. New York, Macmillan, 1936.

12. Rice, O. Trained listener helps ill by saying nothing. New York World-Telegram, August 1, 1945.

13. Lowrey, L. G. Psychiatry for social workers. New York, Columbia University Press, 1946.

14. Berkhart, R. A. The church and the returning soldier. New York, Harper, 1945.

15. Dunkelberger, H. A. Mental convalescents among fellow believers. The Lutheran 27:8–9, August 1, 1945.

16. Federal Council of the Churches of Christ in America and Christian Commission for Camp and Defense Communities. The church and the returning service personnel, p. 27. New York, the Council and Commission, February 1945.

17. Bickham, M. H. The emergency of the new morale. Religious education 11:92–96, March–April 1945.

18. Cabot, R. C. What men live by. Boston, Houghton Mifflin, 1914.
Fromm, E. Escape from freedom. New York, Farrar & Rinehart, 1941.
Liebman, J. Peace of mind. New York, Simon & Schuster, 1946.
Menninger, K. A. and J. L. Love against hate. New York, Harcourt, Brace, 1942.

19. Bell, B. I.   The church and the veteran; an American forecast.   Atlantic Monthly 174:64–68, December 1944.

20. Wuebbens, E. P., Chaplain, Commander, U.S. Navy.   Chaplains say soldiers need living religion.   New York Herald Tribune, June 25, 1945.

21. Ylvisaker, N. M.   The chaplain views the church.   The National Lutheran 13: 30, Fall 1944.

22. Mobilizing the church for demobilization.   *In* The church and returning service personnel.   Indianapolis, Federal Council of the Churches of Christ in America, March 1945.

23. Fritchman, S. H.   The world you want—or do you?   The Link 2:22, published by the Servicemen's Christian League.

24. Welles, Sumner.   Religion and peace.   The Link 2:32, published by the Servicemen's Christian League.

X

MENTAL HYGIENE IN INDUSTRY

In America, there are one or two gainfully employed workers in most families, totaling fifty to sixty million people. Any phase of life that uses so much of the time of so many people is sure to be significant for individual and family well-being. Aside from the sheer logic of numbers, it is generally agreed that congenial working relations and genuine job satisfactions contribute much to the mental health and social adjustment of workers, and also to the mental health and stability of their families. This is true of everyone, from the high-salaried executive to the lowest paid unskilled workman. And not only does much of the well-being of the individual, while engaged in work and in off-duty hours as well, hinge on his employment and work satisfactions; the social and economic stability of the country depends on insuring these values for its workers. It is equally true, of course, that the family and home relations and attitudes affect the man's performance and satisfaction at work. With extensive unemployment or with much employment which does not do justice to the emotional and social nature of workers, we reap not only personal bitterness and resentment but also loss of faith in democracy and a lowering, if not disintegration, of national morale.[1] We have just come through a war which was fought for the preservation of our democratic way of life. The essence of democracy lies in respect for the inalienable rights and responsibilities of individual man; not the least of a man's rights is productive and satisfactory employment. Only in very recent years has this right come to be acknowledged. Refusal or failure to acknowledge it fully is still at the root of some of our industrial strife. We must, of course, go beyond tacit acknowledgment of the right to satisfactory employment. We must make it possible for everyone to exercise this right.

Wanted: A Workable Philosophy of Work

Industry in America, with its genius for organization and for simplified formulations of intricate processes, has operated under these two formulas: (1) proper materials plus technology (patterns, tools, and power) plus workers plus good management equals products at lower costs and therefore higher standards of living; (2) sales value of products minus cost of production equals profit. American industry has proven conclusively that it has the know-how of all parts of these equations except the worker-plus-good-management factor. That seems to outsiders, and is often admitted by insiders, to be at a hit-or-miss, pre-scientific, kindergarten stage of development. Whether industry makes for health, stability, and full production or for anxiety, strife, and lowered production depends very much upon the accepted philosophy of work and the extent to which both employees and managers are able to derive genuine personal and social values from their work. That either the philosophy or the method has been inadequate is quite clear. As Ford stated in an address to a group of automotive engineers, "In a free, competitive democracy mass production is a tool for raising the standard of living by reducing costs and thereby bringing more and better products within the budgets of more and more people. We have not yet solved the problems of mass production, for our failure in human engineering is creating waste and inefficiency which handicap the very purpose of mass production —lower costs." He backed this up by noting that 216,000,000 man-days of labor had been lost through strikes during the period 1927–1941 and that productivity per worker in industrial plants declined more than 34 per cent during the war period. He then added:

I do not have the answer to this problem, but I am sure that workable solutions can be found if we will only bring to it the same insistent objectivity and willingness to experiment which you have given to the mechanical difficulties in mass production. . . . What is needed today is industrial statesmanship—from both labor and management. If we are to have industrial relations programs and labor relations staffs and spend as much money on them as we do, we should do it expertly and efficiently, bringing to the task the same technical skill and determination that the engineer brings to mechanical problems. We must act on a more human and professional plane.[2]

We may distinguish between various levels of work in terms of the respect shown for the individual and the quantity and variety of satisfaction obtained. At the very lowest level is the chain gang or slave labor where men work purely because they must to save their lives and avoid extreme and abusive treatment. The person is not consulted, he is not a free agent, he merely conforms for the elemental protection of his life. He gets no positive satisfactions.

At a little higher level, men work for income only. While few jobs are totally lacking in personal and social value over and above those relating to income, work primarily for income has little intrinsic value and gives the worker small joy. There is no zest and no team spirit. The worker merely drives himself in the performance of a task for the sake of a wage and the things it will buy. In work for income only, there is no regard for maximum creativeness, job satisfactions, or benefit to others, and no reward except what can be purchased from the wages earned.

Work which makes for mental health and stability—and for full productivity—is on a very different level and provides many personal and social values. Most people find it good to make things, to operate machines, to sell, to instruct, to manage, or to direct an organization. Work in which one is interested and for which one is fitted supplies a very basic need and satisfaction, like eating when one is hungry. When a man says "I," he means not only the person he is but also what he does. Just as the meaning and value of a watch or of an automobile are determined more by its function than by the stuff it is made of, so the significance of work for an individual depends more on what his work accomplishes for him than on the intrinsic value of the product of his labor. The more talents he uses in work, the more fully integrated is his personality and the greater his sense of achievement. Work which makes it possible for a person to translate his energies into useful things or helpful services nurtures his self-esteem. Unlike the ancient crafts-man who expressed his personality through his craft and had a loving care for the product he made, men in modern industry work on impersonal machines turning out impersonal products. As a re-sult, the workers may lose some of their sense of personal creative-ness, although in many instances, through the control of speedy and powerful machines, they get a sense of creativeness on a much grander scale. In any event, success in America means skill and ac-complishment in work quite as much as money. This is proved by the fact that almost all our wealthy citizens work and that no emo-tionally healthy man is willing to remain on relief rolls when op-portunity for work is offered or to stay on a "dead-end" job when opportunities for advancement are available. The philosophy of "getting ahead" is so widely accepted in America that it cannot be ignored, either when individuals seek advancement or when union groups do it concertedly.

Moreover, work provides a major means of social relationship. Few people are happy alone. Our social nature demands expres-sion. We must relate ourselves to others and we do so at work for-mally or informally. Shared tasks are more exhilarating than soli-tary ones and the approval of fellow workers and supervisors means much to most people, for our estimates of ourselves are largely the reflection of others' treatment of us. In modern, mass-production industry it is of course difficult to insure close give-and-take between employees and managers. There are, however, no insoluble conflicts between the goal of mass production and the social and psychological needs of workers. The bigness of industry adds to the complexity of the problem, but as leaders in both man-agement and labor become as realistic on the human side as they have become on the mechanical and the technical side, their re-spective aims—more goods at lower cost and permanent and sat-isfactory work—can both be achieved.

It is essential, however, to accept the fact that workers—all classes of workers—are people, real, whole people, which means that their feelings, attitudes, and problems, on the job and off, their personalities and group identifications and loyalties, are quite as important as their brains and manual skills and that well and happy workers are the best workers. Any philosophy of work or theory of industrial management which discounts people's deep emotional and social needs or which does not accept an industrial or business organization as an organic whole is doomed to fail both in terms of maximum production and worker satisfaction. In short, industry must serve the twofold social purpose of producing more goods for more people and of providing more and fuller satisfactions for all who work, artisans and managers alike.

Many leaders whose educational background and administrative experience have stressed technology and economics have found it hard to accept the provision of worker satisfactions as a legitimate and necessary function of industry, but the number of voices demanding it is increasing at a more rapid rate than ever before. Leaders who are concerned with research into management and labor relations are stressing the importance of a practical knowledge of the social structure and of the psychological needs of workers, individually and in groups, as essential for sound management. They point out that an industrial philosophy which regards technology and finance as more real than human factors is a "truncated realism"; that "the administrator today requires, perhaps above all else, insight into the dynamics of human behavior, insight into the forces that make both for conflict and for cooperation"; that it is necessary "to provide employees a socially significant way of life and maintain a condition of balance within the internal organization such that employees, by contributing their services, are able to justify their desires and hence are willing to cooperate."[3-6]

Mental Health and Morale

Mental health and morale are not quite identical but they certainly are reciprocal. Each has meaning for and promotes the other.

Just a few workers with unhealthy attitudes can very soon weaken or destroy the morale of a group. Vice versa, where high morale and good teamwork prevail, the less stable and less self-assured become more comfortable and work with greater efficiency.

Three major influences have been operating to further the promotion of mental health and morale in industry and, while the approach of each is different, the conclusions arrived at are similar.

MORALE IN THE ARMED FORCES

In the business of war it has been discovered that certain kinds of work, of risk, of responsibility, and of discipline improve men's spirits and that other kinds break them. As was pointed out in Chapter I, new methods were devised to test and index trainees' aptitudes and abilities and to relate these to their mental and physical powers and their emotional stability. Job analyses of all occupations in the Army were matched against these "profiles" of enlisted men and women to determine the best possible placement.[7] Though the range of jobs in the armed forces was very limited compared to that of peacetime occupations and consideration of immediate needs restricted it even more, the experience in the Army has demonstrated the value of this scientific approach to placement. Persons who had been poorly placed and trained were retrained for jobs suited to their capacities and all records of the work and medical history of each individual were preserved and moved along with him from the beginning of his war service up to his discharge. Plans for the use of these data about each service person in his readjustment to civilian life have advanced further in Canada[8] than in the United States. But the value of the system for peacetime vocational guidance and placement and its applicability to the whole field of industry are recognized in the United States. As Ford stated recently, "We know that general masses of men work constantly at points below their top capacities, and it is one of our jobs to see that ways and means are provided to help them rise to these opportunities. . . . American industry should be a place of opportunity—a place in which men and women can grow and develop into better jobs."[2]

Besides selecting and training for the job, the armed forces developed methods of building morale; particular consideration was shown for each man's personal welfare and value in the cooperative effort, and emphasis was placed on teamwork and social solidarity. These methods were effective in producing higher morale and efficiency in units whose officers had the necessary qualifications for social leadership. It has been pointed out by Selling[9] that work habits which involve self-sacrifice for the good of the group and flexibility in getting along with other men have not been cultivated in industry and workers do not have a feeling of fellowship such as the Army cultivated. Eadie, however, sees a new spirit, born of military experience, already appearing in some plants.[10]

The concept that each man's potential in production is much higher than has generally been realized and that men are capable of great accomplishment and discipline when they share closely in a common enterprise under leaders whom they trust and admire proved its practical truth during the war. The time is ripe for its application to industry. Advocates of such a concept are not only the psychologists, psychiatrists, and social workers who were largely responsible for making it effective in military life, but also the businessmen and their advisers in the armed forces who saw it work and helped to make it work.[11, 12] The skilled personnel required to build up this esprit de corps in industry is to be found in substantial numbers among the veterans themselves, many of whom left the ranks of industry to join the Army and have now returned to the same level of employment with an equipment for leadership which can be put to use. Their training and experience in understanding and managing people can readily be transferred to the industrial setting. Literature issued by industry to its management stresses the fact that veterans must be assured in a practical way that industry is concerned with their personal welfare and happiness.[13] At least one leaf has been taken from the book of the military psychiatrist and the morale services officer.[14]

The British were so impressed with the improvement of their soldiers when consistent attention was given to building morale that at the end of the war they took most of the officers and enlisted men who had served in education and personnel work in the Army and set them to work in industrial plants. These veterans now train foremen to conduct group discussion and, with the full knowledge and approval of top management, a certain amount of time each week is devoted to free discussion by the workers under the foreman's leadership. No subject is taboo and full and free expression is encouraged. Observers have reported an amazing degree of improvement in the workers' sense of participation and in the morale of entire plants.[15]

MORALE AS SEEN BY EXPERTS IN INDUSTRIAL RELATIONS

Experts in industrial relations note four major sources of trouble. The first is a misconception as to the nature of human beings and their motivation for work. Referring to top management Roethlisberger points out:

This group's whole explicit theory of human cooperation—but not necessarily the practice of it—dates back to the 18th century: (a) Society is composed of a "rabble"; (b) whose interest is in the pursuit of profit and pleasure; (c) in the pursuit of these ends the individual is essentially logical. . . . All the evidence of modern investigation shows: (a) Society is composed of people related to each other in terms of group association; (b) the desire to belong, to be a part, the desire for continuous and intimate association in work with other human beings remains a strong, possibly the strongest desire of man; and (c) in the pursuit of these ends man is essentially non-logical and at times irrational, that is, willing to die or, as management should know, only too willing to "cut off his nose to spite his face."[6]

Roethlisberger ascribes to this misconception much of the failure to provide effective "human administration" so essential for morale. The anomalous position of the foreman he traces to the same source and goes so far as to say: "Master and victim of double talk, the foreman is management's contribution to the social pathology of American culture."[3]

The second major source of difficulty is the relation of subordinates to superiors and the consistent efforts of the supervisory staff to indoctrinate workers with the idea of advancement. As Roethlisberger suggests:

If the man hours spent by subordinates both on and off the job in preoccupation about what the boss thinks were added the total hours would be staggering—not to mention the results this phenomenon has produced in nervous breakdowns and other forms of mental anguish. Stranger still, it almost appears as if modern industrial organization, which prides itself so much on its efficiency, has aggravated rather than reduced the amount of this preoccupation, with disastrous consequences for health and thus for efficiency. . . . The foreman, like each individual in the modern industrial structure, is in effect painfully tutored to focus his attention upward to his immediate superiors and the logics of evaluation they represent, rather than downward to his subordinates and the feelings they have. So rigid does the conditioning of supervisors and executives in the industrial structure become in this respect that it is almost impossible for them to pay attention to the concrete human situations below them, rich in sentiments and feelings. For them the world of feeling does not exist; the territory is merely populated with the abstractions which they have been taught to see and the terms in which they communicate—"base rates," "man hours," "profits," "cost curves," "production schedules," etc.[6]

The third source of difficulty is in the failure of management to understand properly and use constructively the informal organization which is characteristic of all employee groups. As Roethlisberger observes:

Informal organization in any organized human activity serves a very healthy function. It binds people together in routine activity. It gives people a social place and feeling of belonging. It provides the framework for the fulfilment of human satisfactions. It gives people a feeling of self-respect, of independent choice, of not being just cogs in a machine. Far from being a hindrance to greater effectiveness informal organization provides the setting which makes men willing to contribute their services. Informal organization cannot be prevented; it is a spontaneous phenomenon necessary wherever coordinated human activity exists. . . . Too often management has mistakenly opposed—or what is worse— ignored this.

Fortunately in business (and in unions too) there are . . . men with extraordinary skill in the direction of securing cooperative effort. . . . Such administrators understand the importance of "getting along" rather than of "getting ahead." They see to it that the newcomer has an effective and happy relationship with his fellow workers as well as getting the work out. Accomplishing their work through leisurely social interaction rather than vigorous formal action, more interested in getting their human relationships straight than their words and logics straight, more interested in being "friendly" to their fellowmen than in being abstractly "fair" and never allowing their "paper work" to interfere with this process of friendliness, they offer a healthy antidote to the formal logics of the modern factory organization previously described. . . . It is the author's impression that a greater proportion of them are found at the lower levels of management because the logics of promotion in business organization seldom realize their skills. Were it not for them, it is the author's opinion that the unleashed forces of modern technology would spend themselves out to doom and destruction. Aware of the two-fold function of industrial leadership, that is, the social organization of team work and the logical organization of operations, they maintain that healthy balance which makes for individual growth and development and ultimately for survival of the organization.[6]

A fourth source of difficulty is an attitude of anxiety on the part of employees and employers alike. Initially, fear and anxiety are individual reactions, but gradually they come to pervade the group as a whole and to cause changes in collective attitudes and reactions. As Selekman observes:

External forces are internalized to become the anxieties, sanctions and expectancies conditioning the behavior of men at work. . . . These worries, strains and stresses obstruct daily production. Rugged individualism gives way as it were to "rugged groupism." Just as the rugged individualist long has equated his own pursuit of self-interest with the general welfare, the "rugged collectivists" now are armored in the righteousness of their own social equation. . . . Thus, all the unsettlement of this transition period seeps into the behavior of men at work. The hostilities of insecure workers seeking ever higher returns from industry become more aggressive as many different groups proclaim their demands as just and beneficent. Contrariwise, the most ardent affirmations of private management take on an undertone of defensiveness. The manager, too, acts under a spur of multiple drives, interests, ideas and values. What he wants and what he does are conditioned by the same complex "partly rational, partly emotional cultural setting" as the aspirations and behavior of the men who cross him in the job. . . . The thought of injury to his way of working and living evokes typically the reaction of fear followed by anger against those whom, logically or illogically, he holds responsible. . . . The manager can hardly afford the luxury of retaliatory resentment. Instead he must grant to the underlying motivation of workers who are always crossing him the validity that adheres in the aspiration to "get on."[5]

The methods used in the Army might be effective in combating this problem of anxiety as it affects industry. In frank discussions with groups of managers and workers—separately or together— fears and anxieties might be traced to their sources and possible solutions to the total problem examined. The "enemy" is less easy to identify for fearful managers and fearful workers than for fearful soldiers, but the process of developing insight and achieving control is not different.

For the most part the answer of thoughtful industrial relations experts to the problem of morale is proper training of administrators which would include the acquisition of certain mental hygiene skills and insights.[3-6, 16] Roethlisberger describes the equipment the coming administrator will have to possess:

1. The new administrator will need to know and understand better the nature of "organization"—its structure and dynamic interrelations. The average executive knows little or nothing, except for what is implicitly registered in his nervous system, about the "social organization"

of his business. Most of his explicit concern, most of his logical thinking is only about "formal organization." About the other aspects of organization he only stews, frets and gets stomach ulcers.

2. The new administrator will have to develop a common language structure—a language which will keep together in words, rather than keep separate by words, those things that are together. . . . This will be a language of mutually interdependent relations, of togetherness, of equilibrium, of adaptation and of growth.

3. The new administrator will have to understand better the purpose of communication—and not only the aspect of communication which by persuasion attempts to sell one's own point of view, but that which tries to understand and has respect for another's point of view. In the systematic practice of taking into account another person's point of view as the first step in obtaining that person's cooperation—a most difficult skill—he should have daily and continuous drill; he should be taught to listen, in addition to being logically lucid and clear.

4. New methods and new skills will have to be developed whereby change can be introduced into the work situation without provoking resistance. For this . . . we shall need to exercise and practice new insights regarding human motivation. . . . Technical change will have to be introduced at the work level so that the group affected will see it, in North Whitehead's phrase, as "an enlargement of its way of life, rather than as an interruption of it."

5. The new administrator will have to understand better the dependent relation of the subordinate to the superior in business organizations and the feeling of insecurity this dependence arouses. He will have to have new methods and techniques of assuring his subordinates of those minimal conditions of security, not merely financial, without which his subordinates' position becomes intolerable. For this he will have to learn something about the principle of individual growth and development through active participation and assumption of responsibility, and these principles he will have to learn to practice in relation to his subordinates in an atmosphere of approval.

6. The new administrator will have to learn to distinguish the world of feelings from the world of facts and logic. . . . He will see that "feelings" cannot be verbally legislated out of existence; that as a first step in their "control" they need to be expressed and recognized.

7. He will have to formulate goals and ideals which make the present in which we live more, rather than less, meaningful, and to achieve these new levels of insight he will have to throw overboard completely, finally and irrevocably—this will be difficult—the ideologies of the "established society" of the eighteenth and nineteenth centuries . . . ours is an "adaptive society."

Can we develop a group of such administrators? To the author it seems that if only one-half of one per cent of the time, effort and money that have been spent in the direction of technological improvement were to be devoted to seeking better and improved methods of securing co-operation, the accomplishment would be considerable—and that is an intentional understatement. It just does not seem possible to suppose that man's ingenuity, if given free scope, would fail in this undertaking. The task is tremendous; the challenge is great; the stakes are high; but only by traveling some such arduous road, in the author's opinion, can business leadership face up to its real social responsibilities.[6]

MORALE AS SEEN BY MENTAL HYGIENISTS

Psychiatrists, social workers, and psychologists in their study and treatment of persons with problems of mental health or social adjustment have learned to recognize the kinds of work situation and relationship which make for personal adjustment and morale.

1. There must be understanding and acceptance of workers by employers or the supervisors who represent the employer. People who feel they are understood are more willing to give their best to their work and experience less frustration and irritation if some of their wishes have to be denied. This is well illustrated by the statements of hundreds of veterans who were counseled by the authors. Almost without exception those who were holding a job mentioned their employer or "boss" either as understanding or not understanding. In plants where the employer appreciated the fact that the veteran had acquired certain skills and in many instances powers of leadership while in the armed forces and took these into account in placing him; where the employer appreciated the natural desire of veterans to make up for lost time; where there was recog-

nition of the team spirit which prevailed in most military units and an acknowledgment of its worth in industry; and where supervisors looked out for their men and stood up for them, morale was usually good. On the other hand, the lack of such understanding on the part of the employer was a major source of discouragement to the veteran, sometimes even making him doubt whether it had been worth while to risk his life for his country.

2. Proper placement is essential for morale and mental health. This has been proved hundreds of times both in the armed forces and in business and industry. Many a worker who failed and was unhappy in one job became a good worker upon being placed at work for which he was properly fitted by knowledge, skill, and aptitude. Perhaps the most frequent mistakes in placement occur not through overestimation or underestimation of a worker's ability, but rather through failure to take into account his wishes, fears, preferences, and group identifications. The authors have discussed these matters in more detail elsewhere.[17]

3. Psychologically sound supervision often makes the difference between good morale and poor, between stability and instability, between effectiveness and ineffectiveness. Workers want to be treated fairly, in reference to other persons and groups. They want to be treated considerately, and they respond much better to requests than to commands, to leading than to driving. They look also for some appreciation and respond to appropriate praise and approval not only with good feeling but with a determination to do their best. They learn faster and put their new knowledge or skills to better use if they are shown how to improve than if they are lectured for their faults or mistakes. They like supervisors to seek and use employees' ideas in job methods. Chase tells of a die repairer who had won an award for an outstanding suggestion in his plant. In response to the impetus given to the worker's initiative by the wartime Training Within Industry Program, he had designed a set of dies which saved both material and operations in manufacturing firefighting equipment for planes and ships. The man had

worked for the firm for many years and had often thought of similar ideas but had kept them to himself for the simple reason that "the foreman might think he was not onto his job and might get sore."[18] There are thousands like him.

4. Good morale and healthy attitudes prevail only when there are congenial relations between fellow workmen. Some workers are naturally more friendly than others. Where such workers are in the majority, congenial relations are likely to develop spontaneously. This is also the case in business establishments or factories where the immediate supervisor is himself a friendly person, stresses the workers' successes and virtues, and gives them other forms of positive attention. Under such circumstances a democratic form of living together develops; and habits of reassuring, encouraging, and helping one another are established. In the Hawthorne experiments in the Western Electric Company the experimental group concluded, "We have no boss."[19] Some freedom to move about and to talk—at least during rest periods—and other opportunities for informal give-and-take go far to develop congeniality and team spirit.

5. Team spirit is almost synonymous with morale. It may be defined as a feeling of "being in the same boat" and of working together for a common purpose. Although different individuals in the group may play separate roles, each counts on his team mates and knows that he in turn is being counted upon. Each stands up for the other. Working as a team united in a common purpose by bonds of friendliness and loyalty not only gives greater effectiveness but adds a zest and interest to the job that are lacking in strictly individual effort. Moreover, as Ford states, "It is good business to see to it that the members of our industrial teams get information to make them conscious of the fact that they are *on* the team. This applies all along the line—shop employees, office workers, and supervisory and executive personnel. . . . Informed employees are more productive than uninformed employees."[2]

In brief, there can be high industrial morale, with contentment and happiness for both employees and managers, and industrial stability only when men feel strongly that what they are doing is worth while and worthy of them, when all have a real sense of participation in the total task, when there is mutual acceptance of one another's contribution to the whole enterprise, and when there is congenial and democratic give-and-take in all working relationships.

Employees with Special Needs

Workers can be fully productive and cooperative with employers and fellow workers only if they are suited for the work assigned and if they are relatively free from personal worries and frustrations. No one is at his best when he is afraid, worried, or angry. If morale and mental health are to be maximal, job placements must be carefully made and some opportunity must be provided for counseling, so that employees with special needs—workers and managers alike—can "get things off their chest," be freed from undue worry, preoccupation, and frustration, and thereby achieve a proper perspective and the ability to apply themselves to their work.

The proportion of workers who, for chronic or temporary causes, are at any one time unable to bear the emotional or physical stress of industrial work is variously estimated at 20 per cent[20] and 40 per cent[21] and their numbers are said to have risen by 10 per cent[22] during the war.

Psychoneurotic and maladjusted employees as a group constitute the largest number of "problem workers." Giberson finds that this group constitutes 25 to 40 per cent of all patients referred to the industrial physician and believes that "by their faulty attitudes and clashes they cause most of the misery in industry. Yet they often need only a bit of medical advice and emotional first-aid from the psychiatrist to set them right."

The same author lists as the more common symptoms of psychoneuroses in workers: (a) personality clashes and habitual rule infractions; (b) accident proneness and habitual absenteeism; (c) emotional disturbances due to age crises or menopause and gerontology; (d) emotional disturbances connected with the beginning and end of employment, lack of promotion, and the "thirty-year social hurdle" (emotional problems a woman faces if she is not married by the time she reaches that age); (e) neurotic manifestations following accidental injury and difficulties of convalescence and rehabilitation; (f) overstressed emotional compensation for physical defects and dysfunctions.[23]

The chief cause of these maladjustments as reported by Giberson and by Selling is emotional immaturity. These workers suffer from a fixation of attention upon themselves, and they react emotionally to difficulties far out of proportion to the stimulus. They suffer from anxieties, fears, and psychosomatic complaints which cause a good deal of absenteeism though no physical cause for their illness can be discovered. Their maladjustment may relate to their families, to plant authorities, or to others. As Markuson states:

Whether these maladjustments should be attributed to home or plant conditions does not matter; the important thing is to determine the cause and thus decrease this tremendous loss in manpower. Many of these causes appear insignificant, and therefore nothing is done about them. However, these little details, if neglected, build up and accumulate into insurmountable obstacles, and, as a result, thousands of workers either stay on a job badly maladjusted or hop from plant to plant, looking for a haven of retreat that does not exist and will not exist until the underlying causes of discontent are discovered and corrected. It is this problem that is so confusing to many plant physicians, and it is here that the psychiatrist can best lend a helping hand.[7]

As Rosenblum and Romano[24] have noted, working conditions are closely related to the incidence of maladjustment among employees. For example, the rigidity of defense employment which precluded moving from one job to another and paralleled the rigidity of military service resulted in casualties similar to those induced by military experience in persons with a weakened personality structure. Some conditions of work awaken childhood conflict or sexual maladjustments and cause panic, paranoid ideas, and psychosomatic ailments. For instance, a passive man cannot stand up to a hard boss or domineering "brother" worker and must repress his hatred. The mingling of men and women in work constitutes a threat to the man who fears heterosexual contacts and is "guyed" by his fellows, or to the woman who arouses the jealousy of men because of her superior work and unconscious rivalry feelings. Thus some knowledge of the sexual adjustment of both men and women is necessary to avoid placement which might result in tensions and difficulties. Complaints about noise, the size of the plant, or other aspects of the work environment are often exaggerated if not induced by a hidden emotional factor. In an environment which fits his particular needs or at least is not too disturbing, a neurotic worker may be quite efficient, but factors which upset the balance of his adjustment must be understood.

Accident-prone workers. The number of accidents in an organization is recognized as having a relation to the extent of maladjustment present. Giberson believes that 80 per cent or more of reported accidents are preventable and perhaps half of these are due to personal causes. As Dunbar notes:

Until recently the accident hazard was not recognized as a disease syndrome, because accidents were supposed to happen by accident. It is now known that, although some accidents are unavoidable, most of them occur as a result of an accident habit which is really an illness. According to the report of the National Safety Council, four million workers were killed or seriously injured during 1941, resulting in a loss of 460,000,000 man days. Analogous figures for 1943 are: workers killed or injured as a result of accidents, approximately 4,200,200. Thus, in terms of industrial warfare, it is estimated that these accidents resulted in a loss of 720,000,000 man days, enough to build 30,000 heavy bombers or 55 battleships. It is known that the persons who have the highest record for accidents on the job also have the highest record for off-the-job accidents.[25]

More studies are needed of the life and work experience of accident-prone workers. It is important to learn whether they were angry at the time of the accident, and why. Many such men express great antagonism to management and shop stewards. A few have taken guards off their equipment in order to "aggravate" the boss or to provoke a reprimand which will give them an opportunity to express their hatred. Selling has found that some of these men "become so vindictive that one would almost suspect their personalities operate as a physical entity to push them into the machines or make them do poor work." He divides the accident-prone of industry into (1) those who have an impulse to suicide, (2) those who have an impulse to hurt others, (3) insecure persons, and (4) persons preoccupied with domestic difficulties, alleged injustices, or strike possibilities.[26]

Adler[27] corroborates these findings. In the group that he studied, the majority of those who had suffered injury by accident showed "a bitter and revengeful attitude towards parents and educators and felt they had been forced into an occupation which they did not like, and one-third of these harbored serious ideas of suicide." The remainder were either persons who had had "bad luck" all their lives and always expected to be "unlucky"; persons who had been pampered in childhood and felt they were happiest after accidents, when taken care of and babied; persons who lived in constant fear of accidents; or persons with extreme ambition who wanted to work faster and better than others and did not use the necessary precautions." Adler concludes that "a harmonious relationship of the worker to his type of work is a prerequisite to avoid accidents."

Psychopathic personalities are hard to get along with and very dangerous to the morale and efficiency of the group. They are hard to detect, especially in places of authority, for on the surface many of them appear cooperative and are past masters in the art of making plausible explanations. Those in subordinate positions are described as "querulous, unruly, undisciplined, malicious and antisocial." They often quarrel with foremen and an occasional one has been known to damage property in revenge for criticism or for excitement.[28, 29] Selling regards this small group of "egocentric individuals" as the hardest to deal with constructively and the most dangerous to the efficiency and morale of a plant. Union rules protect most of them from dismissal, and if they are dismissed they soon find new employment. Many are chronic truants. A law aimed to check absenteeism in general would partly control the problem, but such a law would be inadvisable because of the danger of misinterpretation. A psychiatric service to differentiate the pathologically egocentric from others whose symptoms may at times be similar is the answer.[9] The best chance of remedy lies with the efficient and regular workers in plants that have developed good working morale. Such workers will themselves demand the discharge or discipline of the egocentric who ruins the attendance or production record of the department.

Absenteeism. A large group of employees are frequently absent because of illness. Sometimes the illness is physical in origin, sometimes it is psychological. In many cases the physical symptoms only are treated and the worker's anxieties are augmented by being focused on his somatic disturbances. In all illness and particularly in cases of psychosomatic disturbance, the mental hygiene or psychiatric approach is necessary. Because changes in muscle tonus are among the most frequent mechanisms of emotional expression, chronic complaints at the first-aid unit of aches and pains after no unusual exertion are fairly common. Such conditions are often amenable to psychotherapy. "Chronic menstrual invalidism" can often be relieved by a similar approach.[29] Many case histories report incapacitating illnesses relieved by the airing of deep personal conflicts and work difficulties.[30, 39]

Particularly in treating compensation and rehabilitation cases, surgeons and general practitioners need to take into account the psychological factor. The proportion of time lost from work after industrial injuries is approximately 20 per cent of the total time lost by illness.[31] A physician employed by an industrial plant reports the program which he uses to salvage patients economically and socially when the diagnosis is neurosis caused by accidental injury. His approach to the patient is basically psychiatric. He responds with sympathy and non-judgmental understanding to the patient's irritability, helps him understand his own behavior, seeks to eliminate the causes of maladjustment on his return to employment, and plans a recreation program with a trained companion. The underlying aim of therapy is to change the emotional dynamics so that the patient prefers recovery to invalidism.[32]

Some *feeble-minded persons* make excellent workers when placed in simple jobs where the operations are few and easily understood and where the worker does not have to maintain relations with very many people. Careful instructions and very close supervision are required.

The *psychotic or the mentally ill person* who has been cured or whose psychosis, though constant, is on a mild level can be employed provided information from unbiased sources indicates that his condition is not getting worse or that he is not making homicidal or suicidal threats. Placement must be carefully made to protect such workers from undue strain; many of them adjust better in more or less solitary work.[17] They should work under constant medical supervision.

The Industrial Physician

Several writers[23, 25, 27, 33] are advising a larger role for the plant physician in selecting and placing new workers so that a better preventive program may be realized. They point out that preplacement interviewing is too often turned over to "bright but inexperienced young men" whereas mature judgment is needed, and that many personnel officers are temperamentally unfit for the patient, intra-personal delving that is necessary. Elaborate tests for determining personality are not very practical, since they are so time-consuming and require such great skill in interpretation that small plants cannot afford them.[34] The three tools for good placement are the applicant's statement on the application form, the findings of the personnel department, and the doctor's interview and examination. In many firms it is the responsibility of the plant physician to draw together the findings of the other two, discover discrepancies, and obtain a clear picture of the applicant which will make possible a wise decision about his suitability for placement.[35] This function of the physician is particularly important in those plants where the personnel department is staffed with unskilled persons; where interviewers are provided for non-medical functions, as in the Hawthorne plant of the Western Electric Company; or where the physician has the assistance of social workers in his department.

The company or plant physician is generally regarded as the pivot of any program of psychiatric service to industrial employees. In his daily contact with workers he is in a strategic position to reduce tensions and frictions if he has the necessary understanding and skill. Equipped with the therapeutic orientation described in Chapter VI, the industrial physician is able to recognize and treat all but the most serious psychiatric problems and to carry out an in-plant preventive program. Giberson[36] believes that the industrial physician who is thus equipped has an advantage over the personnel manager in handling problems of personality adjustment because he has been trained to regard the worker as a total personality and his non-administrative and professional status protects him from the suspicion of partiality and gives him the confidence of both management and worker.* By bringing a manager and a labor leader together one industrial surgeon made three

---

* The industrial trained nurse holds a somewhat similar position. She may find herself in a state of conflict which involves the ethics of her profession because conditions for promoting the welfare of her patients in industry are so far from the ideal to which she has been trained in the hospital. She may have to fight for the welfare of her patients and press home to management the importance of adequate convalescence and other concessions. See Bethel J. McGrath, *Nursing in Commerce and Industry* (New York, The Commonwealth Fund, 1946), pages 126–144.

strikes unnecessary, thus preventing a loss of $100,000 per day.[21]

Very few plants have been able to obtain the full-time services of psychiatrists. Giberson,[36] Himler,[37] Ross,[21] and Thompson[38] believe the situation calls for considerable extension of the scope and responsibility of the industrial physician. Giberson[36] outlines seven procedures which the industrial physician can learn to apply: (1) he can expect and trace emotional complications which will come with every injury and illness, and he should keep as full a record of each case as possible; (2) he can *listen* to the patient, for listening has therapeutic value for the patient and gives the doctor the opportunity to observe the connection between surface symptoms and serious underlying conditions; (3) he can diagnose the industrial trouble spots (foremen, environment, group maladjustment, fatigue) by analyzing his case material and interviewing some patients at regular intervals; (4) he can spot the worker who is prone to accidents; (5) he can recognize the obvious maladjusted types and dispose of them by advising transfer, outside treatment, or education in the simple principles of mental and physical hygiene; (6) he can help prevent maladjustment: (a) by actively exercising his advisory function; (b) by repeatedly bringing to the attention of management each proved instance of preventable maladjustment; (c) by encouraging foremen, section hands, and superintendents to come to him for advice and information; (d) by doing all he can to bring the extra-industrial factors to bear upon any interpretation of employee difficulties; (7) he can conserve manpower and uphold morale through fighting to secure *medical* immunity for the *emotionally* ill.

In Canada the supervision of the health leaves and sick leaves of 35,000 federal employees is being carried on successfully by the regular medical officers, only the most severe cases being referred to the neuropsychiatric division. All persons presenting in their diagnosis what appears to be a neurosis, such as "nervous breakdown," "insomnia," or "overwork," are called for examination. By the end of the second interview the medical officers are able to gain the confidence of the patient and to establish a psychotherapeutic relationship whereby the patient can get a true perspective on his problem. They discuss the patient's situation with his family physician to the mutual advantage of both, since the latter is able to throw light on irritations arising at home and the federal physicians can appraise difficulties arising from the work situation. Slight psychoneurotic disorders that threatened to develop into disabling illnesses have been cleared up and the cooperation of the two physicians serves to give to the patient a fair degree of medical immunity from emotional ills.[39]

Recently a few firms have been extending the functions of their medical divisions to include those formerly carried out by the personnel and training divisions. In the Caterpillar Tractor Company, for instance, testing, counseling, and training of interviewers and supervisors are now all part of the work of the medical division. The psychiatric and psychological procedures used are found to have these values: (1) "they place industrial personnel in positions which make possible the full use of their capabilities while reducing to a minimum the possibility that personality disturbances will be elicited or fostered"; (2) "when such situations do arise the machinery for combating them is ready with counsel and therapy through which the efficiency and satisfaction of employees can be maintained."[40] Many articles dealing with the mental hygiene aspects of industrial medicine have appeared recently, in a number of which this same emphasis is borne out.[41]

Non-Medical Counselors

The experimental studies made in the Hawthorne plant of the Western Electric Company, 1929–1933, seem to prove that the morale and mental health of workers improved and production increased when employees were provided with opportunities to discuss with trained interviewers their worries and problems on the job and off. Until the beginning of the war few firms took advantage of Western Electric's findings but during the war there was a rather rapid growth of counseling services. Along with this development went the evaluation of both the new counseling programs and the more highly formalized procedures of personnel departments.[42] These counseling services, which have taken various forms, are summarized by Baker as of four principal types:

1. A counseling service which provides information on many matters, handles a number of activities previously the responsibility of other members of the personnel department, encourages employee consultation on any question of concern to the employee, and, on the basis of its contacts with employees, advises management on personnel policies and procedures. This is the type most frequently found in war industries and is based on an acceptance of the value to management of specific help to employees. It gives some consideration to the therapeutic aspects of employee interviews, but counselors in these programs do not often go beyond serving as friendly listeners. Employees are given information on company policies and on such special matters as housing, transportation, rationing, and the availability of community social services and medical care. They are referred to their supervisors for decision on problems directly concerned with the job and to outside agencies for extensive assistance in the solution of difficult personal problems.

2. The extension of the personnel department into production departments. The principal objective in the assignment of a personnel representative to production areas is to facilitate employees' adjustment by improved understanding and coordination of personnel policies and procedures. Stress is laid upon assistance to supervisors in their personnel responsibilities. Interviews with employees are more likely to be regularly scheduled induction, follow-up, and exit interviews than informal consultations sought by the employees.

3. Counseling in which emphasis is placed on employee interviewing as a specific aid to individual adjustment. This type of counseling, in particular, requires well-trained, skilled interviewers and in most cases is under the direct supervision of a psychiatrist, psychiatric social worker, or someone especially trained and experienced in personnel counseling. Arrangements of this nature more than any other type of counseling program in industry bring up questions of the extent to

which a company can or should assume responsibility for preventive psychiatric medical service or direct psychotherapeutic counseling for its employees.

4. Direct assistance to foremen on the supervision of women workers. Women supervisors, sometimes called counselors, who are responsible to a department foreman or a shift superintendent but without line authority have been appointed in some companies to relieve the foremen of certain responsibilities in the interpretation of personnel policies and the disciplining of women. Counselors and personnel executives are critical of this arrangement and feel that the assumption of disciplinary duties not only prevents a satisfactory relationship between the counselor and the employee but also is likely to weaken the status of the foreman, without improving appreciably the personnel relations within the department.[43]

The question may be raised as to the future of such counseling programs. The necessity for this service will decrease as employee conditions become more stable, but human relations throughout management and supervision will be a continuing need and will receive increasing emphasis. To quote Radosta and Baker:

The business man is aware that accident rates, absenteeism, material scrapped and labor turnover are costly. Many companies have developed some understanding of the relation of these difficulties to the individual employee's problem. Just as the companies have established a maintenance department which the operator and supervisor call upon when they have trouble with the machines, so the counselors are being called upon when difficulties crop up in the individuals' relationships. The counselor's function does not overlap that of the supervisor's, the union's or any of the company services.[44]

For the long run, management is not likely to accept as a matter of course the ineffectiveness of supervision in personal matters, nor to extend its personnel activities haphazardly into social case work and psychotherapy. The lasting effect of today's valuable experience in counseling may be a greater emphasis on human relations throughout management and supervision. It may also indicate the need for a more closely defined specialized function to help the individual employee and to prevent serious maladjustments. The degree to which this specialist function will be handled within the personnel department of a company or through greater cooperation between the company, the community services and the union, will be determined by management, employee and union attitudes, the location and size of the plant, the availability of community services and many other factors.[43]

Supervisors and Foremen

While plant physicians with some psychiatric training are handling an increasing number of the personality disorders of employees, they cannot meet the whole problem, and supervisors and foremen must be the next line of defense. Wide recognition is being given today to the importance of the supervising staff in the success of any mental hygiene program on a mass scale. The War Production Board, in its Training Within Industry program, engaged in a vast supervisors' training program attended by more than one million supervisors and foremen.

Since foremen must be responsible for harmonious relations and wholesome attitudes on the job, they should be chosen as much for qualities of leadership as for technical skill.[44] They should have the opportunity to attend training courses in mental hygiene and to get acquainted with their men. It is important for them to know the temperament, characteristics, and moods of the men so that they can recognize change, preoccupation, or lack of usual energy on the job, and take steps to intervene when such changes constitute a danger. Selling[9] says the foreman must be taught to recognize fatigue, malnutrition, worry, and the early appearance of physical ailments and to understand that fatigue, worry, and even inability to get up in the morning have psychological causes so that the sufferer should not be regarded as lazy or treated as a "bum" or a "faker."

Supervisor training programs with a mental health orientation can be developed by mental hygienists—psychiatrists, psychiatric social workers, clinical psychologists—in cooperation with personnel workers and plant physicians. Himler[45] outlines a plan for training foremen that includes group lectures and conferences supplemented by individual interviews and consultations. The response of foremen to questionnaires indicates that they are eager to learn more effective methods of handling people. The need for careful placement and supervision of war veterans has given an excellent opportunity to review with foremen the steps involved in placement, medical follow-up, transfer, handling of problem cases, and methods of referral for specialists' attention.

Experience gained from study and analysis of specific individual and departmental problems can be woven into the context of the training program and presented in the form of case histories. The observations and suggestions of Himler are so valuable as to warrant quoting at length:

Although his work is seldom dignified by that name, the good foreman must in effect be a psychotherapist, even if only on an amateur standing. Among other things, this means that he never uses rule of thumb procedures in handling individual contacts with his men, and that he aims to treat and prevent causes rather than symptoms of undesirable work habits and attitudes. Like psychiatrists, foremen are constantly faced with the need to boil down problem situations to their ultimate elements, which can then be dealt with. Foremen realize that interest, ingenuity, and time are required to uncover the worker's inner emotional wants and needs and to redirect his energies into mutually constructive channels. They are especially eager to learn brief interview techniques which will render their daily contacts more effective.

While there will always be a considerable number of employees who are in definite need of special psychiatric care, industry will never be able to provide enough psychiatrically trained physicians or other personnel to carry out the necessary therapy on an individual basis. A logical compromise approach is through increased training and use of foremen as therapists. The industrial psychiatrist can readily serve as a consultant to foremen and can use the individual cases that are referred to him as teaching material in the training of foremen. In this way foremen can gain confidence in methods that are scientifically approved. Artificial and misleading distinctions between industrial and non-industrial causes of adjustment difficulties must be removed if the understanding and therapy are to be truly effective.

In this work with individual foremen, the industrial psychiatrist encourages them to formulate personality factors in their own words and focus attention on features of each situation that they can influence. Attentive, considerate listening and an atmosphere of objectivity must be demonstrated by the psychiatrist's own actions. Traits of interviewing employed in foremen contacts can thus be taught by example.

Sometimes it is advisable to carry out employees' interviews in the foreman's own office, with him present in a joint consultation. Here the psychiatrist has a dual object of giving the worker an impartial hearing and at the same time demonstrating to the foreman a technique of interviewing that uncovers springs of motivation, and enlists the worker's active participation in the solution of his own problem. Quite often foremen who are impressed by the success of this method are frank in appealing for help in regard to their own personality problems. It goes without saying that the insight thus gained has a reciprocally beneficial effect both on the foreman's attitude and on his management of subsequent problem situations involving the human element.

The development and application of such a pragmatic in-service psychotherapist technique is a challenging, but virtually untouched front of industrial psychiatry. The tooling of psychiatric methods for effective use on the foreman's level is clearly one of the outstanding needs in the field of industrial human relations, and this need will certainly increase in the post-war period.[45]

Many labor leaders have become convinced that shop stewards, union counselors, and members of labor-management committees should have as much understanding of human beings and skill in relationships as managers and foremen. The clinic approach in handling grievances has proved more effective than formal legalistic procedures (see Selekman[16]), and unions are setting up training programs for those who represent to the employers the interests of the workers. As a rule, these programs are independent of the in-service training provided by management. There is some reason to believe that well-qualified people who are not too closely identified with either management or labor could well conduct courses in the science of human behavior. These would be equally profitable to foremen and to shop stewards and union counselors, thus breaking down what may soon be recognized as an artificial barrier between the two groups.

Cooperation with the Community

The importance of the individual's family and community life to his adjustment has led industry to cooperate more closely with community agencies and to concern itself with community problems. Good mental health programs in industry can be developed only in those localities in which community organizations cooperate with business organizations and industrial plants.

Several years ago in Michigan an industrial mental health council was created made up of representatives from government, management, labor, the medical profession, and the state society for mental hygiene. A subcommittee of the council has prepared material to be used in training stewards, shop foremen, and personnel men to recognize sudden changes in the employees' behavior that indicate impairment of mental and emotional fitness. The council plans to sponsor foreman-training through conferences on industrial mental health. Material will also be used by labor-management committees of the unions. This industrial council is encouraging closer cooperation with and greater utilization of community health and welfare agencies in helping to reduce those problems that cause worry, fatigue, fear, and tension. In several industrial communities child guidance clinics, staffed with a full-time psychiatrist trained in children's work, a psychologist, and a psychiatric social worker, have been set up cooperatively by the state and the local community.[46]

In a number of other states the desire to meet the needs of war veterans, and particularly the neuropsychiatric dischargees, has stimulated efforts to draw communities and their industries together to work out their problems. In Connecticut a clinic for the rehabilitation of veterans has been established by the joint efforts of labor, management, physicians, and psychologists. Suitable jobs have been found for handicapped persons, and the cooperation of labor and industry with professional groups has been exceedingly valuable and successful.[47] In Peoria, Illinois, a survey was made of jobs available to the physically handicapped and, as a result, more than a thousand handicapped workers were given employment by the Caterpillar Tractor Company alone. In the same town a community clinic was established to expedite the proper placement of NP dischargees and to provide psychiatric treatment for those who needed it.[48]

Hitherto programs of mental health in industry have been developed sporadically by individual companies but some observers are of the opinion that to be most effective programs should be established under impartial auspices and on a city-wide or area-wide basis.

In England a dozen firms employed neuropsychiatrists who specialized in detecting neurological disorders and in eliminating conditions causing them. In Germany and Sweden neurological and psychiatric centers are operated on a cooperative basis to detect and treat disorders among industrial employees of a specific city or industrial area. Work of the same sort has been carried out in the industries of France, Switzerland, Russia, and—to a minor extent—Italy. In the United States, the leading industrial nation, there is a complete absence of any such program. Some program paralleling the European experience is bound to come.[49]

Dumas,[50] McFarland,[51] and others have advocated that industry provide itself with a "psychological fact-finding unit" or "orientation unit," composed of psychiatrist, psychologist and psychiatric social worker, which would offer a scientific means of adjusting workers to the jobs for which they are best fitted. Out of his experience as a consultant on placement problems to the staff of federal employment offices in New York City, Kubie[52] has likewise concluded that many disciplines (clinical psychology, employment counseling, psychiatric social service, and many aspects of education) must be integrated into a united service in any practical application of psychiatry to employment problems. Such a unit of service would have the following functions: (1) to screen out the unemployables and provide for their treatment; (2) to allocate to special tasks or workshops persons who need a sheltered work environment; (3) to allocate persons to jobs for which their aptitudes fit them and which are consonant with their personality; (4) to use therapeutic principles within the industrial setting and for individual workers; (5) to cope with out-of-plant problems; (6) to carry on research into the incidence of neurological disturbances, the relation of such disturbances to types of work and working conditions, and the efficiency of different types of job training.

The acceptance of such a program will depend upon the way in which it is established and how it affects the vested interests of labor and industry. Kubie believes that it can succeed only if it functions under impartial auspices as a joint labor-management council, with joint financial support and supervision; or under the auspices of a local, state, or federal labor relations board. Moreover, it cannot run counter to the accepted policies of organized labor. The seniority principle is highly prized, and a worker who would be better off on another type of work must be assured that he will not lose his rating should he transfer to work more suited to his personal abilities.

These opinions are substantiated by Fountain, a representative of labor.[53] He believes that an enlightened labor movement and an enlightened mental health program aim for the same thing: to establish the dignity of the worker as a human being and to help him feel that his job is important to himself and to society. He emphasizes that labor unions must participate fully in programs of mental health and that such programs must not interfere with the proper use of grievance procedures.

REFERENCES

1. Menninger, W. C. Unemployment and mental health. Ment. Health, January 1946. Published by the Provisional National Council for Mental Health, London, England.

2. Ford, Henry, II. The challenge of human engineering. Advanced Management 11:48–52, June 1946.

3. Roethlisberger, F. Management and morale, p. 194. Cambridge, Harvard University Press, 1941.

4. Gardner, B. B. Human relations in industry. Chicago, Richard D. Irwin, Inc., 1945.

5. Selekman, B. J. Wanted mature managers. Harvard Business Rev. 24:228–245, Winter 1946.

6. Roethlisberger, F. The foreman—master and victim of double talk. Harvard Business Rev. 23:283–299, Spring 1945.

7. Markuson, K. E. The role of the plant physician in an industrial mental health program. Ment. Hyg. 29:110–113, January 1945. Available as a reprint.

8. Hincks, C. M. A memorandum concerning the qualifications of Major Gen. G. Brock Chisholm in connection with the Lasker Award in mental hygiene, October 1944 (unpublished).

9. Selling, L. S. A psychiatrist looks at industrial truancy. Indust. Med. 12:189–201, April 1943.

10. Eadie, G. A. The over-all mental-health needs of the industrial plant with special reference to war veterans. Ment. Hyg. 29:101–106, January 1945.

11. Proctor, C. S. Wake up, Mr. Employer! The Villager (Bronxville Women's Club, Bronxville, N. Y.), October 1944.

12. Radcliffe, R. A. C. The ex-service man in industry. Indust. Welfare & Personnel Management (London, England) 25:289–291, July–August 1943.

13. Jenkins, I. D. Re-employment of the ex-servicemen and women; obligations of employer. Indust. Med. 13:805–807, October 1944.

14. Kraines, S. H. Industry's role in the readjustment of returning veterans. Texas Personnel Rev. 3:55–61.

15. Bullis, H. E. Personal communication. May 1946.

16. Bakke, E. W. Mutual survival the goal of unions and management. New Haven, Yale University Press, 1946.

McGregor, D. Conditions of effective leadership in the industrial organization. Massachusetts Institute of Technology Publications, Social Science Series, no. 2, 1944.

Selekman, B. J. Administering the union agreement. Harvard Business Rev. 23:299–313, Spring 1945.

Selekman, B. J. Handling shop grievances. Harvard Business Rev. 23:469–484, Summer 1945.

17. For fuller discussion see Woodward, L. E., and T. A. C. Rennie, Jobs and the man, chapter 3, Springfield, Ill., Thomas, 1945; also, same authors, with Swackhammer, G., Toward industrial mental health; an historical review. Ment. Hyg. 31:63–89, January 1947.

18. Chase, S. Men at work, p. 36. New York, Harcourt, Brace, 1945.

19. Roethlisberger, F., and J. Dickson. Management and the worker. Cambridge, Mass., Harvard University Press, 1939.

20. Markuson, K. E. Mental hygiene and industry; mental aspects of industrial employment. Ment. Hyg. 28:28–36, January 1944.

21. Ross, H. G. Human behavior and its relation to industry. Indust. Med. 13: 310–314, April 1944.

22. Giberson, L. G. Industrial morale. Indust. Med. 12:164–172, March 1943.

23. Giberson, L. G. Industrial psychiatry; a wartime survey. The Medical Clinics of North America 26:1085–1103, July 1942.

24. Rosenblum, M., and J. Romano. Psychiatric casualties among defense workers. Am. J. Psychiat. 100:314–319, November 1943.

25. Dunbar, H. F. Screening and remaking of men. Survey Graphic 33:412, October 1944.

26. Selling, L. S. Psychiatry in industrial accidents. Indust. Med. 13:504, June 1944.

27. Adler, A. The psychology of repeated accidents in industry. Am. J. Psychiat. 98:99–101, July 1941.

28. Selling, L. S. Industrial psychiatry in wartime; employability of certain mental cases. Indust. Med. 11:407–411. September 1942.

29. Hackett, J. D. Mental hygiene. In Health maintenance in industry. Berwyn, Ill., Shaw Publishing Co., 1925.

30. Wishart, J. H., and L. G. Lobb. Personality problems in the first aid unit. Indust. Med. 13:243–245, March 1944.

31. Bell, D. E. The problem of functional disease as seen in industry. Canadian M. A. J. 48:108–110, February 1943.

32. Solomon, A. P. Psychiatric problems in rehabilitation. J.A.M.A. 121:865–866, March 13, 1943.

33. Brooks, A. L. Mental hygiene and the industrial physician. Ment. Hyg. 28: 37–40, January 1944.

34. Van Kleeck, M. Social work on the industrial frontier. The Compass (130 East 22nd St., New York 10, N. Y.) 26:3–7, November 1, 1944.

35. Eadie, G. Who can work? Symposium; neuropsychiatric aspects. Indust. Med. 13:533–535, July 1944.

36. Giberson, L. G. Psychiatry in personnel work. Indust. Med. 12:164–172, March 1943.

37. Himler, L. E. Psychiatric technics in the management of employee problems. J.A.M.A. 128:638–639, June 30, 1945. Read before the Section on Preventive and Industrial Medicine and Public Health at the 94th Annual Session of Amer. Med. Assn., Chicago, June 14, 1944.

38. Thompson, G. N. War-engendered psychiatric problems in industrial medicine. Indust. Med. 13:686–689, September 1944.

39. Parney, F. S. A practical approach to supervision of mental health in industry. Indust. Med. 9:72–77, February 1940.

40. Vonachen, H. A., B. Mittelmann, M. H. Kronenberg, A. Weider, and H. G. Wolff. A comprehensive mental hygiene program at Caterpillar Tractor Company. Indust. Med. 15:179–184, March 1946.

41. Brodman, K. The organization of a mental hygiene unit in industry. Indust. Med. 15:259–262, April 1946.

    Irwin, E. A. Psychosomatic consultations in industry. Indust. Med. 15:1–5, January 1946.

    Leggo, C. Industrial relations values in industrial medicine. Indust. Med. 15: 330–332, May 1946.

    Leggo, C., S. G. Law, and E. K. Clarke. Industrial psychiatry in the community of Oak Ridge. Indust. Med. 15:243–253, April 1946.

    Whitney, L. H. Emotional first-aid stations—on the job. Indust. Med. 15:336–338, May 1946.

42. Cantor, N. Employee counseling; a new viewpoint in industrial psychology. New York, McGraw-Hill, 1945.

    Garrett, A. M. Counseling methods for personnel workers. New York, Family Welfare Association of America, 1945.

    Rogers, C. R. Counseling and psychotherapy. Boston, Houghton Mifflin, 1942.

    Rogers, C. R., and J. L. Wallen. Counseling with returned servicemen. New York, McGraw-Hill, 1946.

43. Baker, H. Employee counseling; a survey of a new development in personnel relations, p. 51–53. Princeton, N. J., Princeton University, 1944.

44. Radosta, V. Human relations on the shop floor. The Compass 26:11, November 1944.

45. Himler, L. E. Psychotherapeutic aspects of foreman contacts. Ment. Hyg. 29:106–110, January 1945.

46. Webster, H. Contributions of community organizations to industrial mental health. Ment. Hyg. 28:49–54, January 1944.

47. Sappington, C. O. Industrial health; its war and postwar significance. Indust. Med. 12:361–364, June 1943.

48. Vonachen, H. A. A practical program for human rehabilitation. Indust. Med. 12:807–810, December 1943.

49. Giberson, L. C.   The technique of listening to the worried employee.   Indust. Med. 9:414–417, July 1940.

50. Dumas, A. G.   Rehabilitation and training for post-war employment; a panel discussion at the Second War Congress of American Industry, 1943.   Pittsburgh, Industrial Hygiene Foundation, 1943.

51. McFarland, R. A.   Physically handicapped workers.   Harvard Business Rev. 13:1–31, Autumn 1944.

52. Kubie, L. S.   Psychiatry in industry.   Ment. Hyg. 29:201–207, April 1945.

53. Fountain, C. W.   Labor's place in an industrial mental health program.   Ment. Hyg. 29:95–101, January 1945.

XI

PRACTICAL CONSIDERATIONS IN INTERVIEWING AND COUNSELING*

The war and the many dislocations and changes it brought have led to an increased appreciation of the importance of interviewing and counseling. As was indicated in Chapter I, much interviewing and counseling were required in the armed forces. In industry the need for top-notch production, the loss of many skilled workers to the armed forces, the employment of numbers of women and other new workers, the amount of special training required, and absenteeism occurring for various reasons made clear the necessity for knowing workers better and giving them help in solving their varied problems. Similarly, the Red Cross, the social agencies, the churches, the USO, the Veterans Administration, the local veterans' information centers, the colleges and universities were faced with a great increase in war-related problems which, in most cases, required for their solution the help of a correspondingly larger group of counselors and interviewers. The need for counseling is not limited to those directly or indirectly affected by the recent emergency. It is reliably estimated that at any given time 10 per cent of the population have serious social and emotional difficulties and that 20 per cent would derive benefit from a proper counseling relationship.

Because of the increased need for counseling in wartime as well as the demand of the armed forces and war agencies for the services of professionally trained interviewers and counselors, there was during the war a dearth of trained personnel in civilian agencies and in industry. Consequently, people who had had lit-

* Much of this chapter is reprinted, with adaptations, from Chapter V, *Jobs and the Man*, by the same authors (Springfield, Illinois, Charles C. Thomas, 1945).

tle or no training for the work found themselves in positions which called for interviewing and counseling skills. This continues to be true now in the post-war period notwithstanding the return of many counselors from the armed forces to civilian positions. There simply are not enough fully trained and experienced social workers, clinical psychologists, and other skilled counselors to meet the demands. The Veterans Administration and the guidance centers in the colleges and universities alone require several thousand more than are available. Consequently, organizations, with or without care in selection, have placed many relatively untrained people in interviewing and counseling positions and set them to work.

Moreover, large numbers of people in various professions and in business and industry who have always been doing a substantial amount of interviewing—and are now doing more than ever—have received little or no training for the interviewing and counseling features of their work. It is estimated that in business and industry there are probably 2,300,000 people in executive, supervisory, and foreman positions who use from 50 to 90 per cent of their time conferring with others. There are close to 2,000,000 professional people whose professional education included little or no specific training in the arts of interviewing and counseling: over 1,000,000 teachers and school administrators, 300,000 nurses, 180,000 physicians in general or specialized non-psychiatric practice, 170,000 lawyers, and 140,000 clergymen. The amount of time devoted to the discussion of personal and social problems varies somewhat with the profession and individually within each profession, but such problems form a considerable part of the content of the interviews.[1]

These men and women whose work brings them into interviewing and counseling relations with large numbers of people constitute a tremendous potential resource for relieving tensions and improving human relations. But their contribution to mental health will be most effective if they have adequate orientation in mental hygiene and a fair degree of skill in interviewing and counseling. Obviously, these groups cannot take time out to pursue long professional training along social and psychological lines. Neither can this brief chapter make thoroughly skilled counselors of them. However, the specific principles and procedures suggested here may give some assistance to those who have had little or no training in interviewing and counseling and are trying to help people to deal with their problems. It is hoped that this chapter may also serve as a review and perhaps as a source of additional suggestions for those in schools, churches, social and health agencies, and in business and industry who feel a need to increase their understanding and improve their techniques in the field of human relations.

Types of Interviews

Interviews are of many kinds, depending considerably on who seeks them and what the objectives are. The objective may be either simple or complex. In many interviews, the objective is to get and to give information. Much employment and student interviewing is of this kind and requires of the interviewer chiefly a friendly approach, systematic inquiry regarding preferences and qualifications, and fair powers of observation. The same is true of most information services.

Many interviews are more complex, requiring sound understanding of people's motives and reliable estimates of their capacities for adjustment. This is true of interviews for selecting personnel for supervisory or executive positions and also of interviews with people who have developed problems which involve personal attitudes or difficulties in getting along with others. Interviews with people who complain of illness may be still more complicated. Perhaps most difficult of all are interviews with people who have emotional or nervous disorders, or serious personality problems which get them into repeated difficulty with other people. In such situations, even though the initial request is for simple information, information and instruction are not enough. The counselor must seek to clarify the issues in the problem and bring constructive influences to bear on attitudes and motivation. In social case work and counseling interviews there is usually both a specific and a more general purpose. The specific purpose is to resolve the complaint of the counselee or bring about changes in which the counselee is interested.* The general purpose is to clarify the issues and bring about maximum adjustment.

It should always be recognized that what appears to be the problem may be only a small part of it. Quoting Hamilton:

We know that problems are created when the demands of the personality are in conflict with the pressures or demands of the situation—as in employment—or when the demands of the personality are in conflict with each other—as when a man wants to be with his family and wants to go to war, or a woman wants a career and wants children, too; and these conflicts are particularly distressing if part is unconscious. In a strong personality these conflicts become more or less unified, or at least harmonized (psychologically speaking, the ego is the unifying device); but in a less well-integrated person, if the reality situation through illness or other pressures becomes overwhelming so that the ego cannot function, the person is caught in an unresolved dilemma.

We know, too (and this is the important point for counseling) that problems do not always come neatly packaged—so many pure environmental pressures, so many inner personality demands—but that problems are psychosocial. Irrational feeling elements are interwoven with all sorts of practical issues. This is why workers have to be trained to understand that it does not matter at which end, practical or emotional, a client begins, and why the two objectives of relieving environmental pressures and increasing insight must be integrated in modern casework counseling.

The skill comes in understanding disguised as well as surface needs—how to release feeling and tension; how to assist in reformulating the problem and to consider alternatives in a nonjudgmental atmosphere.[1]

---

* The term counselee, while not entirely satisfactory, is used consistently to designate the person interviewed in a counseling situation. It is used only because it is applicable to all situations, although the counselor in specific situations would more appropriately refer to the person being interviewed as member, client, student, employee, parishioner, or patient.

The counseling interview establishes a "zone of neutrality" in which the counselee can talk out his troubles instead of continuing to act them out in ways that handicap himself or others. Skill in the art of listening is, of course, essential for this kind of interviewing and requires unobtrusive search for basic factors while the counselee discusses the superficial aspects of the problem which at the moment seems to be the cause. The counseling interview aims to guide the counselee into talking out, thinking through, and planning steps which he himself can put into effect to solve his problem. The counseling interview, if properly conducted, should free him from the painful and bewildering phases of his situation, so that he can more effectively work out a solution. The counselor is primarily a catalytic agent. Counseling offers no ready-made solutions but motivates people to healthy self-guidance and self-direction. In short, it helps them to help themselves.

Where counseling interviews are conducted by persons who have no administrative authority in the organization, as in the Hawthorne plant of the Western Electric Company,[2] in the Workers' Service Bureau in Cleveland,[3] and in much social work and psychological and vocational counseling,[1] the interviews can be, and usually are, entirely non-directive. Counselees are simply given an opportunity to "talk out" their troubles with an understanding and attentive listener whose sole job is counseling and who has no power to make decisions or to take any action which might conflict with the counselee's interpretation of his own interests.

Counselors who are part of the operating organization and have some administrative authority can maintain a sympathetic and listening attitude and help to objectify the real problem but cannot conceal their authority merely by appearing neutral. They should minimize the amount of advice given, for it is an accepted rule in counseling that merely offering general advice to persons under emotional stress is seldom effective. They may, however, be obliged sometimes to advise or persuade counselees to discuss or think over a number of possibilities or plans before deciding upon a final course of action.

Attitudes of Counselees

The counselor can assume that the people he interviews will show various attitudes toward him and varying degrees of readiness to accept and use his assistance. Some counselees who keenly feel their need for assistance tend to become too dependent and look to the counselor as a person who will solve their problems for them. They may come too often to the counselor's office, take up excessive time, and constantly ask for guidance in trivial matters. This attitude is something of a nuisance to the counselor, but brusque dismissal is not the solution. Each person seeking help must be dealt with on an individual basis. Some of these dependent people idealize the counselor and think of him as all-wise. An explanation to the counselee to the effect that he is expecting too much brings to his attention his own attitude and also explains the counselor's position and his many other responsibilities. The counselor will find it helpful to break the adjustment tasks down into simple parts and to give liberal praise for every evidence of progress which the counselee makes in managing his own affairs. This gives him hope and stimulates him to keep on making further efforts. The counselor must always guard against doing too much for counselees of this type. Inexperienced counselors have often become so interested in their counselees that they have been too anxious to please them, and thus have fallen into the trap of making their decisions for them and carrying their responsibilities. The aim should always be to help them or teach them to come to grips with their problems and to do things for themselves with greater effectiveness.

Other counselees have a negative attitude, refusing to talk spontaneously, answering questions grudgingly, or breaking appointments frequently. Such an attitude may have several causes: they do not like the counselor; or the prospect of talking frankly seems too painful; or they think they have already talked too much and are resentful of the fact that the counselor knows so much about them. If further interviews are possible such thoughts and feelings can be talked out and brought into the open; and antagonism, suspicion, or dread can be reduced if not eliminated. Sometimes, too, an apparently negative attitude is merely the counselee's unwillingness to be dependent on anyone else for assistance. This is a natural attitude and, if recognized, is not a serious barrier. In fact, in the end it is the patient's major asset in finding solutions to his problems.

Fortunately, the attitudes of many counselees are more favorable than the two extremes described. As a rule, the counselee is fairly open-minded, direct, and frank, eager for help in understanding his problem, and predisposed to make his own decisions and carry on without leaning unduly on others. Obviously, counseling with such persons is easier and it is with this group that relatively untrained and inexperienced counselors have most of their early success.

It should be noted that this range of attitudes is shown not only by people who are confronted with fairly serious personal problems which bring them to the attention of a counselor, but also by staff members, business associates, committee members, and others who have occasion to confer and collaborate on problems of mutual interest. Many a professional or business conference has broken up without achievement of the desired result because of the failure to recognize and to deal wisely with the negative and defensive attitudes of one or more members of the group.

Qualifications of Interviewers and Counselors

The significance of skill in interviewing is coming to be more and more appreciated, and it seems likely that in the future more emphasis will be placed upon proper qualifications for such work. As was pointed out in a recent report of the National Industrial

Conference Board, "The successful interview depends largely upon the interviewer himself. Although this staff member represents the company to the job-seeking public, it is unfortunate that in many instances appointment is made with little or no thought of his qualifications, or of the far-reaching effects of his attitudes on both the employer and the prospective employee."[4] Industrial firms have no monopoly on such disregard of qualifications for interviewers. Many other institutions and agencies are equally indifferent.

Whether interviews accomplish their purpose depends largely on what the person interviewed thinks of the interviewer. Everyone engaged in interviewing might well ask, "What do the people I interview think about me as a counselor? Do they think I am understanding? Do they credit me with having good sense? Do they think I will not blame them? Do they believe I am genuinely sincere and that I will keep confidences? Do they find it pleasant to talk with me? Do they think I can really help?"

How those who are interviewed answer these questions in their own minds depends very much on how the interviewer thinks and feels about people and on how he shows it. If he has an air of superiority and assumes that everyone who has any personal problems which he can't solve by himself is a stupid bungler or a sinner, if beneath his polite exterior there is an undercurrent of antagonism, superciliousness, or distrust, the people he interviews will usually sense his attitude and be politely evasive and eager to bring the interview to an end. If, on the other hand, the interviewer or counselor has a fundamental liking for people, accepts and enjoys individual differences, and assumes that those who develop problems do so because of unfavorable elements in their situation or because of limitations which their experience has placed upon them, then those who are interviewed are likely to discuss their problems frankly and with some real hope of getting assistance from the interviewer. We may note a little more specifically a few of the primary qualifications for interviewers and counselors.

1. The good interviewer is genuinely interested in people and finds most of them likable. This means that the interviewer is sensitive to human relationships. He is readily aware of the significance which the things he says and does have for others. He observes changes in people's behavior and catches the subtle meaning of tone of voice, hesitancy in speech, or impulsive action. One who lacks these capacities is not likely to make a good counselor, even with much specific training.

2. The good counselor tries to deal objectively with people. He tries always to see the counselee and his situation as they actually are, without letting his own feelings, convictions, or prejudices influence him unduly. The good counselor realizes that the person he is interviewing will respond to his attitudes. He is careful to show neither anger nor undue sympathy. Difficult though it may be, he strives to keep his eye on the good of the counselee rather than on his own reputation. The good interviewer is able to put himself sufficiently in the place of the other fellow to understand him and his situation, but at the same time he is able to keep a certain detachment so that he does not confuse his own interests and feelings with those of the person he is interviewing.

3. The good interviewer has a thoroughgoing respect for the individual and is predisposed to allow each person he interviews the freedom to be himself. He carefully avoids trying to make over the counselee in his own image. He accepts him as he is and allows him freedom to work out his own solution to his problems, insofar as such solutions do not interfere seriously with the liberties or effectiveness of his associates.

As Rogers has pointed out, "In client-centered or non-directive counseling, there are two basic assumptions. (1) It is assumed that we should respect the integrity and the personal autonomy of the individual. It is felt that each person has a right to make his own decisions. He has the right to seek help and to take help, or he also has the right to refuse help. He is responsible for his own life and every precaution should be taken to build this sense of responsibility rather than tear it down. (2) A second assumption is that the individual has an enormous capacity for adaptation and for readjustment. Put in broader terms, the individual has a tremendous drive towards growth and maturity and positive health. The war has shown with striking clarity the capacities for adaptation and for growth which exist within each individual. The primary aim of client-centered counseling is to release these forces, to free the individual to go on growing when conflict or circumstance or doubt has halted him. It is this strength within the individual, not the strength within the counselor, upon which we must rely."[5]

The significance of personal attitudes in conversation and interviewing is well illustrated by Stevenson:

> In conversation with a more or less unknown person, I should expect that the first question to confront him, consciously or unconsciously, would have to do with whether or not he likes me, and if I do not respect him as a person, if I do not allow him to be himself, if I show no interest in him, if I am restless and fidgety, his answer, more often felt than expressed, will be, "No, I don't like that fellow." Having gotten past the question of whether he can like me or not, he is then concerned with whether or not he can trust me. His answer will be negative if I burden him with moral judgments, blame him or express too much commendation or enthusiasm. He next wants to know whether I have something of real value to give him; and if my response to his illness, his financial difficulties, his family, his educational plans or his vocational quandaries are mimeographed answers that leave him as a person entirely out of account, he will probably rate my contribution as low. If, on the other hand, he finds encouragement to proceed, he will want to try me out in various ways. He will get my reactions to rather indifferent issues, then he may step ahead to present his needs in fuller and fuller form. It will be necessary for me, without being a dead pan, to use the art of saying nothing as we talk, or at least of saying nothing that he would say for himself.

> A beginning is best made with conversation that surely will not get us into argument or conflict. The weather is a common subject of probing between two people at this point of acquaintanceship. In discussing the weather I test the other fellow's willingness to talk to me. If he talks

willingly, I feel that it is not enthusiasm for the weather, but a willingness to accept me as a person to talk to. He, on the other hand, is more or less alert to the way I receive his conversation about the weather. Do I lend an ear interestingly because I respect him, or am I grudging? Do I compete for control of the conversation? Do I dead-pan him, or really show interest? Do I encourage him to move along to express other thoughts? Do I moralize with him and advise him, or do I by listening and exchange of ideas help him to arrive at a better understanding and clarify matters for both of us? Do I argue to reshape him in my own image, or do I like him for his own personality?

As part of this art of saying nothing in words, I may say much without words. I may use my facial expression or gestures to make him feel at ease. An occasional "and" or "yes" is helpful, but they do not mean and or yes as defined by Webster. Also, if I am somewhat professional in this situation, I will be conscious of his delaying tactics that reveal insufficient confidence, and I will not be irritated by these tactics, since I will know what they mean. If he repeats his story over and over again, introduces irrelevant topics, spends time on trivial matters, or lapses into silence or throws the burden of conversation on me, I know that he is not yet ready to go ahead. . . .

I should like to describe an interview with a man that reveals just how this occurs. This man sought help for a stomach discomfort, fullness and belching. His initial step in talking with the doctor was to blame his difficulty on overeating. In our culture overeating has no more moral implications than the weather, and so he has no resistance to admitting this weakness. After a little discussion along this line he suggests that his difficulty may be due to his having to drive a truck in traffic. In this he admits to the doctor the possibility of an emotional element, although he softens this by saying that he knew a man who drove in traffic and the strain of handling the steering wheel was responsible for his getting appendicitis. Shortly he abandoned the idea of an organic determinant in his complaint by saying that it may have something to do with his job which is inspecting airplanes and if he should make a mistake it might result in someone's death. He had now arrived at a complete emotional explanation for his difficulty and brought himself face to face with the question, "Do I like this fellow? Can I go further with him? Can I trust him? Can he help me?" Apparently he reached a sufficient degree of assurance to end these delaying tactics, for he suddenly blurts out, "You do not know what I have been through for eight years with my wife. She has nagged me constantly. I go home at night hungry and the food is burned. I get so upset that I have to leave the house without eating." But this is not all. He follows this up with a statement that this has become so intolerable and his wife so ill that they have had to have her committed to a mental hospital. In response to a direct question he will not tell which hospital. Why? Because as it turns out, the hospital is not a private sanitarium and her family is critical of him for not giving her that luxury. Now it sounds as if we had reached the center of the difficulty, but he is still trying out the doctor before presenting his real difficulty, which finally comes out in a statement that he is very much concerned for his daughter who has been very nervous and who a neurologist says is apt to go the same way as his wife. This is not a succession of interviews covering weeks or even days. It is an interview of twenty minutes to half an hour.

Whether I'm professional or not, my attitude toward things that are different from me or my way of life will be important to my getting along in such a contact or to go further in being of help. If I oppose things that are different, my uselessness is soon discovered. If I merely tolerate things that are different, I may be tolerated, but my usefulness will be extremely limited. If I can enjoy difference and respect it I cease to be threatening. Then my partner in conversation, having no need to be defensive, can gain perspective himself. We may be very tolerant in one sphere and very narrow in another. If one wishes to discover how useful he may be to a returning veteran, it might not be bad for him to look into different spheres of his life and test his capacity to accept difference—attitudes toward race, creed and color offer valuable tests.[6]

Some Things to Look for and Emphasize

Next in importance to the counselor's personal qualifications are his major aims and objectives in the counseling process. Much depends on what he looks for and what he emphasizes throughout. Skilled interviewers advise that emphasis be placed on the following:

1. Assume that as a rule problems are somewhat complex and have not one but several or many causes. For example, a worker who was normally productive begins to make an increasing number of mistakes. He pulls the levers of his machine at the wrong time, forgets to remove his tools from hazardous places, and gets involved in quarrels with his fellow workers. Investigation reveals that he has become much worried about a son in the armed forces, from whom he has not heard for several weeks. This in turn has caused some loss of appetite and loss of sleep, with consequent results in terms of fatigue and irritability. A foreman, at the end of a day when he had made many mistakes, threatened him with loss of his job if he did not improve. Irked by this threat and feeling tired and worn out, he fell into a dispute with his wife over rather trivial matters, which finally ended in uncomplimentary comments as to why he wasn't as successful as his brothers. Clearly this man's problems are "snowballing," and attention to any one part of his situation without knowledge of the various complications could not hope to get results. As doctors and social workers put it, "Find out the causes—do not treat the symptoms."

2. Remember in every counseling situation that you are dealing not only with a person who has a problem, but with a person who has both a problem and a history. Watch out for themes which occur over and over again in an interview, such as a fault-finding or critical attitude toward everyone with whom the person is associated, or frequent apologies and expressions of self-depreciation. As a rule there have been antecedents to the present difficulty. The resentment of the authority of the supervisor has usually been preceded by similar resentment of former supervisors—in the case of veterans, by marked resentment of the authority of their officers —and by overreactions to the authority of parents and teachers. So-called day-dreaming and wool-gathering which result in a student's failure or a workman's accident today have usually been preceded by other occasions of preoccupation with personal worries and in-

terests. Try to discover the person's major personality trends and characteristics.

3. Recognize that talking with people and sharing one's feelings with them are healing processes in themselves. Much of the art of interviewing is well expressed in the phrase, "the ministry of listening," which incidentally gave title to an interesting pamphlet that has been used widely.[7]

4. Learn to accept and respect aggression and don't let it get a rise out of you. Recognize that an aggressive or disagreeable counselee is apt to be a very troubled or even a sick person. Remember the proverbial truth that "A soft answer turneth away wrath," and that the softest answer is an unafraid and kindly look and poise born of understanding.

5. Recognize that in a counseling relationship a strong bond springs up between the counselee and the counselor. The importance of this bond must not be underestimated. Use it to increase the counselee's ability to direct his own affairs, and do not let him become more dependent upon you.

6. Seek out and make special mental note of the counselee's strong points and the things he is sure he does well. If he is to be helped to make an adjustment, it is just as important to discover his abilities as to learn his failures and weaknesses.

7. Keep constantly in mind the counselee's ability to adjust and also his limitations. Suggest, if anything, only such efforts as give good promise of success. Keep in mind the next practical step for the counselee, that is, the next step which he can take successfully, rather than the far-off, desirable goal from the viewpoint of the counselor. Especially in dealing with a person who is unsure of himself, be careful not to give him too many tasks to accomplish. Some succeed much better when they solve their problems in a piecemeal fashion. It is well for the counselor to formulate in his own mind the various adjustments that will eventually have to be made; but he should take them up with the counselee step by step, as the counselee discovers the need to tackle them.

Do's and Don't's in Interviewing and Counseling

As has already been implied, effective interviewing and counseling cannot be reduced to a simple set of rules. Much depends on the basic understanding of the counselor, the attitude of the counselee, and the spirit which prevails throughout the interviewing sessions. Certain procedures, however, are helpful and with practice become the counselor's second nature.

1. Whenever possible make some advance preparation by learning or reviewing at least a few pertinent facts about the person to be interviewed. For example, where a person has been referred to the counselor by someone else, the counselor should have information on the reason for referral. The counselor need not have a great deal of advance information. Too many facts, and especially too many opinions on the part of others, may make it difficult for him to be natural and friendly in his approach. One or two facts, such as, "This veteran fought at Guadalcanal," or "This one was wounded in Italy, although he now appears to be well," make it possible to start the interview in an easy and natural way. If the interviewer has a single opening wedge of this kind, he can build a half-hour discussion from that start.

2. Interview in complete privacy if at all possible. Nobody likes to talk confidentially in an atmosphere which does not permit him to feel at home. Interruptions spoil the spontaneity of conversation. In an industrial setting the counselee should be relieved of all work responsibility; otherwise he cannot give his undivided attention to the interview.

3. See that the counselee does not have to wait and that he is physically comfortable and at ease. It is significant that most arguments occur when people are standing up. Provide a consulting room and not a witness stand, and arrange the furniture with that idea in mind. Make sure that the person interviewed is not placed in the bright light while you sit in a shaded corner. The reversal of these positions creates a better atmosphere for counseling.

4. Give your undivided attention to the person you are interviewing. You cannot conduct a successful interview while looking out the window. Much looking away will be resented as disinterest, and a wish to avoid the counselee's eye may be interpreted as embarrassment in your role as counselor.

5. Be natural, informal, and courteous. Excessive dignity or ceremony is apt to make effective counseling impossible. The counselor's interest in the counselee and his problem must be genuine and not forced. Make it clear that you are not going to "put him on the spot" or "pin something on him," but rather that you want to share with him your thinking about problems in which both of you are interested.

6. If it seems hard to get the interview started, begin with some comment of a favorable nature. This makes the counselee feel he is noticed and appreciated for himself and opens the way to talk about things in which he is interested. When you talk, speak plainly, without sentimentality, and in a calm and even voice.

7. Try to be a good listener, that is, listen silently until the person you are interviewing has fully expressed himself. You may need to ask him a few questions for fuller information, but be careful not to sidetrack the counselee in giving his story. When he has finished his account, it is often desirable to guide the conversation into channels which will reveal aspects of the situation unrelated to what he considers his chief source of difficulty. If he makes a vague statement, ask him to give you an example in his recent experience. It is surprising how often the use of examples clarifies the person's problem, both to himself and to the interviewer. Remember always that you are counseling, not prosecuting; that you are seeking facts, not judging; that you are striving to help, not condemning.

8. In the course of listening to the counselee's story, the counselor often gains confidences and confessions of a very personal nature. Sometimes these offer important clues to the crux of the problem, but it should be emphasized that merely uncovering intimate

and private facts is not the primary purpose of the interview. The real aim is to search out and reveal the relationship of those factors which have direct or indirect influence on the person's poise, work efficiency, social adjustment, or whatever his goal may be. The degree to which this aim is achieved gives the only true basis for measuring the success of the interview. There is some danger that the relatively inexperienced counselor will lose proper perspective through too great an interest in the details of the counselee's personal affairs.

9. Both in listening to the counselee's own account and in the questions he asks, the counselor should:

a) Note especially the counselee's characteristic attitude toward himself and the degree of his need for approval and reinforcement.
b) Try to determine his characteristic attitude toward others, whether friendly, frank, distant, aggressive, or hostile.
c) Note especially whether certain kinds of problem occur over and over and the kinds of situation in which such difficulties arise.
d) Seek to get the counselee to define in his own words aspects of the problem he has hitherto avoided or overlooked and to plan his own course of action. The following are examples of the "who-what-when-where-how" questions, which in an easy and natural way emphasize the part which the counselee must play in remedying the situation. "What are your ideas concerning the causes of the difficulty? What have you done thus far to improve the situation? What stands in the way of working things out? Do you have someone to whom you can take your problems? In what way do you think the interviewer can be of help?"

10. Don't hurry the counselee and avoid interrupting him until he has had the opportunity to give his story in full and to explain the problem as he sees it. Resist completely the temptation to lecture or moralize.

11. Don't pry into personal affairs. For example, if you are interviewing a worker and have reason to believe that his home life or other personal experiences have something to do with his problem

on the job, introduce the subject by asking some such question as, "How are things at home? Do you bring any worries to the plant with you?" This assures the worker that you are sticking to the business at hand and are interested in his out-of-plant affairs only as they may have significance for his work efficiency.

12. Invite and encourage the counselee to discuss his feelings frankly, even though some of them are negative and even though they may be directed against you or the organization you represent.

13. Try to get the counselee's slant on things and don't bias his responses by asking leading questions; by telling him your own views on the subject; or by indicating, through your speech or facial expression, that you strongly disapprove of what he is saying or thinking.

14. Try not to permit the counselee to commit himself to false statements which he will later feel required to defend. While he is "feeling you out" to see if you are understanding and can be trusted, he may tell you only part of the truth, or even some untruths. If you challenge him immediately, you may only cause him to get angry or to "close up." Casual questions are more apt to be answered truthfully than questions which sound like a cross-examination. A suggestion to "think the matter over further" or an inquiry as to other possible explanations of a situation is much more effective than to accuse the counselee of lying, or in other ways to force him to take a defensive stand.

15. Don't be afraid of silence. Silence on your part is apt to draw out the other person. If you think of it as "an expectant pause" in which the person interviewed has time to compose his feelings and collect his thoughts, you will not be so strongly tempted to fill every gap in the conversation with comments of your own. In interviewing a woman who bursts into tears, the stereotyped "Now don't cry" is apt to add to her embarrassment or irritation. Simply wait for her to compose herself, realizing that many people talk more freely after a brief shower of tears. Neither should weeping be re-

garded as an automatic signal to stop the interview, as is often done out of mistaken kindness. Too much silence, of course, can become burdensome; when the silence becomes too prolonged, the conversation can be shifted to some other phase of the problem which needs clarification.

16. Don't disclose information obtained confidentially in interviews. One breach of confidence may completely destroy a counselor's opportunity for helpfulness, for knowledge of such a breach usually spreads like wildfire. Every person is entitled to a private life and if part of this is shared in the counseling process, the confidence should be kept inviolate. The only exception—and in spirit it is not an exception—is the sharing of knowledge with a professional person who will make constructive use of the information on the counselee's behalf. Even then it is well to obtain the counselee's permission before transmitting information to a physician or other person who might give professional service.

17. Don't give premature advice or make promises. Be sure that you understand all the important factors in the counselee's problem before you give any advice, and then limit your counsel to things which will be practical from the counselee's viewpoint. Be careful never to commit yourself to promises which you may not be able to keep. Sometimes the only promise that can be made is to investigate further the problem which the counselee feels is an obstacle to his full cooperation.

18. Plan the guidance or treatment along the line of the counselee's abilities and his major aims and suggest only such activities as he can undertake comfortably with some assurance of succeeding.

19. Insure progression during the interview by summarizing briefly what the counselee has said and then asking if this summary gives a true picture of the problem as he has discussed it up to that point. Written notes outlining the main points are sometimes helpful. Make it clear, at least near the end of the interview, that there must be some way in which the two of you working to-

gether can improve the situation. Coming to grips with some of the issues involved advances the counselee toward a solution, even though parts of the total problem remain unsolved.

20. Before ending an interview, see to it that you both understand just what can and will be done by the counselee, what will be done by the interviewer, what by others. Many times the problem is so complicated that all the counselor can do at the end of the interview is to express an interest in learning more about the situation, to suggest that the matter needs more thought and to arrange a definite time for this. Be sure to follow up such an appointment. Sometimes it is well to end an interview in which the counselee is "spilling the beans" too fast by saying that what he has said is so important that it would be better to think it over and discuss it in another meeting in the near future.

21. Be fully acquainted with the resources of your community and use them wisely. Avoid leaving an impression that you can solve all problems single-handed. Make it clear to the counselee that you will not consult with anyone to whom you refer him unless you have his full consent and permission.

22. Don't be afraid to admit frankly your own mistakes or errors. People respect a man who can admit that he makes mistakes and does not consider himself infallible. Instead of weakening the contact, such admissions, when they are in order, may actually serve to strengthen the counselor-counselee relationship.

Follow-up Interviews

Not all counseling problems require follow-up interviews, but it is usually a good plan for the interviewer to express his willingness to continue the discussion at a later time. It is often effective to "hit the iron while it's hot" and to inquire briefly as to the counselee's progress after an interval of a few days. Follow-up interviews are seldom as time-consuming as the first interview, and the results from the small amount of additional effort required in following through are often very rewarding.

Interview Records

No rules can be made regarding the taking of notes. In interviewing most people, note-taking during an interview should be kept to a minimum, if used at all. If it is deemed helpful to take notes, they should be in plain view of the counselee. They should be limited to dates, figures, or facts; or graphic examples of some phase of the problem or situation. After the interview has been ended, it is desirable to make a brief summary of the problem presented, the issues faced, the issues remaining unsettled, positive steps taken, and referrals made. Notes of this type act as a quick memory refresher for later follow-up.

The Need for Training

Some day educational, vocational, religious, and other personal interviewing and counseling may all be highly skilled occupations. If so, much more adequate training will have to be provided. Good interviewers and counselors have not "just growed" like Topsy. The two professions which rely mainly on interviewing techniques, psychiatry and social case work, have not only provided basic courses dealing with the mental, emotional, and social life of individuals but have also provided internships or field work under skilled supervision. For these professions from one to three years of actual work under the direction of more experienced doctors or social workers have been required. It has been proved a thousand times that an intellectual grasp of psychological principles does not necessarily mean that one is able to use that knowledge skillfully in interviewing situations. Techniques can be refined only through use and correction.

If interviewing and counseling in the various fields are ever to achieve real occupational status, those who are to engage in them will have to be provided with training similar to that of social workers and psychiatrists, but with more emphasis on the particular relationships and adjustments that especially pertain to each given field. A substantial body of material from the various fields in which counseling is done is now available for prospective counselors (see below, *For Further Reading*).

Even if all the organizations interested in counseling desired to import trained professional personnel from the fields of psychiatry and social work, it would not be possible at this time to do so in sufficient numbers to supply the need. Industry, schools, churches, and rehabilitation agencies will doubtless have to train most of their own staffs for this work. In such training, simple, dynamic courses in psychology and mental hygiene should be required. Still more important will be provisions for adequate supervision and direction on the job. Those who are learning to use counseling procedures and trying to increase their effectiveness should have the benefit of supervision by experienced professional workers.

REFERENCES

1. Hamilton, G. Counseling as social case work. Social Service Rev. 17:127–143, June 1943.

2. Roethlisberger, F. J., and W. J. Dickson. Management and the worker, p. 287. Cambridge, Mass., Harvard University Press, 1939.

3. Palevsky, M. Counseling services for industrial workers, p. 51. New York, Family Welfare Association of America, 1945.

4. Re-employment of veterans. Studies in Personnel Policy, No. 69, p. 4. New York, National Industrial Conference Board, 1945.

5. Rogers, C. R. A counseling viewpoint. New York, Federal Council of the Churches of Christ in America, 1945.

6. Stevenson, G. S. The rebirth of a civilian. *In* Readjusting with the Returning Servicemen, p. 57–66. Chicago, Illinois Society for Mental Hygiene, 1945.

7. Dicks, R. L. The ministry of listening, p. 23. New York, Federal Council of the Churches of Christ in America, 1944.

FOR FURTHER READING

Dicks, R. L. Pastoral work and personal counseling. New York, Macmillan, 1944.

Gardner, B. B. Personnel counseling. *In* Human relations in industry. Chicago, Richard D. Irwin, Inc., 1945.

Garrett, A. M. Counseling methods for personnel workers. New York, Family Welfare Association of America, 1945.

Garrett, A. M. Interviewing; its principles and methods. New York, Family Welfare Association of America, 1944.

May, R. The art of counseling; how to gain and give mental health. Nashville, Cokesbury, 1939.

Rogers, C. R. Counseling and psychotherapy, p. 450. Boston, Houghton Mifflin, 1942.

Rogers, C. R., and J. L. Wallen. Counseling with returned servicemen, New York, McGraw-Hill, 1946.

Whitehorn, J. C. Guide to interviewing and clinical personality study. Arch. Neurol. & Psychiat. 52:197–216, September 1944.

XII

THE MENTAL HYGIENE OF FAMILY LIVING

THE burden of the last six chapters has been to indicate additional sources of mental hygiene help for the large numbers of people who need such assistance. It has been recognized throughout that mental health problems are to a large degree socially conditioned and that to promote mental health it is necessary to give attention to groups as well as to individuals. Opportunities to correct faulty attitudes and develop group morale have been noted, especially in connection with industry and church life, but it remains to come to grips with the preventive and constructive side of mental hygiene.

In this connection one is reminded of an old Cornish custom which was a very simple but effective test for sanity. The patient was put into a room in which there was a bucket under a tap. The tap was turned on and the patient was given a cup and told to bail the bucket. If the patient turned off the tap before he began bailing the bucket, he was considered sane. If, on the other hand, he started bailing the bucket without turning off the tap, he was deemed to be insane. In dealing with social and mental health problems we act somewhat like the patient who bails the bucket without turning off the tap. We keep on spending sixteen to twenty billion dollars a year on police departments, courts, and prisons without getting at the sources of social pathology. People keep on getting married, but the only preparation we provide is a civil contract that requires one minute to execute or a religious ceremony that requires from five to ten minutes to perform, plus physical examination and a Wassermann test in some states, and then we bail out a large proportion of married couples through the divorce courts. (In several cities and at least one state the number of separations equals or exceeds the number of marriages.) We keep more than half of our hospital beds filled with mentally ill persons without making consistent use of what knowledge we have of the causes of mental illness. We know that many of the serious behavior problems of children—and of the undesirable and unhealthy personality patterns of adults—result from a misunderstanding of the nature of children and from their early misguidance in the family group, yet we have done almost nothing to educate for family living.

Preventive medicine and public health made headway only after the causes of various diseases became known and systematic efforts were made to remove the causes. The same principle holds in the field of mental and social health. To prevent crime, delinquency, marital discord, serious child-behavior problems, psychoneurosis, and mental illness, we shall have to know and, as far as possible, remove their causes.

In the field of mental health, it must be admitted that our knowledge of the causes of mental illness is very incomplete. In case of organic conditions, such as paresis, toxic psychoses, and mental diseases resulting from traumatic injury, causes are specific so that if we can prevent the contraction of syphilis, the absorption of toxins and drugs, and the occurrence of head injuries, we can prevent mental illnesses resulting from such conditions. These are the main conditions in which absolute prevention is possible. As yet we know too little about the causes of schizophrenia or of manic-depressive and other functional psychoses to be able to prevent them with any degree of certainty. Our knowledge of psychoneuroses and their motivations is more adequate. Although their prevention is presumptive rather than absolute, there is good reason to believe that in most instances early diagnosis and treatment and the alleviation of family and other social stresses reduce the intensity of the intrapsychic conflicts and prevent the development of more severe forms of psychoneurosis.

Public health has been promoted not only by controlling known sources of infection but also by strengthening people's resistance to disease through improved nutrition and more hygienic habits.

By analogy, in mental health we need not await the completion of research that will tell us all about the causes of mental and emotional illness. We can use what we know about the processes of personality development to establish a program that not only will help to prevent illness, but will promote people's emotional maturity and thus strengthen their security and increase their stability and social effectiveness. That is the positive goal of mental hygiene.

The Need for Maturity

Immaturity stands out as "Number One" trouble-maker in bringing about mental, emotional, and social ills. It accounts for practically all neurosis, is a major factor in much mental illness, and seems to be at the root of many social problems. On the other hand, emotional and mental maturity is the only hope of maximal personal satisfaction, physical and mental health, social progress, and enduring peace. Put so tersely this statement may seem to be too sweeping. If space permitted it could be well documented, but here we can note only a few of the many strong demands made recently for maturity in our people. It is recalled that 25 per cent of the eighteen-year-olds not accepted for service in the armed forces were rejected on the ground of emotional immaturity and that pointed questions are being asked about the effectiveness of our homes and schools. Major General Chisholm of the Canadian Army recently put his diagnostic finger on immaturity as the basic cause of wars and demanded an educational program to free people from blind and unthinking allegiance to false and local loyalties, however revered, and to make possible realistic thinking and planning.[1] One of the most searching and constructive articles, in the opinion of the authors, dealing with management-labor strife is entitled, "Wanted Mature Managers."[2] Similarly, a thoughtful article by a strong friend of labor ends with a plea "for a thorough study of labor's own responsibilities—for a cleaning of its own house, as it were, and for an intellectual and emotional maturity in keeping

with its own physical development."[3] The increasingly critical reaction of large numbers of people to the irresponsible filibustering
and pussyfooting which legislators sometimes engage in and to the
occasional bickering of other public servants suggests hopefully
that we may soon demand maturity in our elected and appointed
officials. In the helping professions—such as psychiatry, psychology,
social work, and the ministry—and in education, maturity is increasingly recognized as essential for the most constructive work. And
most significantly, it is now recognized that in the home it is the
emotional and social maturity of parents that counts most in the
constructive guidance of children. Thus observations from virtually
all fields of human endeavor point to emotional maturity as perhaps
the most significant need of human beings in the modern world.

How very important maturity is becomes clearer when we define
the term and see the many lines of constructive effort which issue
from it. Selekman[2] defines it this way: "The emotionally mature
person is one who accepts unpleasant facts, whatever their genesis,
as concrete situations to be handled rather than hated." This is an
oversimplification, but it does get close to the root of the matter. It
takes little exercise of the imagination to see how many human
situations could be improved, and the participants made happier
and more secure, if they were accepted as challenges to straight
thinking and cooperative effort rather than as occasions of anger,
hatred, and negative emotions which yield no practical solution.
According to recent definitions by Strecker and Appel:

Maturity is a quality of personality that is made up of a number of
elements. It is stick-to-itiveness, the ability to stick to a job, to work on
it, and to struggle through until it is finished, or until one has given all
one has in the endeavor. It is the quality or capacity of giving more
than is asked or required in a given situation. It is the characteristic
that enables others to count on one; thus it is reliability. Persistence is
an aspect of maturity: persistence to carry out a goal in the face of difficulties. Endurance enters into the concept of maturity: the endurance
of difficulties, unpleasantness, discomfort, frustration, hardship. The
ability to size things up, make one's own decisions, is a characteristic of

maturity. This implies a considerable amount of independence. A mature person is not dependent unless ill. Maturity includes determination, a will to achieve and succeed, a will to life. Of course, maturity represents the capacity to cooperate: to work with others, to work in an organization and under authority. The mature person is flexible, can defer to time, persons, circumstances. He can show tolerance, he can be patient, and above all he has the qualities of adaptability and compromise. Basically, maturity represents a wholesome amalgamation of two things: (1) dissatisfaction with the status quo, which calls forth aggressive, constructive effort and (2) social concern and devotion. It is morale in the individual.[4]

In very simple terms, a mature and mentally healthy person is one who (1) respects and has confidence in himself and because he knows his true worth wastes no time proving it to himself and others; (2) accepts, works with, and to a large extent enjoys other people; and (3) carries on his work, his play, and his family and social life with confidence and enthusiasm and with a minimum of conflict, fear, or hostility.

How can we educate for maturity, which is so essential for personal stability and social progress? Analyses of the growth experiences of those who are eminently happy, successful and mature, and of those who are burdened with indecision, worry, dependency, and frustration, enable us to chart the essential features of an educational program. It becomes clear at once that educating for maturity cannot be accomplished by instruction in the usual sense. Feelings of confidence and strength and habits of friendliness and cooperation cannot be induced by talking about them. They must be built out of the living material of daily experience.[5] It is clear that we shall have to encompass the childhood and adolescent years if we are to understand and foster the elements in a child's total experience of family, school, and community living that contribute to the development of emotional maturity in the adult individual. In educating for maturity, as in a painting or a symphony, it is the total effect that counts; nothing is neutral or insignificant.

The Significance of the Home and Parental Guidance

The importance of the home has become more fully appreciated as we have learned more about the instinctive endowments and emotional needs of people. Normally home is a place where an individual feels he belongs. Whatever difficulties and frustrations he may meet elsewhere, he expects to be accepted and liked by members of his family and to be counted as one of that intimate group even though he sometimes fails to conform to what is expected of him. For people who are emotionally dependent and immature, home often becomes the place of escape and protection in a way that is unhealthy. But even under such circumstances they are more nearly healthy and secure than they would be without the emotional support which home supplies. To educate for maturity we obviously must begin in the home for the home has the earliest and most constant effect on personality development and on the formation of lifetime patterns of behavior.

The meaning which home has for growing children depends initially on the relationships which the father and mother have with each other. If there is genuine affection, mutual respect, true pleasure in the person and personality of the other, and something approximating equality in the sharing of privileges and responsibilities, an interpersonal atmosphere is created in which the budding personalities of children can thrive. If instead of understanding and mutual regard and pleasure, there are friction, tension, and animosity, children suffer no matter how systematically the father and mother may try to observe psychological principles in the guidance of their children.

The full potentialities of the home for the personality development of children is realized only through the parents' understanding of children's needs and their ability to meet them. Whether children grow up to full maturity or become arrested at some immature level depends on how well the parents set the stage and insure the step-by-step maturing of emotional and social behavior.

The brief discussion which follows will emphasize the dynamic factors in family living which contribute to mental health and will serve to outline a program of parental guidance.

It is clear from a large body of clinical experience that the re-action patterns which offer the greatest hazards to mental health are: (1) strong or frequent fear and anxiety; (2) withdrawal from people and retreat into fantasy; (3) strong feelings of guilt or shame, from whatever source derived; (4) intense and prolonged hostility, whether expressed through undue aggression or con-verted into neurotic symptoms. Home situations and relationships which tend to develop these patterns in children are therefore to be avoided or corrected if already present.

Stated positively, the primary goals of mental health in family living are the establishment of a basic sense of well-being and security and the progressive development of all the natural endow-ments and interests of children so that they can understand, accept, integrate, and use them with increasing satisfaction and social competence. To insure such growth the following secondary goals are likewise essential: (1) the consistent development of self-confi-dence and a genuine sense of adequacy; (2) the development of sociability and habits of cooperation which enable children to enter into the give-and-take of family life and prepare them to participate effectively in work, play, and citizenship; (3) the emotional and psychosexual maturing which is necessary for mental health and for successful marriage and parenthood.

ESTABLISHING BASIC SECURITY

A child's initial confidence and sense of well-being is built upon the security of parental affection. The gentleness with which the mother picks up the baby and moves him about, the tender care with which she meets his simple needs, and the pleasantness of her voice and expression during all her ministrations form an emo-tional atmosphere which is quite as real as the air the baby breathes. A baby needs love as much as he needs food, and the love that helps him most in getting his start in the world is the love that prompts and accompanies the systematic care by which the mother satisfies his need for food, comfort, movement, and sleep. This is most necessary before the young child can start growing up wholesomely. A repotted plant starts to grow only after its roots have taken firm hold in the new soil around it. If it is moved repeatedly before it gets established or if it is deprived of sunlight, it is apt to die or at least to become dwarfed. Similarly, a child has to be established in his daily routine and have about him an atmosphere of warmth and affection before his personality can grow. As Ribble has shown, loving affects his capacity to respond to objects, to food and vitamins, to human relations, noises and language, thought, ideas and future goals based on past experience.[6] How very true this is, is dramatically and convincingly shown in Bender's study of 6,000 children who in the first two or three years were cared for in baby homes, nurseries, and other institutions:

The structure of the personality of these children we see is characteristically undeveloped. The first processes of the unfolding of the budding personality did not occur in the early weeks or months of life in the warm environment of the daily care of the same mother person. In the early months of life the brain itself and nerve tracts to and from the outside world are growing, and physiological patterns are being set and established by being lived. The organism is perceiving the outer world both physical and social for the first time, and the individual gradually becomes aware of people and things about him by virtue of their influence on him and his influence on them. It is absolutely imperative that these processes shall all occur in the secure environ of a human relationship. This is the only matrix upon which the pattern of human life can grow. The pattern of growing, of learning, of self-expression, of trial and error, of reaching forward into the future and looking backward into experience is only possible by living these experiences with a human being. . . . From this experience must grow the identification processes which enable the child to utilize his inborn capacities to identify himself with other persons and their causes and problems, to relate himself to others, to work with them, to give and take. This is the source of the democratic way of living. Also from this identification process comes the capacity to have understanding and judgment of situations and concepts, the difference between right and wrong, social aims, the value of the individual, the social concept of time which involves learning from the past and living into the future, and the capacity for symbolic self-expression which is the basis of all higher learning, art, culture and science.

Children who have had no early mothering experience for one or two or three years are not able to accept the experience when it is offered them. . . . They all appear retarded, untrained, impulsive, unpatterned in their behavior. As they grow older and the demands of society upon them increase, their behavior becomes progressively more asocial. . . . The worst of it is that they can never make up for the experiences they have lost. Their personality will never develop beyond the infantile stage where it was first deprived. . . . So far we have found no educational or psychotherapeutic method whereby unpatterned, impulsive behavior can be modified into organized or patterned behavior. The child is driven by impulses which demand immediate satisfaction. . . . Once the early childhood has been passed without adequate opportunity for normal relationships and personality development, the organization of the personality and retardation in development seem to permit no modification.[7]

While the child greatly needs the consistent love of the mother or mother substitute, the mother must have such a degree of maturity as will enable her to love the child for his own sake and allow him the freedom to become an independent individual. The exploitation of children by parents who use them as outlets for their own emotions or as a source of selfish satisfaction is the basis of an amazing amount of psychoneurosis. Parents should enjoy their children but not at the expense of the children's development. Undue dependence on parents not only is frustrating to the child, but soon becomes disappointing to the parent and in due course of time the dependent child responds with strong hostility, open or repressed.[8] The most violent intrafamilial hatreds which the authors have ever seen expressed are those of adults whose overdependence on parents had been deliberately fostered. The statement that children need an atmosphere of affection as much as they need air or food, carries with it the implication that this is something freely available to them but is not imposed in a way that prevents or arrests normal development.

In addition to a continuing and satisfying relation with the mother the young child needs plenty of opportunity to get satisfactions in accordance with his developing interests and changing needs. The primary role of the parents is to observe the child's changing and growing interests and to insure that adequate satisfaction is obtained at each level and that the child progresses normally through the natural succession of interests and activities which make growth and maturity possible.

LEARNING TO UNDERSTAND, ACCEPT, INTEGRATE, AND USE CONSTRUCTIVELY NATURAL ENDOWMENTS AND INTERESTS

While it is of great interest to most people to watch the budding consciousness and the changing interests of young children, many parents do not observe these changes carefully enough or understand their significance well enough to guide their children in accordance with their psychological needs. Instead they rely on crutches, imposing on children the rules of thumb which have been handed down for generations or in some instances training them strictly in accordance with some new theory which pleases their fancy. In either case, they miss the opportunity to understand the real desires, needs, and strivings of their children; and without this understanding they often fail to foster and direct the children's growth through all the stages necessary to achieve full maturity and integration. Consequently, development is arrested through the "short circuiting" of growth processes and neurosis and other forms of immaturity result. We can here discuss only those interests and activities which are most important in the development of children's personalities and which are most likely to be ignored or handled in a way that fixes attention at an immature level and prevents full growth and integration.

For good reasons the young child has much interest in putting things into his mouth and sucking on them. At birth the mouth is the most highly developed part of his body and he has better voluntary control over the oral muscle than the other skeletal muscles. Also the mucocutaneous junctions of the mouth, like those of other body orifices, are more largely supplied with sensory nerve endings than are the skin and mucous membrane generally. Thus sucking, through the friction and muscle activity involved, not only expedites the taking of food and stimulates breathing and blood circulation, but is a very pleasant activity as well. In fact, it is the baby's major satisfaction, and the baby who may suck as much as he pleases is usually satisfied and contented.

Culturally, sucking has been accepted as a means of taking food. But children who do not get enough satisfaction while taking their food and who thereupon suck their thumbs or other objects are often scolded, punished, and deprived, with the result that their anger, hostility, and anxiety are unduly aroused. Their need for solace then drives them to seek further satisfaction by sucking more, and the habit tends to become fixed. If no attention is paid to it, except to provide a small-holed nipple for taking water or food, and if the mother continues to be as loving as ever and provides additional opportunities for play, the habit is given up, sometimes quickly, sometimes gradually, and the child moves on to more mature activities better prepared to enjoy them because he has had his sucking satisfactions.

As infantile sucking is given up for more mature self-feeding with spoon and cup, the new method of eating takes on emotional as well as nutritional significance. While children "mouth" their food partly for pleasure, social satisfactions are soon linked with this pleasure, particularly if mealtime is made pleasant and if the child receives the warm approval of his parents when he eats in a grown-up way. The surest way to establish good eating habits and to give them pleasurable associations is to accept the child's appetite as the best indicator of his food needs, as to both quantity and kind, and in a cheerful, matter-of-fact way to place before the child small quantities of food which are replenished on request. When parents do not trust the child's appetite as a sound indicator of need, are anxious, or make eating an occasion for a battle of wills, the child is likely to respond with anxiety or hostility and the gastrointestinal tract easily becomes an avenue for the release of nervous tension. Gastrointestinal disturbances in the later years are often found to have their roots in parental anxiety, overfeeding, and disciplinary use of the feeding situation.

Another natural interest of every young child, which is fraught with danger to mental health because of the cultural taboos which surround it, is his interest in the various parts of his body, and particularly in the organs and processes of elimination. Once he has pretty well solved the problem of getting food and has begun to distinguish "me" from "not me," he is likely for a little while to be acutely interested in the elimination of body waste. If parents and nurses accept this as a natural interest entirely devoid of moral implications, answer the child's questions simply and directly, and encourage normal control of body function by approving and praising him when he uses the customary facilities, the child, after a brief period of fairly intense interest in elimination, moves on to other and more social interests with confidence and eager expectation. On the other hand, shaming, punishing, and depriving the child on account of his curiosity or his failure immediately to control his body functions are apt to have several undesirable results. Such methods and attitudes tend to prolong anal interests unduly, to induce negativistic attitudes toward parents and others, and to prevent the establishment of hygienic habits. These behavior patterns may continue into adulthood. Chronic constipation, stinginess and inordinate emphasis on material values, and restricted compulsive personalities are often traceable to this source.

Another natural interest about which parents find it hard to be objective is the young child's interest in his genital organs and his curiosity about birth and sex differences. In practice, sex education should not be divorced from the rest of a child's education. But we are obliged to give special attention to it because it has so often been neglected or woefully mishandled, with the result that it has been a major source of emotional maladjustment. Guilt about sexual ideas, wishes, or practices is not only at the root of many marital difficulties but is often a contributing factor in psychoneuroses and other mental disorders. These ill effects are largely the result of the unhealthy repression caused by the strong social taboos of a moral and religious nature which have surrounded sex in our Western culture for several hundred years. A prurient curiosity and a public thirst for scandal are other outcroppings of this campaign of silence and shame. We shall see the dawning of a new day in mental hygiene when all parents can accept sex as a fact and a force in human life which is quite as worthy as sight, hearing, or any other faculty and is to be understood and intelligently controlled to the advantage of a richer personal experience and a wholesome social life.

At some time in the preschool years all children discover that the genital zone is particularly sensitive to touch and that touching or handling is pleasurable, just as sucking was formerly found pleasurable. This interest, if accepted by the parent as natural and normal, soon runs its course and the child is the better equipped for the next step forward by virtue of having made this discovery and obtained its attendant satisfactions. If the child is shamed, scolded, punished, or made to feel "bad" or "naughty," it gives the interest and habit, if it has become a habit, undue importance. Moreover, partly as solace and partly as retribution, the child uses masturbatory activity more frequently and continues it longer if punitive or corrective measures are used. In all psychiatric literature it is virtually impossible to find a single case in which masturbation became a fixed and excessive habit in early childhood unless the child had been shamed or punished for it or had been so deprived emotionally that he had recourse to it as a substitutive source of satisfaction.

When it comes to giving children essential information regarding the origin of life, parents are clearly in the most natural and advantageous position, but strong cultural taboos have stood in the way for generations. Fortunately, these taboos are weakening and an increasing number of parents are able to be fairly objective and frank in answering children's questions. Except where shame has been associated with sex in their own minds, they can first tell children, in answer to their questions, quite simply and naturally that babies grow in the body of the mother until they are big enough and strong enough to be born and later, as the children become interested, can inform them regarding the father's role in procreation. Parents' fears that the child will ask endless questions are usually without foundation for the small child is usually content with the main fact that satisfies his curiosity. Nothing is so powerful in fixing in a child's mind and emotions a wholesome attitude toward sex as loving, respectful, and truthful handling of his questions. It strengthens his sense of security and gives him a feeling of relatedness to his parents. On the other hand, he is bewildered and confused by stories of being brought down from the clouds by the stork, pulled out of the doctor's medicine case, or plucked from the gooseberry bush, or by other local myths of "where babies come from." Frankness and honesty within the limits of his understanding lead him to associate sex with love and home, and the emotional concomitant is one of joy and tenderness rather than of shame and guilt.

It is important also that both boys and girls should understand the essential differences in the sexes and that they should be able to identify themselves with their own sex group. When there are both boys and girls in a family and the differences in age are not too great, children tend to observe each other and accept the fact of sex difference without much difficulty. The discovery of sex difference, however, is fairly frequently somewhat of a problem to the little girl. Because the male genitals are more external than the female, it appears to the observing little girl that the boy has something that she lacks and she doesn't like this. To assure her that all little girls and mothers are like her and that all boys and fathers are like her brother definitely helps her to accept this difference. Care should be taken also to provide the girl with as many privileges as her brother or she will tend to protest against her feminine role and strive to develop a masculine psychology with the possible end result of spinsterhood, marital difficulties, or psychoneurosis.

Thus children progress in the discovery and use of their body parts, particularly when their parents are able emotionally to accept their children's curiosity, explorations, and practices and to permit them full satisfaction at each stage. Children pass from one stage to another much more easily if they have attained their full measure of satisfaction in each. A lack of satisfaction tends to arrest emotional development at the phase at which frustration occurs. Parental approval and guidance and progressively satisfying experience go far in establishing in children a genuine sense of well-being and strong feelings of personal worth, which are so essential for emotional stability and mental health.

DEVELOPING SELF-CONFIDENCE AND A SENSE OF ADEQUACY

Simultaneously with interests which are closely connected with physical functions and bodily satisfactions, children have an increasing need for self-activity that requires the use of their total musculature and relates them to the world of things and people. Even the infant needs opportunity for self-activity, so that he can learn early to get satisfactions out of his own efforts and not become too dependent on others for care or emotional support.[8] Opportunities for self-activity cannot be provided too early. Even in the first weeks loose-fitting clothes which permit the baby to kick and move his arms freely give him a chance to begin to feel his own powers. Placing the bottle on a pillow beside him so that he can learn to hold it, encouraging him to push his arms through sleeves rather than having them pulled through for him, allowing him a chance to handle the spoon and cup, and providing opportunity to explore all corners of his home, to handle everyday objects, and to dig in the earth give the young child a succession of enjoyed experiences in which he discovers new powers and develops new skills. Every new success and every additional satisfaction provide stimulation for further effort. The common adage that nothing succeeds like success is eminently true in child development. Children become self-reliant as they see themselves succeeding in doing the things they try to do. For maximal benefit children must be allowed to work at their tasks without being interrupted with warnings and premature corrections.

Parental approval and affection shown during children's many trials and errors add much to their feelings of confidence and help to build up their faith in their own ability. Thus it is desirable to reward with approval their successes—and even their stumbling efforts—and largely to ignore their mistakes and failures. This makes it all pleasant and stimulates them to try again.

Sometimes simple instruction, largely by example, is also necessary and helpful when children are actively interested to learn a new skill. With a small amount of showing at the right moment, particularly if praised in anticipation of success, they learn quickly how to pull on clothes, to hold a cup, climb stairs, put toys in order, throw a ball, and master the hundreds of other skills involved in growing up. As the warp and woof are woven into a fabric, so children's successes and the living faith and love of their parents combine to build their confidence.

DEVELOPING SOCIABILITY AND HABITS OF COOPERATION

In the course of this early training parents help or hinder children's social development and foster habits either of cooperation or opposition. They must be careful to avoid pressing children too hard and forcing them to do too many things against their wishes.

When pressed too much the only recourse children have to prove their individuality is to say "no." Parents who are uninformed on the subject or have not disciplined themselves have little regard for the personalities of small children and usually underestimate their ability to make choices and manage their affairs. Such parents tend to give orders and expect to be obeyed. Children whose parents characteristically have this attitude may develop habits of negative response. This is particularly true if parents show a great deal of excitement or anger when met with an emphatic "no." Parents who make as pleasant as possible the things they ask their children to do, and who allow or encourage them to work at these tasks without rigid insistence on immediate results, help them to develop a cooperative spirit.

There is substantial clinical evidence that people who in their adult years are uncooperative and antagonistic—husbands and wives who quarrel excessively and workers and managers who cannot get along agreeably—were emotionally deprived, harshly disciplined, socially restricted, or subjected to unfavorable comparison in the family group. Forced feeding, forced attention to toilet needs, extreme restrictions on play, frequent and violent punishment, and other forms of pressure are commonly found in their histories. Children develop patterns of hostility and overaggression not from too much consideration of their needs but rather as a defense against domination or as compensation for feelings of inferiority. Children need a large balance of satisfactions as over against their deprivations. The security of being loved constantly, the satisfactions obtained from interesting play and other self-initiated activities and experience of give-and-take in the family group provide the basis on which cooperative relationships can be built. Children who are sure of their parents' love and trust and who enjoy a wealth of daily activities with them can accept some restrictions without becoming seriously upset or fundamentally hostile. They can effectively discipline themselves to conform to parental standards of sociability and cooperation.

In the course of their habit-training and family living it is inevitable that children will sometimes become angry and show marked hostility to their parents. The parents' handling of this is very important, as it either aids the children's maturing or tends to fix habits of hostility and aggression at a childish level. If parents can accept such displays of negative feeling as natural and inevitable and allow the angry child to talk it out, the anger subsides very quickly. If, on the other hand, parents respond with unwarranted excitement and anger, or by punishing or scolding, the child's anger and hostility is accentuated and, if repeated often enough, becomes a fixed pattern of behavior.

The hostility of young children is usually accompanied by wishes to destroy, but such wishes are quickly dissipated if the parent does not respond in kind. To illustrate, a two-year-old during a moment of anger at her father because he did not grant her wish at the moment blurted out, with two-year-old vehemence, "Daddy, if I had you in the cellar I would chop you up and throw you in the furnace and shut the door on you." Feeling quite safe and accepting the outburst as natural and normal, her father responded with a simple, unemotional, "You would." The child's fury subsided in less than a minute; when she went to bed a little later she said, "Daddy, I want to give you three kisses tonight" (instead of the usual one). The secret was in making her anger of no account and keeping faith in spite of the momentary outburst. Blaming and punishing young children for their destructive wishes only drive the hostility inward where it festers and comes out in neurotic symptoms or is stored up in mounting resentment and aggression.

The first three years of life represent a period of almost constant struggle or conflict between the child's instinctual urges and desires and the demands of society, represented mainly by mother and father, for the control and repression of them. The infant must increasingly adapt himself to mature society with its insistent repetition of "no." Love, desire for approval, acceptance, and security are inevitably mingled with anger, resentment, hostility, jealousy, and rage. The ultimate price paid for acceptance and love is compliance with the parents' demands and abandonment or repression of immediate satisfactions.

Children must, of course, learn to discipline their natural impulses and integrate them into their ego and superego. They must develop a conscience and moral sense and be able to relate themselves acceptably to other people. In the past it has been rather naïvely assumed that children can be made morally and socially responsible by teaching them concepts of right and wrong and of socially acceptable behavior and by making personal demands upon them for achievement in these areas. We now know that children learn to discipline their own impulses and to set acceptable moral and social goals for themselves in the concrete rather than in the abstract. They grow up morally and socially by having a pleasant, satisfying experience with someone whom they love and trust, in short, by hero worship, the "hero" being most commonly the father or mother. They then think and feel themselves to be like the "hero" and consciously strive to become more and more like him. With a high estimate of the hero's personal worth and a strong feeling of affection for him, the child's emotions and wishes operate consciously and unconsciously to increase his own likeness to his ideal. It is almost entirely through this process of identification that children develop conscience and standards of conduct and come to place high value on personal integrity. Many of the group of persons known clinically as having psychopathic personalities were found never to have had a warm, congenial, and sustained relationship with a person with whom they could establish an identification and thereby achieve an adequate sense of personal worth and a satisfactory mode of life. Like water which never rises above its source, parents and teachers cannot induce a child to develop beyond the degree of maturity and virtue which they themselves have achieved.

To help children grow up socially, it is necessary to provide them with companions of about their own age from the time they are two or three years old, particularly if they do not have brothers and sisters. Children learn sociability and consideration for others largely by living with other children. There is no substitute for this. Children who live entirely with adults until they go to school have a definite handicap. They must rub elbows with others, take some knocks and give some knocks, sometimes dominate and sometimes submit, if they are to learn to play and work together easily and with satisfaction. In this as in habits of self-activity, a chance to work it out themselves, plus parental approval when they do well, is the best procedure. This is true for older children and adolescents as well as for those who are younger.

EMOTIONAL AND PSYCHOSEXUAL MATURING

Family living can make another significant contribution to the maturing of both boys and girls: it can insure such progression in their love attachments and emotional growth as will make it possible for them to select and win mates and to succeed in marriage and parenthood.

The emotional maturing of the boy is a little different from that of the girl. The boy needs the love of his mother to establish his basic security and prepare him for subsequent feelings of intimacy with women. He requires a large amount of friendly experience with his father to enable him to wean himself from the more dependent relationship to the mother and to enable him to identify himself with his father and to strive to develop manly interests and virtues. Both the psychological weaning process and the achieving of manliness are further fostered by association with boys of his own age during the preadolescent period and all his previous experience of affection helps to prepare him for selecting a mate and maintaining a congenial relationship with her. If the child has had almost no friendly or loving contact with the father in early infancy, it may become an acute problem for the child to accept him later, since he appears as a competitor for the mother's love and, as such, arouses the child's jealousy and hostility. In such cases, the child can accept the father into his world only by repressing his negative feelings. This conflict when severe and unresolved is a major source of psychoneurosis in both children and adults, and when it leads to overdependence on the mother and complete failure to identify with the father or a father substitute, it may result in character disorder and severe problems in social adjustment.

The girl, like the boy, needs a mother's love to establish her basic security, but she tends to become very much interested in her father at an early age and not infrequently delights in teasing her mother about this. It is very valuable to the girl to have enough experience of friendliness and intimacy with her father to allow her to develop normal interest in boys as she grows older and later to choose and love a mate. But in turning to her father for affection she must not turn completely away from her mother, for she needs the continued friendly experience with her mother to enable her to accept her as an ideal. Unless she is fond of her mother, she will not strive to become like her and will not develop an essentially feminine psychology. If her relationship to her mother is marked by antagonism rather than love, the girl is in danger of rejecting the mother's role, of wishing she were a boy, and striving to become like boys. This trend, if developed to a marked degree, complicates her later adjustments in family life or may even develop her aggressiveness to such a degree that she has difficulty in getting along with people in other relationships.

Every boy and girl needs both a father and a mother and a group of companions for his or her emotional maturing. Each needs the love of the parent of the same sex to make acceptable the characteristic role of persons of that sex, and each needs a continuing feeling of affection for the parent of the opposite sex to establish a pattern of intimate response to persons of the opposite sex. Each needs the group for the further development of these patterns and for a proving ground. Neither boys nor girls can mature fully or take their rightful places in the adult world without going through these changes of love-interest and attachment.

In connection with the emotional and psychosexual maturing of boys and girls opportunities should be given them to acquire some knowledge of the physical and emotional aspects of puberty and of their subsequent heterosexual interests.

Parents who have learned to answer their children's early questions frankly and with ease have little trouble explaining to their adolescent children the nature and meaning of their sexual maturing and the changes in social interests which then take place, but as Laycock has noted, many parents cannot do so.[9] Girls should of course be told the meaning of menstruation, preferably in advance to forestall the risk of fright and worry, and should be advised as to the hygienic measures to follow. Boys should understand their sexual maturing so that they will not be frightened by feelings of tension or by nocturnal emissions. Masturbation should be viewed as a habit associated with sexual growth and adolescent sexual tensions and should not be charged with moral and religious implications. Actually, unless indulged in excessively, there is no evidence of harmful results from the habit, aside from the psychological harm caused by the feelings of guilt induced by cultural taboos or by actual misinformation given unwisely by parents, teachers, or others in the false hope of scaring youth into giving up the habit. Serious injury to the mental health of many children and adolescents has been done by such misguided efforts.

Parents should not only see that boys and girls understand the physiological maturing which equips them for biological parenthood, but also help them to understand—what they are more interested in—the emotional and social significance of their interest in a certain person or persons of the opposite sex and the reasons for periodic excitations of a physical and emotional nature in relation to such persons. Only with understanding can they learn to manage their love interests and sexual excitations in ways that are healthy and conducive to proper mate selection and marital adjustment and meanwhile pursue their education, work, and social interests without the all-too-common frustrations of guilt and fear. Not only do wise parents consistently associate sex with love and respect for personality as they inform their children about the process of procreation and adolescent maturing; they also wholesomely interpret sexual relations as a major and mutually satisfying way in which a man and wife express their love for each other.

The best educators for maturity are parents who have achieved marital happiness themselves and who are able to share with their children the knowledge, the affection, the mutual respect, and the methods of give-and-take by which they live their daily lives. How they handle money, how they live with their neighbors, how they meet disappointments and solve problems, how they sense each other's moods and meet each other's needs, how they make up after a quarrel, how they reinforce and inspire each other—these are all priceless parts of the living heritage they give their children. These are the things out of which the children in turn construct their purposes, mold their patterns of thought and feeling, and fashion their spirit.

Educating for Marriage and Family Living

We shall hardly be able to educate for maturity through family living unless we first educate potential mothers and fathers so that they can play these roles satisfactorily. It is a well-accepted fact that the most significant factors in the development of adult personality in all its individual, moral, and social aspects are the feeling and action patterns which become established in the early years of family living. It is equally well established that maladjustments between husbands and wives who have become fathers and mothers are one of the chief sources of personality disorders, neuroses, and social maladjustments, and that parents are able to foster psychological maturity in their children only when they are well adjusted in their relationships to each other.[9] Consequently, anything which helps to put marriage on a sound basis will contribute materially to the mental health of the next generation.

There is great need in this country for an extensive program of education for marriage and family living. Admittedly, young men and women who are very immature or whose personalities have been partly warped will not correct their personality patterns merely through a course of study, but a large majority of essentially normal young people do get from well-designed and effectively conducted courses in marriage and family living, a fuller appreciation of the psychological principles involved in the inevitable interplay of personalities and sounder knowledge of and more wholesome attitudes toward the sex side of marriage which will prepare them to adjust with greater objectivity and confidence to their role as parent and spouse. A record of the questions asked of many who have given courses on marriage and family living reveals an amazing amount of uniformity. There is always interest in a discussion of how love develops and matures, of the values which men and women expect to get out of marriage, of personality assets and liabilities, of the physical, intellectual, and spiritual aspects of sex, health, heredity, recreation, and religion, of the understanding and guidance of children, of the adjustments of "in-laws," the management of finances, and virtually every other aspect of family living. There is interest in courtship and the early days of marriage and also in the understanding and techniques required for continuing adjustments.

Some young people need and want individual counsel and this should be provided. But the majority express a preference for group study because it is less personal and enables them to maintain their independence and at the same time to reap the advantage of the questions and ideas of fellow members. They point out that what one does not think of, another does, and so they acquire better perspective.

There is some question as to the auspices under which such courses can best be conducted. It appears to the authors that the more we get down to fundamentals in education the less we shall need to divide people into separate groups in order to educate them.

But in view of the difficulty in achieving objectivity in discussions of sex, religion, and morals, there is some advantage in working with a fairly homogeneous group. It is perhaps partly for this reason that education for marriage and family living has been conducted most often under church auspices. At the same time, many communities are sufficiently homogeneous to permit such courses to be offered in the secondary schools without endangering the cherished beliefs of the boys and girls or of their parents. And in so far as differences in religious beliefs and social customs have been accepted without evaluation, a respectful yet realistic discussion of these differences is definitely educational and promotes intellectual and social maturity.

There is still strong resistance on the part of school administrators to the inclusion in the secondary school curriculum of courses in marriage and family living. This was shown dramatically by an effort to introduce into high schools a book designed to help the boys and girls understand themselves and improve their relationships with others. Consistently, school administrators in three states, where experimental efforts were made, and several prospective publishers insisted that the chapter dealing with marriage and sex be eliminated on the ground that it was "dynamite." The chapter "What Are Children Like" was quite acceptable. Ironically enough, in one school where there was strong opposition to inclusion of information on premarital sex education, eight girls at the time of their graduation were involved in out-of-wedlock pregnancies. In spite of such resistance, however, there is a growing trend toward including education in family living in the curricula of our secondary and higher schools of learning. An increasing number of communities, though still a small minority, have become sufficiently impressed with the need for this to undertake a communitywide program in family education.[10]

The schools have no monopoly on the neglect of opportunities for family education. A majority of doctors who complain of the dire effects of ignorance on the health and personality of mates and parents have done nothing to remedy the situation except through individual treatment, often after it is too late. Social agencies and social workers have participated very little in community-wide education which would be helpful to families, notwithstanding the fact that the need for education for family living is obvious from their records and those of the divorce courts and guidance clinics. Similar evidence is provided by the many family difficulties which never come to the attention of professional people but which mar the happiness and block the maturity of the children exposed to them. If we are going to educate consistently for maturity through family living, our schools and social agencies, our psychiatrists, psychologists, social workers, and pediatricians, and all thoughtful people will have to do more than they have done in the past to prepare young people, married and unmarried, for family life.

The promotion of family education by the National Council on Family Relations, the Home Economics Education Service of the United States Office of Education, the Committee on Marriage and the Home of the Federal Council of the Churches of Christ in America, and local efforts by various organizations are commendable, but still reach only a minority of American homes.

Books which have contributed to the preparation of many people for family living are listed at the end of this chapter (see *For Further Reading*).*

Parent Education

Equally great is the need for more extensive and better parent education. Most parents, even those who are fairly well informed and whose attitudes are essentially constructive, would benefit by opportunities to learn more about child growth and development

---

* In the Circulating Branch of the New York Public Library, books in the classification which includes philosophy and sociology as well as marriage, family relations, child training, and psychology, averaged five readers last year. The circulation of books in this classification is increasing.

and the fuller significance of their parent roles. Many good books for parents have appeared in recent years (see *For Further Reading*). *Parents' Magazine* starting from scratch twenty years ago has arisen to a circulation of more than a million. The Child Study Association of America throughout the past twenty-four years has actively promoted the better education of parents. Some state departments of education and a few city school systems promote parent education fairly actively and in rural areas the extension divisions of departments of agriculture reach approximately 500,000 parents each year with courses or pamphlet material. Valuable as these efforts are they reach but a minority of parents.

Programs must be extended much further if all or a majority of parents are to be reached, and more attention will have to be given to cultural influences and the significance of emotionally charged attitudes. As Frank has pointed out, we would probably get farther by discussions of the cultural sources of our numerous ideas about children and the expected roles of parents than by attempting to impart directly the findings of social and psychological science.[11] As Plant has stressed, parent education must be in terms of people living together, in terms of what they mean to each other and not what they do for each other. There must be sensitive recognition as to when the parent is ready for this or that sort of information or help and we must be concerned to create in parents a faith in their ability to do a good job and accept the fact that some knowledge must come to them within a framework of "those things we accept without the need of proof."[12]

We have little indication of what constitutes the best media for parent education. Direct information can, of course, be given by radio, informal address, or printed material. Discussion under skilled leadership is probably most effective in dealing with attitudes and in reassuring parents as to their ability to play their role well. They discover that other parents have similar problems in the home guidance of children; they are apt to see more forcefully the significance of their own attitudes and conduct and are encouraged to study the *cause* of children's behavior and to substitute intelligent control and guidance for emotional appeal and personal domination. The limitation of the discussion method is chiefly that there are insufficient numbers of adequately trained personnel.

The authors have no last word on educating for maturity. People must first be convinced of the need for maturity to solve the complicated problems of interpersonal and international relations in our modern world. They must then utilize the potentialities of family living to insure opportunities for children to mature progressively from infancy to adulthood. Parents play the leading role in the drama of life in which maturity is attained or blocked. When enough people become convinced of the vital significance of the parents' role and when all who have knowledge and skill are ready to contribute their aid, we shall be ingenious enough to devise ways of carrying out an effective program. Once we are agreed on the desirability of the goal and equipped with adequate knowledge of personality development, we can make constructive use of this knowledge, just as we have adopted public health measures to build physical health. Churches and other community agencies should do more and all professional groups should assist, but if the program is to be carried out on a nationwide scale, the schools will have to extend greatly their work in family-life education as well as to foster by direct means the mental health and maturity of the children under instruction.

REFERENCES

1. Chisholm, G. B. The reestablishment of peacetime society. (*In* The Psychiatry of Enduring Peace and Social Progress, William Alanson White Memorial Lectures.) Psychiatry 9:1–35, February 1946.

2. Selekman, B. J. Wanted mature managers. Harvard Business Rev. 24:228–244, Winter 1946.

3. Wolfson, T. Labor's coming of age. New York, New York Society for Ethical Culture, 1946.

4. Strecker, E. A., and K. E. Appel. Psychiatry in modern warfare. New York, Macmillan, 1945.

5. Preston, G. H.   The substance of mental health.   New York, Farrar & Rinehart, 1943.

6. Ribble, M. A.   The rights of infants.   New York, Columbia University Press, 1943.

7. Bender, L.   There is no substitute for family life.   Child Study 23:74–77, Spring 1946.

8. Levy, D. M.   Maternal over-protection, chapters IV and V, p. 53–100.   New York, Columbia University Press, 1943.

9. Laycock, S. R.   How parents hinder adolescents' adjustments to the opposite sex.   Understanding the Child 14:35–39, April 1945.

10. Education for family living.   Annual Report of the Superintendent of Schools, Highland Park, Michigan, 1945.

    The Box Elder County (Utah) Community Program of Education for Home and Family Life.   Salt Lake City, Utah State Department of Education, 1945.

11. Frank, L. K.   What is ahead in orthopsychiatry (Round Table, 1946).   Am. J. Orthopsychiat. 17:5–8, January 1947.

12. Plant, J. S.   The vital need for parent education; an address before the parent education conference, May 1946 (unpublished).

FOR FURTHER READING: EDUCATION FOR FAMILY LIVING

Bowman, H.   Marriage preparation must be modernized.   Ment. Hyg. 30:74–82, January 1946.

Duvall, E. M., and R. Hill.   When you marry.   New York, Association Press, 1945.

Exner, M. J.   The sexual side of marriage.   New York, Norton, 1932.

Foster, R. G.   Marriage and family counseling.   New York, McGraw-Hill, 1945.

Gesell, A., and F. L. Ilg.   Infant and child in the culture of today; the guidance of development in home and nursery school.   New York, Harper, 1943.

Groves, R.   Conserving marriage and the family.   New York, Macmillan, 1944.

Groves, R.   Preparation for marriage.   2nd ed.   New York, Emerson Books, 1944.

Levy, J., and R. Monroe.   The happy family.   New York, Knopf, 1938.

Stone, H. and A.   The marriage manual.   New York, Simon & Schuster, 1935.

Strain, F. B.   Sex guidance in family life education; a handbook for the schools.   New York, Macmillan, 1942.

Strecker, E.   Psychiatry speaks to democracy.   Ment. Hyg. 29:591–605, October 1945.

Travis, E. L., and D. W. Baruch.   Personal problems of everyday life.   New York, Appleton-Century, 1941.

Wood, L. F.   Harmony in marriage.   New York, Round Table Press, 1939.

Wright, H.   The sex factor in marriage.   New York, Vanguard, 1931.

FOR FURTHER READING: PARENT EDUCATION

Aldrich, A. C. and M. M. Babies are human beings. New York, Macmillan, 1942.

Baruch, D. W. Parents can be people; a primer for and about parents. New York, Appleton-Century, 1944.

Education for better parenthood. Baltimore Bull. Educ., Winter 1945.

Gruenberg, S. M. We the parents. New York, Harper, 1939.

Isaacs, S. The nursery years. New York, Vanguard, 1937.

De Schweinitz, K. Growing up. 2nd ed. New York, Macmillan, 1935.

Senn, M. J. E., and P. K. Newill. All about feeding children. Garden City, N. Y., Doubleday, 1944.

Spock, B. Common sense book of baby and child care. New York, Duell, Sloan & Pearce, 1946.

Strain, F. B. New patterns in sex teaching. New York, Appleton-Century, 1941.

Taylor, K. W. Do adolescents need parents? New York, Appleton-Century, 1938.

Washburn, R. M. Children have their reasons. New York, Appleton-Century, 1942.

Wolf, A. M. The parents' manual; a guide to the emotional development of young children. New York, Simon & Schuster, 1941.

XIII

MENTAL HEALTH IN EDUCATION

Mental hygienists, while holding firmly to the view that family living is the most important influence in the development of character and personality, look to the school hopefully as the second line of defense. The school assumes great importance in the further development of children partly because children normally spend much of their waking lives in school—five or six hours a day, five days a week during eight to ten months each year. A complete discussion of mental health in education would require a book such as Ryan's *Mental Health through Education*.[1] We can here discuss briefly only the most important ways in which mental health can be promoted in and through education.

The modern disciplines of psychiatry, psychology and social work, and the mental hygiene movement which largely has emanated from them, have done much to restore to education its etymological meaning; they have focused attention on the endowments and potentialities of children and on the need to "draw out" or develop these into patterns of behavior and personality that will be individually satisfying and socially effective. The more we have learned about the immediate psychological needs of children and the social demands that are made of them as they grow to adulthood, the more obvious it has become that education should focus upon and develop the potential resources of individual children in ways that fit them effectively for work, family living, and citizenship.

Learning is one of the natural activities of children. Healthy children have a need and desire to acquire information and skills that will give them greater control over their environment. The primary goal of education has always been to provide an opportunity for children to learn in this particular sense. Only recently has it been realized that learning is not the activity of a single function but is bound up with the total personality of the learner and that mental health is as essential to the learning process as intelligence. Moreover, what children learn in school has no value in itself, but only as it can be used and applied in their daily living as children and as adults. Therefore, the school has the responsibility to develop attitudes and resources, a point of view toward themselves and others, an inner balance and security, which make it possible for children to function as human beings in a human society. In short, mental health is an inseparable part of education.

Many aspects of school experience contribute to mental health. Of these, three are particularly important: teachers' personality, aims, skill in human relationships, and understanding of children; the techniques and methods of instruction; the content of the curriculum. Less immediate in their effect on children but basic to the other factors are the viewpoints and policies of administrators and supervisors.

It is almost axiomatic that the mental health of pupils can be promoted consistently only by teachers who are healthy minded and who understand the children they teach. But teachers' mental health like everyone else's is tied up with their status in the community. If public apathy and penuriousness refuse them an adequate income, they will seek more rewarding employment. If they are not respected or accepted in the community, if their value does not receive the recognition given to other professional men—ministers, doctors, dentists, lawyers, and engineers—young people will not turn to teaching as a satisfying way to earn their living. As a matter of fact, since 1941–1942, 280,000 teachers have abandoned the profession; and whereas in that year only one teacher in two hundred failed to meet the legal requirements for a certificate, in 1945–1946, one teacher in eight held an "emergency" permit, and the enrollment in teachers' colleges in 1945–1946 was only 62 per cent of what it was in 1941.

This is a problem the community must face. Certain facts assembled by the National Education Association and cited by Amidon are significant.

The greatest single reason why trained teachers have been leaving the profession in such numbers in the past six years is to better themselves in income and status. . . . It must be borne in mind that workers in private industry without higher education and professional training earn on the average of at least $500.00 more a year than the typical teacher. Further, the 25% increase in median salaries is substantially below increased costs of living for the same period. . . .

A less typical, but very persuasive reason why so many teachers have abandoned the classroom in recent years and are now reluctant to return to it is the lack of respect accorded teaching as a profession. In spite of the high educational standards set by law in many school systems, and in spite of the importance of the teacher's influence on the children entrusted to her, many American communities refuse to accept the teacher as they do their other professional members—the minister, doctor, dentist, lawyer or engineer.

To the harassed taxpayer who argues that, "We can't afford it," some comparisons cited by the National Education Association are revealing. The total annual cost of public elementary and secondary education has for some time remained at about $2,500,000,000, which constituted less than 3 percent of the national income in 1940, and 1.5 percent in 1943. But between 1939 and 1942, our annual national expenditure for beauty treatment and cosmetics increased from $1,800,000,000 to $2,400,000,- 000; for alcoholic beverages, from $3,400,000,000 to $5,200,000,000. Comparable increases in school budgets would mean a new measure of security for the teaching profession; and for our children, a better chance to grow into informed and responsible men and women.[2]

In addition, educational goals must be dynamic enough and sufficiently related to current life situations to challenge teachers and give them a sense of contributing substantially to preparing children and youth to take their places creditably in our modern, complex world. Such goals as Counts lists in *Education and the Promise of America*[3]—education for individuals of maturity and excellence, for a society of free, equal, and cooperative men, for an economy of plenty, a civilization of beauty and grandeur, an enduring civilization and an emerging world community—have a definitely challenging quality and when pursued effectively give teachers a true sense of mission and importance.

The Relation of Teachers to Children

A child's relation to his teacher is of crucial importance to him. Fear, frustration, or hostility induced by his school experience can develop or exaggerate patterns of behavior which will determine his whole life adjustment. Teachers who realize this recognize that one of their chief qualifications is to understand the needs of children and to use methods that develop confidence, trust, and cooperation.

Understanding children involves emotional values which transcend ordinary knowledge of psychological principles. Beneath all human behavior are truths which are so thoroughly verified by experience that they are almost axiomatic, and which if fully accepted by the teachers profoundly influence their relations to children. Prescott elaborated these in an article, "Helping Teachers Understand Children,"[4] later published in book form.[5] We may state them in summary form.

1. *Behavior is caused.* A child's present actions are based upon his past experiences, shaped by his present situation, and influenced by his desires and hopes for the future. This means that a child's behavior can be understood in the light of his past experiences, the meaning which his present situation has for him, and the desires and hopes he has for the future. It also implies that every child is educable, that unacceptable behavior can be changed, and that desirable and effective action can be evoked. This point of view is in sharp contrast to the common conception of child behavior as capricious and impulsive and therefore to be controlled by adults without reference to its causes. Teachers whose relations

to children are based on this concept are able to accept all children emotionally because what a child does is natural under the circumstances. Teachers who believe this cannot seriously reject or blame a child for what he does because his behavior is seen only as a symptom of underlying causes. This does not imply, of course, that undesirable behavior is condoned. Quite the contrary; inappropriate behavior defines some of the teachers' tasks. Understanding teachers try to gauge what conditions, relationships, and experiences have been and are exercising an unwholesome influence on any child's actions, and attempt to arrange or supply others that will neutralize or replace these undesirable influences. This is important for what they experience now will determine what they will be like in the future. This fundamentally optimistic belief is a challenge to teachers to arrange conditions and situations that are appropriate to children's needs, to maintain relations with them that are supporting and reassuring, and so to provide them with experiences that will help them to understand the world and people around them.

2. *All human beings are inherently valuable.* This axiom which lies at the core of our religion and of our American democracy carries with it the implication that each individual has something in him of intrinsic worth which must be respected, encouraged, and put to work for the common good. Teachers who thus accept and value children feel it a privilege to help every child, no matter what his capacities and behavior, to realize his potentialities.

3. *Each individual is unique.* Every child differs from all others in the pattern and combination of the many factors which determine his characteristics and actions at any given moment. Some of these highly variable factors are: body build, physiological stability, available energy for activity, rate of timing of growth, mental capacities, knowledge and skills, attitudes and values, relationships to parents and siblings, status with peers, and way of regarding himself. Because of these many variable factors that influence development and behavior, a child can be understood only by a

person who knows a great deal about his personality as well as his general background and the unusual experiences to which he has been subjected. An understanding teacher recognizes this and continuously gathers and organizes information about the children, uses it to distinguish significant differences between individuals, and attempts to help each boy or girl in ways that subtly take this uniqueness into consideration.

Teachers who wholeheartedly accept these three basic principles and put them into practice in their daily association with children create the psychological conditions necessary for good learning and make it possible for children to identify themselves with their teachers and find security in the pupil-teacher relationships. The mental hygiene implications of this are obvious.

The authors would add a further qualification for teachers, that is, that they themselves should have a good balance of satisfactions as over against their frustrations and deprivations. Teachers must have a certain zest and enthusiasm for living with a ready capacity for enjoyment and a melioristic if not optimistic outlook on life. In the foregoing chapter it was noted that the secret of psychological growth and maturity is in the attainment of adequate satisfactions at each level of development. Other things being equal, teachers who have had that kind of growth experience throughout childhood and adolescence and whose adult relationships are satisfying are best qualified to teach others how to grow and live zestfully. The policy of many school systems in barring married women from teaching is unsound in this regard. While marriage and parenthood offer no guarantee of a full and satisfying life, it is the authors' observation that teachers who are happy in their marriage and secure as parents more consistently and spontaneously promote the security of children and induce in them cooperative attitudes.

Modern science has also added to the effective equipment of teachers by making available a wide range of knowledge about human beings, facts concerning human growth, development, motives, learning, and social living. Its greatest value is in helping teachers to understand the child as a totality, to appreciate that while he is a psychobiological organism, the member of a social group, and the sharer of a cultural tradition, yet he lives and acts as an indivisible unit, as a unique individual. Teachers who understand this are continuously aware of the interrelationships of the many forces which have made each child what he is and accordingly are better able to direct these forces toward making him the best that he can become. In one other way modern science adds to the understanding and effectiveness of teachers. We quote directly from Prescott:

The understanding teacher habitually uses *scientific methods* in making judgments about any particular boy or girl. This means checking the validity of all information about the child and recognizing when the facts are too few to permit a sound judgment. It implies knowing what further facts are needed and how to set about getting them. It means that initial conclusions will be regarded only as hypotheses, that alertness in looking for new information will not be relaxed, and that the teacher will be emotionally ready to modify, or even completely to reverse preliminary judgments about a child when new evidence merits such a change. It means being so thoroughly habituated in using these scientific procedures for making decisions during the daily routine of classroom activities that reasoning back and forth between data about a child and scientific principles becomes virtually second nature.[5]

Relating the Educational Process to the Needs of Children

To promote mental health and maturity, education must meet the intrinsic needs of children. In the first place, the tasks set for children must be understandable and meaningful to them. Frequently the failure of pupils to achieve satisfactory learning is due to the fact that instruction has no clear purpose or meaning for them whereupon they soon become preoccupied in fantasy with their own particular interests which are meaningful. Children give best attention and put forth enough effort to learn new skills only when the learning tasks are related to previous satisfying experience, to a real and active current interest, or to the possibility of obtaining pleasure and achieving higher status as a result of such effort.

The immediate goal of a child's effort must be attainable. The learner must be able in imagination to see himself accomplishing what he sets out to accomplish and, especially if he is very young, he must make some noticeable progress fairly soon. No relatively inexperienced student of music attempts a Chopin étude or Wagnerian aria, but most students will accept a new assignment that is somewhat more difficult than the previous one. No fifth-year class would undertake to catalogue the 4,483,683 books in the New York Public Library, but many fifth-grade classes have both assembled and catalogued for use in their class projects a library of a hundred or more books and built and painted shelves to house them. Moreover, educational measures to help children extend their control over themselves and their environment must not impose too strict a regulation of their primary instincts or demand the negation of basic needs. Frequently children are forced by false standards of education to suppress their need for physical activity, their sexual interests, and their feelings of hostility to an extent that is almost as foolhardy as to attempt to teach them to get along without food. As a result, they feel guilty over some of their natural endowments and lose faith in themselves. As a group of mental hygienists have noted:

> Not the least important task in mental hygiene is to create a belief in human nature. . . . We could believe more in human nature if we realized that children have potentialities for growth and achievement which we can rely upon to help them mature. If they are not blocked, frustrated, coerced or deprived of the understanding or affection they need, they will meet the requirements of socialization effectively.[6]

The tasks a child is set to do must challenge all his powers if they are to make him an all-round person. The more faculties he is called upon to use, the more integrated and whole he will become and the stronger and healthier will be his sense of worth. Integration is basic not only to the learning process but to the application of what one has learned to wider fields of experience. It is in recognition of this principle that personality is rapidly becoming the primary concern of education and that the personality of the teacher is assuming increasing importance. As Melvin points out:

The wholeness and the balance of internal relations is preserved only when the human personality is regarded as the primary goal of education. To make human personality is the primary goal of both learner and teacher. It is only with this goal that people can become desirable as individuals and as groups. For the group is not the antithesis, but the synthesis of individuals. To provide a child with a concrete living embodiment of a good man is the primary goal of education. The first thing of importance to the teacher is who and what he himself is. There is a sense in which the intimate and private life of the teacher is the most important thing to the school for the teacher himself becomes the person who is the learner's goal—many teachers, many goals.[7]

A sense of futility and uselessness about what one does in study or work is one of the worst enemies of mental health. In contrast, if the child is acquiring knowledge or developing a skill that fits him for the vocation of his choice or for next steps in his relations to other people, he works with zest because the emotions attached to past satisfying experience and projected in anticipation to new and fuller satisfactions are fully activated.

Schools and all other agencies that attempt to educate children and at the same time to promote their mental health must distinguish between immediate and lifetime goals and make clear provisions for intermediate steps in achieving the latter—steps which take into account the child's stage of growth and maturity. This gradation of goals is particularly important in relation to the development of personality and character, because of the danger to mental health presented by the apparent conflict between natural interests and instinctive endowments, on the one hand, and religious and social ideals, on the other. It seems more difficult to relate the steps in personality and character development to the degree of emotional maturity than to grade lessons in reading, spelling, or arithmetic. But this is perhaps because it is only recently that attention has been directed to the problem. As a matter of fact, the gradation of instruction by scholastic norms was achieved only after many years of study and evaluation and even now modifications are being made, as, for example, postponing instruction in reading well beyond the age of six. As emphasis shifted from the subject to the learner, it became clear that' gradations in learning had to be made more flexible to suit the needs of children with varying degrees of intelligence and with varying social backgrounds. Now that the development of mature personalities and social responsibility has become a major goal in education, it is recognized that the degree of emotional maturity is an equally important factor in the learning process. There is real danger to mental health if adult standards of feeling and behavior are imposed on children before they are ready to measure up to them. To expose children to standards which they are unable to achieve or set goals for them toward which they cannot see themselves making any progress is to give them feelings of frustration, if not of despair; and in qualities and relationships which have a "good" or "bad" connotation they are likely either to develop a strong sense of guilt or to reject the goal. More specifically, complete truth telling, complete freedom from anger, and complete lack of manual aggression toward an offending child can hardly be achieved by first-graders, at least without an occasional slip; and when slips do occur, consideration must be given to the stage of emotional maturity reached by the offender, as well as to the occasion and the motivations which prompt the behavior. To quote again from Prescott:

We believe that the various sciences concerned with human growth and behavior have demonstrated that children, during the several phases of their development, face a series of common *"development tasks."* They have to learn to walk, to talk, to dress themselves, to get along in groups, to behave as boys or girls, to act conventionally in a thousand situations, to read, write, figure and spell, to use money, to respect property, to respect the values that characterize American life, to find a way of earning a living, to select and win a marriage partner, to fulfill civic responsibilities, to arrive at a satisfying explanation of the meaning of life and of the universe—and much else. We believe that children naturally tend to work at these tasks when they reach the appropriate maturity levels, and that they are disturbed when they fail to accomplish any of them. Understanding teachers know: what these tasks are, their sequence and timing in relation to physical, social, and mental maturity, what complications often arise as individuals with different characteristics and backgrounds work at them, and what conditions, relationships, and experiences are most helpful to children in mastering each of them.[5]

In religious education, even more than in public secular education, there is need for attention to variations in emotional development. Many an adult has come near to developing a neurosis because as a child he was expected to behave like a grownup and felt secretly guilty when he failed to meet the standards of the adult world. Ethical standards should be presented as ultimate goals toward which one moves in progressive steps and with the hope of realizing them fully in due time. It should be made clear to the child that improvement rather than complete achievement is the immediate aim. Honest admissions of failure on the part of instructors and other adults help the child to recognize that "to err is human" and relieve his sense of guilt, if he has already experienced one.

Just because people are people they inevitably strive for integration. One of the things which most distinguishes them from other forms of life is their ability to gather up their past experience, express it in the present, and thereby work out their destiny. The integration process includes the child's total experience, not only in school, but in the family and in his immediate social group. The school must take into account this total experience if it is to aid the child in developing and rounding out his personality. In other words, the educational goals of the school must be orchestrated with those of parents, the church, the clinic. If this is not done, conflict is almost sure to result. Health instruction in schools has sometimes failed to take into account the dietary laws and food habits of racial or religious groups. School efforts to teach truthfulness have often been countered by parents who expected the child to lie to certain people on certain occasions. Parents sometimes find their efforts to encourage emotional maturity and critical thinking largely cancelled out by the authoritative methods of certain teachers. Teachers who are trying to develop pupil initiative, resourcefulness, and critical thinking sometimes fail because of the autocratic control and unreasonable domination of parents. In all such situations, mental and emotional conflicts are generated or increased.

Again, failure on the part of the school to take the child's total experience into account often results in certain gaps in the child's preparation for life. One of the more common of such omissions is an explanation of the meaning of life and the universe which the child will find satisfying. The school often assumes that the child is associated with a church or religious organization, but he may have no such contact—less than half of school children do—and his efforts to get help from his parents may be met with refusals or with mythical explanations which do not explain. Frequently there is a gap also between what adolescents want to know and the information given them by the schools and youth-serving agencies. As has been pointed out:

A program of mental health for adolescents should be directed to the clarification of the many and often acute curiosities of young people, their perplexities, and, above all, their aspirations. This is where the schools can be of immense help if they would increasingly organize their programs around the questions which adolescents are vitally interested in, as contrasted with the usual procedure of expecting adolescents to conform to a curriculum which may largely ignore what they want to know and what they would like to do.[6]

During adolescence when young people are trying to grow up, become responsible self-directing young adults, often in the face of resistance and even bitter opposition from their families, the adolescent boy and girl need all the reenforcement and assistance which the school and youth agencies can provide but which at the present time they often fail to offer because they are more interested in their own special programs and purposes than they are in the needs and difficulties of youth.[8]

Education in Human Relationships

Children should of course be taught to develop habits of careful observation and critical, objective thinking, but considering their emotional and social needs, they should also be taught the importance of learning to understand other people and of achieving successful relationships with them.

Like the family, the school is a laboratory in the techniques of relationships. A teacher in the kindergarten or first grade carries the children's projection of a mother. If she is not a "good mother," the first days of school are traumatic. There must be a continuation of the atmosphere of warmth and trust that the young child needs if he is to develop a sense of personal security; and special consideration and attention have to be given to children whose home life has given them the handicap of overdependence or patterns of negative response. Levy has shown how very important freedom from such patterns is for actual school learning.[9]

As the children grow older, their personalities develop through identification with someone who carries other values than those which are characteristic of the mother—someone who crystallizes their need to use and develop their innate social and intellectual powers. The teacher often becomes the object of such identification, the ideal woman who is interesting and socially adapted, or the hero who excels intellectually or by force of personality. This identification can occur only if the instructor is understanding, considerate, friendly and gives each child a feeling that he rates. An emotionally positive relationship with the teacher adds to the children's social sense and gives them experience in relating themselves to adults and to persons in positions of leadership, as well as to their peers.

The school also provides children with their best opportunities for building relationships with their contemporaries. With opportunities for joint planning, with division of labor that takes into account children's varying interests and skills, and with the chance to learn from one another, they learn to get along well with people and cooperatively accomplish tasks which no one of them could do alone. The child who is inclined to withdraw from association with others or who has few inner resources can thus be helped while at school to achieve a balance which will make him a helpful member of society, unafraid of others because he has worked and played happily with them in his early years.

It is important, too, that the content of the school curriculum should provide children with information about the nature of people and the significance of wholesome and satisfying social relations. It may not be obvious in some classrooms, and certainly not in most textbooks, but actually people and their relationships are more interesting to children than most subjects to which they traditionally have been exposed. Yet it is only very recently that the content of instruction in elementary and secondary schools has concerned itself with getting an understanding of human relations and teaching children to distinguish between what is desirable and constructive and what is undesirable and destructive in this area.

Some interesting experimentation in human relations classes has been done in the last several years under the aegis of the Delaware Society for Mental Hygiene. It was found possible to include discussions of personal attitudes in human relations in all grades beginning with the first. In the upper grades actual relationship situations within the class, community, or nation are made the basis of discussion. In lower grades much use is made of stories rich in attitude and relationship concepts and having the quality of human warmth and interest even though the characters are animals. Class discussions of such stories as *The Barnyard Guard,* for example, provide abundant opportunity for helping five- and six-year-old children to acquire psychological insights.[10, 11]

In the secondary schools and even in colleges and universities, the teaching of the social sciences can be related to the underlying problem of how people have striven to understand each other and get along together. A study of group relationships, of racial and religious prejudices, of cooperative societies, taps deeper emotions and gives learning larger meanings when related to practical situations, to the present or future problems of the individual and society. Courses in marriage and family living and in personnel administration or labor relations which really get at the motivations of people and the bases for security are not only valuable because they add to the necessary store of knowledge, but because young people are able to apply what they learn to their own practical problems of living.

Chisholm has pointed out that, if we are to evolve a peaceful and progressive society, we must examine various concepts and loyalties which have been accepted unthinkingly and interpret them as experimental ways in which certain groups have sought to solve some of life's problems; we must not view them as finalities. It is important, as he says, to foster and strengthen the child's native ability to observe and to reason about his observations, for only in this way shall we develop a generation of people who will not drift into situations leading to social disaster such as war and economic depressions. At all levels of school, habits of thinking critically and objectively and insight into the behavior of persons and groups can be best acquired through the study and critical evaluation of human relations.[12, 13] In such content, much more than in the traditional disciplinary subjects, the learner finds elements which are related to his own experience and which can be applied to his own situation. Just because human relations involve emotions, ideals, and prejudices, as well as events, there is both need and opportunity in such a course of study to develop critical discrimination. In line with this need, some educators are giving larger place in the curriculum to those areas of human experience in which value judgments are operative. For instance, in the introduction to *Gen-*

eral Education in a Free Society, President Conant of Harvard University states:

Unless the educational process includes *at each level of maturity*, some continuing contact with those fields in which value judgments are of primary importance, it must fall very short of the ideal. The student in high school, in college and in graduate school must be concerned, in part at least, with the words "right" and "wrong" in both the ethical and mathematical sense. Unless he feels the import of those general ideas and aspirations which have been a deep moving force in the lives of men, he runs the risk of partial blindness.[14]

It is noteworthy that in professions which make most use of mathematics, science, and technology, demands are now being made for a broader education which stresses human values and relationships. Fine, in his recent study, notes the fact that the Society for the Promotion of Engineering Education recommends that "undergraduate curricula should be made broader and more fundamental through increased emphasis on basic sciences, humanities and social studies."[15]

Likewise, in out-of-school education, which has been growing rapidly, we see this demand for better understanding of human relations, not only between individuals but cultural, racial, national, and international groups. In discussing out-of-school education the Harvard Report in its final paragraph states:

Enlargement of the common concern is indeed the distinctive character of our age. Not very long ago the mass of mankind could and did leave peace making, for example, to statesmen. Today most people feel some of its weight on their shoulders. Even one generation back, how other people lived was not their business; but all men are neighbors now. Among and beyond all the local and personal motivations which drive men to pursue education, this budding collective responsibility year by year grows in power. And as it grows it profoundly influences some immediate motives. The desire to get on in the world or to advance the status of workers, the two chief drives which have animated out-of-school education hitherto, are being transformed by it into wider interests far more favorable both to growth in democracy and to the final causes for which society itself is only a means. "War is the great educator," as enemy propagandists have said, though hardly with this in mind. It has shown us that in technical instruction we have been sadly unambitious and unenterprising. It has shown us clearly that in general education the strongest incentive comes from the whole man's awareness of his share in the common fate, of his part in the joint undertaking.[14]

Healthy School Administration

In schools as elsewhere administration is primarily an organizational tool for getting the whole job done. Its function is to keep all parts tied together so that the purpose of the organization is effectively achieved. The administrator must possess unusual capacity for encompassing both the whole and the parts. He must firmly sustain, with resiliency and enthusiasm, the total work of the school and at the same time allow staff members as much individual freedom as will not divide or defeat the school's major purpose. It is in the administrator's office that the many cross-currents meet and flow continuously to and from the community and to and from the internal organization of staff and pupils.

For this reason mental hygiene can be effectively promoted in and through education only if the administrators and supervisors fully believe in it and are able to sustain it through appropriate curricula and teaching methods, and particularly through the kind of supervision that promotes confidence and security in both teachers and pupils. When emphasis on mental hygiene has been made an official policy in a school system there is very real danger that some administrators, with an eye to their own advancement, will get on the bandwagon though they do not really believe in it and do not have sufficient knowledge and skill to maintain that emphasis consistently.

Actually the principal sets the tone of a school. His real attitudes filter down to the teachers and the pupils. Teachers take cognizance of what he says about mental hygiene, but they act upon what he thinks, feels, and does. The principal should have all the qualifications of an understanding teacher and apply this understanding specifically to all members of his teaching staff as well as to children. He should be an emotionally mature person who recognizes and brings out the good qualities in teachers and pupils. Admittedly, some of the traditional emphases in education definitely run counter to the kind of administration which makes for the mental health and security of both pupils and teachers.[16] Over-authoritative attitudes, the imposition on teachers of policies which they have had no part in making, and an undue emphasis on the mechanics of what someone has called "school keeping" tend to create a school atmosphere which is essentially unhealthy. Constraint rather than spontaneity pervades it; lip-service rather than frank give-and-take becomes characteristic; morale is essentially the morale of fellow sufferers.

To administer schools in the interest of mental hygiene it is necessary to select or develop administrators who fully accept its principles, who genuinely accept and respect teachers as persons and give them unstinted support and encouragement in the use of classroom methods which make for child security and growth. It is the opinion of the authors that skill in the group-discussion method is to be preferred to skill in the authoritative lecture-directive method and that in the selection of school administrators more weight should be given to maturity of personality and to ability in securing the free and full cooperation of the staff and maintaining a high level of teacher morale. Strang has reported that in a discussion of mental hygiene and school administration, one principal, "not entirely facetiously, proposed the inclusion of a test of blood pressure and evidence of good digestion as part of the examination of principals."[17] This would not be a bad idea, especially if the test could be administered during and following a candidate's conference with staff or an interview with a parent, child, or teacher in a critical situation.

Sound administration strengthens the morale of the teaching staff by (1) inviting and encouraging their evaluation of all school procedures and accepting their thinking and planning; (2) recognizing differences in teachers as well as in pupils and assigning work which utilizes their special aptitudes and skills; and (3) giving a quality of supervision that is characterized by warmth and confidence and a real sharing of responsibilities. In short, effective administration emphasizes the social and emotional maturing of pupils, and not only supplies teachers with such materials and tools as are needed, but most of all reenforces their morale by providing strong, democratic leadership. The secret of good administration, like that of good teaching, is effective leading.

Guidance and Clinic Work

Thus far we have stressed mental hygiene in education as a viewpoint and a method which schools can use to insure the maximum growth and personality development in each and every learner. No matter how thoroughly imbued with this viewpoint school staffs may be, education cannot always achieve its goal of mental health and mature personality. In some children unhealthy patterns have been fairly well established by the time they enter school. In others, destructive forces in family and community cause continuing conflicts so severe that they cannot be fully resolved no matter how favorable the school environment may be.[18]

Consequently, there are in virtually all schools some children who need individual assistance. Where neuroses have already been established or there are other serious maladjustments, the special skills of the psychiatrist, psychologist, and social worker may be needed. The percentage of children needing such service varies somewhat with schools and communities, but it has been estimated from studies in several communities that about 5 per cent of the children in elementary school at any one time require special study and treatment on account of social, psychiatric, or behavior problems. To serve these children the full-time services of a clinic team consisting of one psychiatrist, one or two psychologists, and two or three psychiatric social workers is needed for every 40,000 children in the elementary school grades. In the opinion of many observers, this should be regarded as minimal. Because of the added tensions associated with puberty, the development of sexual interests, and efforts toward emancipation from the parents, the percentage of high school students who would profit greatly by individual consultation or clinical study and treatment is believed to be considerably higher (on the basis of the Cincinnati study,[19] 45 per cent).

The work of a mental hygiene or child guidance unit must be carefully and fully integrated with the work of the teaching and administrative staffs.[20] When clinical services are first provided there is a tendency for school staffs to unload on such a unit all their responsibility for variant children who have outstanding needs and to set them apart in a way which makes it impossible for them to obtain acceptable standing with their classmates and teachers. In the New York City schools where the Bureau of Child Guidance has worked since 1931 as an integral part of the system, an increasing amount of the time of the staff has been devoted to developing sound procedures of guidance for administrators and teachers and for instructing them—through courses, conferences, and interviews—in the principles of mental hygiene applicable to classroom use. In individual cases served by this bureau exchange of information between school and clinic staffs has been found necessary. In fact, there has to be a unified approach on the part of all people who are in a position to influence the children, as is pointed out in the 1945–1946 Report of the Superintendent of Schools. Guidance concerned with the total growth of the individual is the dominant theme of education in the New York school system, the superintendent states, and not a special or distinct function of a special department. In line with this view he recommends:

The guidance program should be continued from kindergarten through secondary school; ... should enlist the co-operation of the home, church, child-serving agencies, public and private; ... should be concerned with the special health, academic, emotional and social development and vocational direction of children; ... should be interested in the prevention of maladjustment as well as in its treatment; ... should aim to make children increasingly competent in self-direction.[20]

Many school systems do not have special mental hygiene clinics. In many of the larger cities some service can be obtained from community clinics. For such clinics to be effective there must be co-operation and mutual understanding on the part of school and clinic. If the two organizations work at cross-purposes, they only increase the conflicts to which the child is exposed. In a majority of schools, teachers and principals have to do all the guidance work without any assistance from specialists.

Teachers can be trained to prevent and reduce somewhat the mental hygiene problems of children and to deal constructively with many problems that have not yet become too acute.[4, 21, 22] Basic training can be given in the teacher-training colleges and later supplemented by the workshop type of in-service training. When Wickman made his comparative study of the attitudes of teachers and of mental hygienists toward the behavior problems of children, teachers very definitely emphasized overt behavior which caused difficulty in the classroom and were not concerned with the behavior of children who were timid and inclined to withdraw from social contacts.[23] In the twenty years since that study was made, teachers in many school systems have received further training which has greatly increased their awareness of the special needs of both types of behavior deviation. In a study which one of the authors made in 1938, the teachers in twenty-eight schools, numbering about 1,000, were asked to fill out a schedule of information regarding every child in their classes who presented problems for which the help of a clinic or social agency was thought desirable.[24] Forty per cent of all the children reported by the teachers showed symptoms of withdrawal, whereas only 20 per cent of the children being served by social and health agencies showed this type of problem.

There is obvious need for mental hygiene services in the secondary schools, although the exact incidence of problems at that level is not known. To our knowledge mental hygiene clinic services have not been available in any one school long enough to yield adequate information regarding the frequency and types of mental hygiene problems in the secondary schools. The special high school unit of the Bureau of Child Guidance in the New York City schools, which was established in 1945 and is being extended further at the present time, may later have some information on this. The accentuation of individual problems during the 'teens is too well known to need proof beyond that which is at hand in the records of social agencies, children's courts and community clinics. There is some evidence in clinic experience that in many cases effective treatment can be carried through more quickly in the adolescent years when the resources of the individual can be used to more advantage than in the earlier latency period when treatment is so largely dependent on the amount and kind of cooperation obtained from the parents.

At the level of higher education, a number of colleges and universities provide psychiatric and mental hygiene services as a part of the college or university health services. A large majority, however, make no provision beyond occasional routine physical checkups. The evidence from those schools which have service suggest that in all probability it is needed in all colleges and universities. At Yale University, during a ten-year period, approximately 1,500 students consulted the Division of College Psychiatry and Mental Hygiene.[25] Of the 1,257 students whose records were full enough to be used in Fry's study only about 8 per cent were considered really "abnormal." The rest, who were considered more or less "normal," encountered difficulties at various times which they could not themselves solve and reacted with emotional and physical upsets. Freshmen constituted about 45 per cent of the undergraduate group. As to the kinds of problems dealt with we may quote a brief statement from Fry's study:

The first group of problems are the problems of personality growth and development shared by most of the patients as human beings in a certain age period. Given our mores and the circumstances of his life, an individual of college age is required to assume more and more responsibility for his decisions and actions in all phases of life. An individual's progress toward maturity is, then, the basic issue of these cases— maturity in attitude toward and management of his personality, in the conduct of relations with his family and with society, in the development of his sexual behavior and attitudes.

There is, however, a series of problems concerned specifically with the student's reaction to the special environment of the university. . . . Problems of social experience are, in a sense, no less personality problems than those mentioned above: they arise out of the relation between the individual and his world. Individual personality differences are, therefore, important here, too, and require study and treatment. In these cases the main issues of disturbance derive to some extent from particular features of life in the special environment where the student finds himself. Issues of social success, vocational choice, and scholastic failure are typical foci of disturbance. The incidence of such problems varies greatly with the composition of the different student groups and the stage of the student's development. Among undergraduates, for example, 48 per cent of the freshman patients came with scholastic problems, whereas only 20 per cent of middleclassmen and a negligible number of seniors had scholastic difficulties. Among graduate students, those in the Divinity School faced special vocational and emotional adjustments of their religious ideas and beliefs, while issues of religious doctrine were of no special concern to students in the other schools.[25]

Thus guidance and clinical work are needed at all levels of school to restore to health and social effectiveness those children and youths whose growth, integration, or socialization is being blocked by inner conflicts or environmental stresses. In short, it is the function of the special guidance or clinic staff to remove the psychological and social barriers to such children's education so that it can proceed more normally. Equally important, if not more so, is the infusion of the clinic staff's viewpoint throughout the school, to the enrichment of teacher-child relationships and further refinement of the educational process. The more closely supervisory, teaching, and clinic staffs work together, the more obvious it becomes that education and mental hygiene have a common goal— the integration and socialization of the individual. As Frank has stated:

Mental hygiene gives no support for the doctrine of unrestrained freedom in the education of the child, but does assert that this necessary socialization should be given to the child with love and affection to avoid damaging his personality. The major emphasis in education should be upon making social life, with its necessary deprivations and inhibitions, and its requirement of prescribed patterns of conduct, emotionally acceptable to the child, so that he can learn these necessary lessons without the resentment or hostility that blocks social order, and without the anxiety and guilt that distorts, and often destroys the personality.[26]

REFERENCES

1. Ryan, W. C. Mental health through education. New York, Commonwealth Fund, 1939.

2. Amidon, B. If we want schools. Survey Graphic 35:258–261, July 1946.

3. Counts, S. Education and the promise of America. New York, Macmillan, 1945.

4. Prescott, D., and associates. Helping teachers understand children. Understanding the Child 14:67–70, June 1945.

5. Available from the American Council on Education, Washington, D. C.

6. Douglas, T., M. Kenworthy, E. Humphreys, E. Weiss, and L. Frank. Mental hygiene for children and youth. Understanding the Child 14:47–54, April 1945.

7. Melvin, G. A. The activity program. New York, Reynal & Hitchcock, 1936.

8. Douglas, T., M. Kenworthy, E. Humphreys, E. Weiss, and L. Frank. Mental hygiene for children and youth. Understanding the Child 14:74–80, June 1945.

9. Levy, D. M. Relation of maternal over-protection to school grades and intelligence tests. Am. J. Orthopsychiat. 3:26–34, January 1933.

10. Bullis, H. E., E. O'Malley, and J. Jastah. Human relations in the classroom—

kindergarten–12th grade. Wilmington, Delaware Society for Mental Hygiene, 1944.

11. Tarumianz, M. D., and H. E. Bullis. The human relations class; a preventive mental hygiene program for schools. Understanding the Child 13:3–10, October 1944.

12. Chisholm, G. B. The reestablishment of peacetime society. (*In* The Psychiatry of Enduring Peace and Social Progress, William Alanson White Memorial Lectures.) Psychiatry 9:1–35, February 1946.

13. Chisholm, G. B. Can society keep pace with science? *In* Proceedings, National Conference of Social Work, 1946. New York, Columbia University Press, 1947.

14. Conant, J. B. *In* General education in a free society. Report of the (Harvard) Committee on the Objectives of a General Education in a Free Society. Cambridge, Mass., Harvard University Press, 1945.

15. Fine, B. Democratic education. New York, Crowell, 1945.

16. Veo, L., and L. E. Woodward. Planned social work in the school. Am. J. Orthopsychiat. 11:1–13, January 1941.

17. Strang, R. M. Health and mental hygiene. 1943 Yearbook, New York Society for the Experimental Study of Education. New York, Thesis Publishing Company, 1943.

18. Hewitt, L. E., and R. L. Jenkins. Fundamental patterns of maladjustment; the dynamics of their origin. (Springfield), State of Illinois, 1946. Obtainable from the Illinois Department of Welfare.

19. Hertzman, J. Mental hygiene survey of high school students in Cincinnati during three consecutive war years. Address before the 24th Annual Meeting of the Am. Orthopsychiat. Assn., February 1947.

20. Superintendent of New York City Schools, 46th Report (1945–1946).

21. Baruch, D. W. Procedures in training teachers to prevent and reduce mental hygiene problems. Pedagogical Seminary and J. Genetic Psychology 67:143–178, December 1945.

22. DiMichael, S. G. Comparative changes in teachers' attitudes from courses in mental hygiene and educational guidance. J. Educational Research 37:656–669, May 1944.

23. Wickman, E. K. Differences in the attitudes of teachers and mental hygienists. *In* Children's behavior and teachers' attitudes. New York, Commonwealth Fund, 1928.

24. Woodward, L. E. Child welfare needs and services in Queens County, New York (mimeographed). Welfare Council of New York City, 1939.

25. Fry, C. C., with collaboration of E. Rostow. Mental health in college. New York, Commonwealth Fund, 1942.

26. Frank, L. K. Summary of discussion on reorientation of education to the promotion of mental hygiene. *In* Mental Health, edited by F. R. Moulton and P. O. Komora. (Lancaster), Am. Assn. for the Advancement of Science, 1939.

XIV

SUMMARY AND PROSPECT: THE INDIVIDUAL AND SOCIETY

THIS book has attempted to show that an individual's mental and emotional ill health is a reaction of his personality to the multiple stresses of the total environment, whether the stresses be in the external environment or in his own complicated emotional imbalances. The point at which any individual becomes sick depends upon his constitutional stability and toughness to withstand stress, upon the severity of the stresses in his external environment, upon the severity of his internal conflict, or upon a combination of these factors. Our knowledge of how these forces interact in any given patient is considerable. If prevention of mental ill health is to become a reality for the millions, we must learn how to remove stresses in the environment as well as to strengthen the inner resources of individuals, and to apply corrective principles there as we now apply them in the treatment of the individual patient.

Mental health cannot be developed in a social vacuum. Powerful factors operate against it as our present society is constituted. To promote positive mental health will therefore require the cooperation and help of many individuals and groups. Medical and social scientists need to look squarely at these factors and, abandoning professional isolationism, cooperate in an effort to counteract them. Mental health can only be achieved in an environment which provides opportunities for self-expression, social usefulness, and the attainment of human satisfactions. Preventive psychiatry is only beginning, and its only sure tool at present lies in educating the public in the meaning and causes of mental disorders and the ways of developing positive mental health.

We have had two world wars in twenty-five years. Obviously

our approach to war prevention and peace building has been ineffective. Hitherto we have relied on moral principles and political procedures. Appeals to morality have had little effect on international policy because nations, unlike individual human beings, are motivated by considerations of their sovereignty rather than by principles of right and wrong, and have no sense of responsibility toward other nations comparable to the average citizen's sense of responsibility toward the people of his community. The political procedure which would establish international machinery for settling disputes and maintaining security has not yet succeeded because nations have not been willing to delegate to an international federation the necessary power and—what is still more important—have failed to win for this organization the loyalty, confidence, and good will which citizens feel toward the nation-state.[1] Lacking loyalty the international organization cannot secure voluntary compliance, and lacking force it cannot compel it. Now that the atomic bomb hourly threatens the actual destruction of civilization, there can be no peace of mind. Blind terror compels us to seek for new solutions.

A warring society is a sick society. As Chisholm has noted:

The necessity to fight wars whether as aggressor or as a defender who could have, but has not, taken steps to prevent war occurring is as much a pathological psychiatric symptom as is a phobia or the anti-social behavior of the criminal who has been dominated by a stern and unreasonable father. They are alike irrational behavior patterns resulting from unsuccessful development and failure to reach emotional maturity.[2]

For the recovery and the acquisition of health, a sick society, like a sick person, needs therapy and the continuing application of hygienic principles. Thus we must seek to develop those healthy behavior patterns, attitudes, and feelings that are the best insurance against war and at the same time fashion the ideational framework and organizational structure for a peaceful world that will enlist the interest and active support of all the citizens. As stated in the preamble to the Constitution of the United Nations Educational, Scientific, and Cultural Organization: "Since wars begin in the minds of men, it is in the minds of men that the defenses of peace must be constructed."[3]

Developing Emotional Maturity and Leadership

Underlying the collective insecurity that precipitates war is the individual insecurity that comes from emotional immaturity. It is in the home, in the interrelations of parents and children, of brothers and sisters, that healthy personalities and constructive social attitudes are developed, and it is there that insecurity, dependence, emotional instability, and faulty habits of thinking most often emerge. Therefore, it is in the home that the training for emotional maturity must begin.

The authors believe that the kind of home training and guidance described in Chapter XII and the emphasis on human relations in education as described in Chapter XIII will go far toward giving the oncoming generation such a satisfying experience in their relations to other people that they can without too much difficulty evolve a workable philosophy or system of beliefs which will serve them as a basis for healthy and cooperative relationships throughout their lives. We express that conviction because the sort of home guidance and school experience we have described not only implants basically sound ideas about human relationships, but develops the even more important patterns of feeling which make a constructive social philosophy possible. Certainly no philosophy will be adequate for the years ahead which fails to draw upon and use the greater depths of human emotion. As Leighton has stated:

Most people use their intelligence to attain ends dictated by their feelings and convictions and not as a matter of their basic motivations. With ourselves, no less than with a foreign or "primitive" people, the choice of a career, of a marital partner, of religion, of friends, of political candidates, of a place to reside, of food, of a doctor, of a lawyer, and many other crucial steps in life are carried out far more on the basis of feeling than on the basis of reasoning—and feeling means systems of belief and related patterns of sentiment in varying combinations, powered by needs, drives, aspirations and insecurities.

Societies move on the feelings of the individuals who compose them, and so do countries and nations. Very few internal policies and almost no international policies are predominantly the product of reason. To be sure, reason and thought are components, but they take the form either of rationalization to justify or of scheming to attain ends already decided upon at the dictates of feeling.[4]

A generation of children who have been well loved, who are wholesomely self-confident, who have disciplined their instinctive drives and harmonized self-interest with enjoyable give-and-take with others, who can think critically and objectively, who have become accustomed to making decisions while adapting to change, and whose personalities are well integrated and mature, are the best guarantee that problems of human relationship can and will be worked out. When the dynamic processes of growing up are made to serve positive and constructive ends, conflict, fear, and hostility can be kept within bounds and the danger of disabling psychoneuroses diminished.

The basic training and education provided by families and schools go far to promote the mental health and stability of children. But the efforts of understanding parents and teachers are likely to be partially defeated unless neighbors and friends appreciate children's psychological needs and encourage the educational processes by which sound personality growth can be fostered. Studies of children have shown that variations in personality structure are largely dependent on the familial and other cultural patterns to which the children are exposed.[5]

During the war, the key to morale in our fighting forces was leadership. In building and maintaining a peaceful society, leadership is equally important. The number of people capable of true leadership in our complex world is of course limited, although much less limited than the self-appointed leaders in fascist governments would have us believe. One of the secrets of a healthy society, nationally and internationally, is the selection and training of potential leaders in all professions and major fields of activity. Such leaders must have an understanding of individuals and groups and of the history and heritage of different nations. They must have a mature personality, enough dissatisfaction with the status quo to call forth aggressive, constructive effort, and enough social concern and devotion to hold them to their course while a healthier society is slowly but surely constructed. They need thorough grounding in the knowledge of human motivation, and their training must include understanding of the findings of psychiatry and the other social sciences.

Strengthening Economic Security

One of the most effective means of building morale and preventing psychiatric disorders in the armed forces was the prompt discovery and alleviation of such environmental stresses as discomfort and inconvenience, wasted effort or unfairness, and defective or untrustworthy leadership. The experience of psychiatrists, social workers, and plant managers shows that in a peacetime society the same relationship between mental health and environmental stresses holds. As stresses are multiplied in number and increased in intensity, there is a corresponding increase in the number of people who can no longer function effectively, and, conversely, as stresses are removed or alleviated, the number of people who are mentally healthy is proportionately increased. One of the most powerful environmental stresses, and one to which millions of people are exposed, is economic insecurity.

The extent to which economic insecurity contributes to psychoses, psychoneuroses, delinquency, crime, and other social problems is not yet clear. There was no appreciable increase in admissions to hospitals for the mentally ill during the economic depression of the nineteen-thirties, but there was a marked increase in the number of psychoneurotic persons whose illness became so serious that they had to be hospitalized. This suggests that "economic factors, whether primary or not, do act as inciting and precipitating influences in functional mental disorders."[6] The total psychological effects of economic insecurity cannot, of course, be measured in terms of gross pathology alone. The anxieties created by unemployment and loss of income have been experienced by so many millions of people, and their expression—in irritability toward members of the family, heightened group conflicts, loss of self-respect and the esteem of the community, and many other ways—has been so commonly observed that statistical proof of such ill-effects is not needed.

Through social insurance in the form of unemployment compensation and old age security and through public assistance, the federal and the state governments have attempted to prevent the worst effects of economic insecurity. As Falk and Hirsch have stated, "To the extent that such measures do provide assurance of income they serve as preventive measures by securing society to some degree against the development of mental deviation arising out of economic fears and worries."[7] There is clearly need to extend social insurance to the many groups of employees not now covered by the provisions of the law and to extend security against accident and health hazards to those who become disabled and are left without earning capacity by reason of non-industrial disablements.

If our free enterprise system is to function adequately, private business and industry must do much more to stabilize employment and guarantee economic security, and labor groups must develop real leadership and take steps to assure full productivity. Both management and labor have great power, but each group is dependent on the other and each lacks an adequate measure of freedom, enterprise, and security. In the opinion of the authors, this situation will continue until the two groups find a positive common goal, in the pursuit of which a more meaningful way of life can develop. During the war period full production for the sake of the

Allied cause was such a positive common goal, with the result that there was not only less distrust and less friction between management and labor than there had been for many years, but—what is just as important—much greater satisfaction in their work on the part of both groups. During the war, to some degree at least, the fiction of economic man motivated only by the lure of financial reward was supplanted by the reality of the individual human being at work on a special task. There was a new realization that managers and workers are creatures of multiple desires, feelings, social needs, and purposes, to whom work is satisfying only when it gives them a sense of comradeship in a shared and truly worth-while enterprise. To retain this gain it is necessary for both groups, perhaps with the financial aid of the federal government, to take aggressive steps to achieve and maintain full employment, that is, to give everyone the opportunity for steady, gainful, satisfying employment on a year-round basis.

Many economists agree that this is both possible and practical. The American Management Association in a recent study of two decades of experience with guaranteed wages concludes that stabilized employment is an obtainable goal. It points out:

> Most companies could make at least a beginning toward the objective of guaranteed employment. Experience has shown that the big stumbling block of seasonal fluctuation can be systematically reduced or even eliminated by many companies. The annual wage can improve morale, increase output by lowering production and labor costs per unit, afford greater utilization of plant and equipment, reduce labor turnover costs, increase versatility and flexibility of employees and provide eligibility for special government benefits which reduce costs. Moreover widespread guaranteed annual wage could reduce savings accumulated in fear of unemployment and thereby stabilize consumption much more to help eliminate seasonal fluctuations.[8]

It has become clear that economic insecurity is one of the causes of war. While ideological differences were the immediate cause of World War II, behind these ideologies and giving them real power were the hard facts of economic need. Leaders in the aggressor nations sold their ideology to the people by promising to remove the causes of their anxiety and to satisfy their economic and social wants.

It appears to the authors that the psychological aspect of economic need has been too much ignored by those who are seeking to prevent war. The affluence of small minorities within a nation or of one powerful nation within the group of nations can be viewed with some equanimity by those who are fairly comfortable, but among the impoverished, the unemployed, the hungry, and those who are poorly clad and housed, such inequality breeds hostility as inevitably as night follows day. Faced with sharp differences in standards of living, the underprivileged cannot avoid the conclusion that there should be a larger measure of economic justice and of social equality. The human submissiveness characteristic of periods of slavery and serfdom has passed in Western civilization, and is slowly disappearing in the East. The common man will not accept hardship and poverty when plenty and comfort abound. Fighting comes easy to those who by fighting hope to gain needed comforts, possessions, and opportunities, and easier still to those whose resources have been exploited by powerful interests in other lands. As many thoughtful people see it, the greatest hope for peace lies in the Social and Economic Council of the United Nations, which among other things proposes to study the economic needs and to develop the economy of the various nations in the interest of fuller opportunity and a higher standard of living for the people of these nations. The greatest danger to peace is that the efforts of the Council will be blocked by powerful groups of self-seeking individuals in all nations.

Building Interracial and International Understanding

Schreiber in a well-documented article[9] has described realistically the interdependence of democracy and mental health and has pointed out that whatever fosters and promotes democracy also guards and advances mental health. Conversely, whatever breeds racial, religious, or other group prejudices and intolerance accentuates the tensions of all the members of the out-groups and gives them handicaps which largely negate the values of democracy.

Prejudicial attitudes are acquired largely from parents, relatives, and neighbors during early childhood, and are confirmed by habitual emotional reactions that are so strong and so deeply imbedded in the personality structure that they yield only to prolonged critical examination in a social situation that puts a premium on their opposite. In the case of many individuals release from prejudice can be effected only by psychological or psychiatric treatment which allows the unconscious hostility to express itself. As Levy has pointed out:

Intolerant people are people who hate. Their degree of intolerance is a measure of their hate. When a person is characteristically intolerant, he belongs to the group of the psychologically hostile, whose features I shall attempt to describe. The most distinctive finding among the psychologically hostile is a stultification of the personality. In a well-known personality test such individuals, for whom hatred is so vital a function, are found to be characterized by a marked narrowing of the thought, feelings and imagination. The generalization applies equally well to the haters who have repressed their hate and to those who express it directly, in words or action. . . .

The disseminator of intolerance, operating on the fertile soil of the psychologically hostile, may initiate an epidemic of hate, as readily comprehensible as an epidemic of typhoid fever. The source of either epidemic, whether of typhoid or hate, would be considered equally dangerous and criminal, if public understanding of mental health were at all effective.[10]

The current interest in intercultural education in primary and secondary schools and in adult education circles is a great gain. In communities where the schools strive to bring about better relations between majority and minority groups in the school world and in the community, much is being accomplished. An outstanding example of this is the work done in Springfield, Massachusetts.[11]

In the last five or six years a wealth of material has been published[12] which suggests constructive ways of dealing with the problems of minority groups who are not fully accepted or who are actively rejected. An interesting series of pamphlets has been recently published by the National Institute of Social Relations under the title *Talk It Over*.[13] A concerted program of education and social action directed to individuals of all ages, utilizing various methods and in all community groups, is required to reduce the tensions to which out-groups are now exposed, be they Negro, Jew, Catholic, Protestant, or immigrant.[14] In at least a few communities, group prejudice is becoming unpopular, and although the federal government has not passed any permanent Fair Employment Practices Act, at least a few states have done so. Even in states having no such law some business firms observe fair practices.[15]

An understanding of the cultural background of our fellow nations and of our own is no less important for the maintenance of peace. A knowledge of the history, the characteristic viewpoints, and forms of government of other peoples will give us an understanding of what they need to make their lives full and secure.

To accomplish a satisfactory degree of mutual understanding and to make it possible for the people of different nations to identify with one another and accept one another as kinsmen and neighbors, free and extensive interchange of teachers, students, artists, and technicians who can develop natural resources will be required. In this field the United Nations Educational, Scientific, and Cultural Organization, if properly implemented, promises much of constructive value. Its fourteen-point program should go far to consolidate the findings of the social and psychological sciences and through the contributions of science, education, and art to create international understanding and cooperation.

A Working Philosophy and a Philosophy of Work

The discoveries and inventions of the physical sciences have bridged time and space and have made neighbors, however unfriendly, of all the people of the world. They have greatly multiplied the number of ways people have to work together. On the other hand, the social and psychological sciences have not put to similar practical use the knowledge of human beings that they have achieved, and have not shown a corresponding initiative in extending the limits of their knowledge to include further areas of human activity, both social and individual.

While applied science has brought about radical changes in our mode of living, most people are guided by the same standards, goals, and attitudes which made for a good measure of security in an earlier age, but which no longer help to deal with today's increasingly complex problems. For example, many are committed to the political dogma of national sovereignty notwithstanding the fact that world federation is possible only on condition that national sovereignty is partly surrendered. Again, multitudes who profess belief in the particular plan of personal salvation that was a part of their religious heritage find that their religion gives them neither peace of mind nor social effectiveness in dealing with the major issues of the day. The tendency to hold to static sets of value in a world undergoing phenomenal changes presents a major threat to mental health and social stability.

What is needed today is a new philosophy which does justice to our social and emotional needs and which builds a new and more inclusive morality based on these needs. We need a clear understanding of the nature of our world and a conviction regarding man's place in it that is scientifically tenable, socially acceptable, and emotionally satisfying. Such a faith springs from an appreciation of harmonies of sight and sound, evidences of cosmic purpose, and a sense of personal integrity—experiences which have been to a great extent the basis of established religion. But it builds also on our scientific knowledge that the natural world is governed by laws which are fully trustworthy and quite as wonderful and awe-inspiring as the mysterious powers of the supernatural to which our forefathers gave allegiance.

A faith adequate for our age must embody a view of man and society which gives purpose and meaning to each man's life, allays men's fears and distrust of one another, and induces and maintains such mutual confidence, cooperation, and support as are needed for living together in families, groups, societies, and nations. To build and implement such a working faith is one of the big psychological tasks of this age, for unless men believe in their own worth and in their ability to manage their lives with self-satisfaction and social acceptance, and unless they have a similar faith in the worth and ability of their fellow citizens and the citizens of other nations, they will continue to be plagued by a sense of futility and by fears of want and of war.

William James[16] suggested many years ago that to maintain peace one must provide moral equivalents for war. That this will not be easy is clear from Flugel's summary of the values that war has for the individual and the nation:

> The problem of providing a substitute for war that shall have something approaching war's peculiar combination of moral and instinctive appeal, is far from easy. In its danger, its hazards, its call for heroism, effort and sacrifice on the part of whole communities, war is without parallel—as also in the sense of social cohesion that it brings and the amount of aggression it permits.[1]

Such a challenge to personal heroism and group morale need not go unanswered in a peacetime world. Proper attention to personal and social values in connection with work would go far to give workers a genuine sense of contributing to a collective effort. Work that is challenging, that gives people a sense of belonging to a worth-while organization, and that helps satisfy the needs of other people, supplemented by concerted efforts toward community improvement, yields a quality and a degree of personal satisfaction and a sense of social cohesion which are essential to both peace and progress. Such a moral equivalent to the values of war can be provided if home and school encourage personality development and social relationships, and if business and industry, government, and voluntary community groups provide maximum opportunities for people to work together in a common cause.

The Responsibility of Medical and Social Scientists

The symptoms of our sick society are multiple. In merely cataloguing them, the authors have added nothing new to the diagnosis. The implications of these factors, however, do need reassertion. For unless individuals are taught to realize the significance of these multiple factors for their own emotional health and security as well as for that of the nation, they cannot be expected to join in concerted efforts at correction. One difficulty is to see the problem as a whole and the other is to break it down into encompassable tasks which individuals and groups can undertake and succeed in. Bomber crews, every man of whom was trained to do a specific job, and who counted on each and every member of the crew to do his part, went out on missions with confidence notwithstanding great danger. Their course was clearly charted. Each man was prepared to do his job and all knew the significance which the success of the mission would have in the total task of winning the war. If our peacetime goals can be defined with something of the same precision, and if the individual's part in the total task can be made as clear and as meaningful for the group, we shall have gone a long way toward removing our basic insecurities and achieving individual stability and group morale.

Multiple factors operate to cause wars, and constant efforts must be made to define and to expose them. Some are ideological, some are economic and sociological, and some operate at the level of the personal emotional motivation of mankind. The latter factors have been long neglected. They need the most vigorous study and research, utilizing all the ingenuity and skill that our social sciences can muster.

An effective safeguard against war would be an international research institute devoted to the study of individual and group aggression, hatred, and fear and their etiology in terms of personality development, cultural heritage, and social conditions. Admittedly, social psychiatry, psychology, and anthropology cannot be as exact sciences as physics and chemistry, for the factors are too complex to admit of control for experimental purposes. There is every reason to believe, however, that research into the causes of aggression and fear and into effective methods of control will yield results just as startling as the discoveries and practical applications of physics and chemistry. Now that the world is becoming one society, it is imperative that we should learn how to live together in groups and nations. The social sciences must take up the challenge. Guesses and fumbling and outworn viewpoints and methods result in too many "accidents" in the form of group conflict and international strife.

It is the peculiar obligation of medical and social scientists—psychologists, psychiatrists, anthropologists, sociologists, social workers—whose field of interest is man as an individual human being and man as a member of human society, to widen their knowledge and to disseminate their findings, thus confirming the experience and stabilizing the inner faith of the more naïve. The security so won will minimize the dangers of conflict, individual and national, will build satisfying human relationships, and will tend to free and direct the energies of man for the service of the community. The safeguarding of mental health and the development of satisfactory human relations are very large tasks, and they must be shared by parents, teachers, doctors—especially psychiatrists—social workers, psychologists, clergymen, business, industrial, and labor leaders, and by all others who are in a position to lead and influence the lives of people.

Public Education in Mental Hygiene

The material of this chapter sums up inevitably to the need for a vigorous program of public education in the principles and dynamics of individual and societal emotional health and happiness. This is the only possible means of implementing the suggested program for health and security. Public education will take much time and great energy, but all of us in our particular specialties have a deep obligation to assume it. And while no direct approach at the intellectual level can hope to touch the deep, unconscious, motivational forces of the human personality, here and there a beginning may be made in applying the principles and procedures outlined in this book toward a fuller mental hygiene program. This is the task for the years ahead.

During the war, it was necessary in the armed forces not only to provide for the prompt discovery and treatment of men who were showing early signs of mental or emotional disturbances, but also to give all officers and enlisted men basic mental hygiene orientation. Such educational measures did not prevent men from being afraid under combat conditions, but it did enable them to understand and accept their reactions as natural and normal under the circumstances, and to use their fear in constructive rather than destructive ways, that is, for their own protection and that of their units.

Although the factors that threaten mental health are harder to isolate in peacetime than in war, and although the tensions of normal civilian life are less acute than those to which military personnel are exposed, it is possible to extend to our population as a whole an orientation in mental hygiene similar in some respects to that which was provided for officers and enlisted men. There are, of course, differences. In the Army a man's interest in himself and his immediate unit occupies almost all his time and energies. In civilian life there are many other influences and relationships, involving people's various roles as workers, mates, parents, club members, and citizens. Consequently, the task of educating people in the mental hygiene of everyday living is more complex.

The major objectives are clear. As an aid to the treatment of the ill such education should (1) strive to remove the stigma which still attaches to mental and nervous disorders and to secure their acceptance as valid and treatable illnesses; (2) supply information in regard to existing and desired facilities, kinds of illness and mal-adjustment that can be treated respectively by private psychiatrists, outpatient psychiatric or mental hygiene clinics, and psychiatric hospitals, and measures to be taken by families in behalf of the seriously ill; (3) create a demand by the people for adequate facilities for the treatment of nervous and mental disorders, including hospitalization and opportunities for consultation and clinical treatment in all communities.

On the constructive and preventive side, mental hygiene education should (1) develop a broad understanding of what constitutes healthy-mindedness at each stage of development, what the danger signs are, and what people can do to prevent psychological liabilities from becoming serious blocks to health and happiness; (2) develop increased appreciation of the dynamic quality of family living and of the special significance of healthy and happy relations in the childhood years; (3) bring about fuller recognition of the stabilizing influence of satisfying work and economic security and of the threat to mental health which lies in neglecting the personal, human values of a job and their importance to the worker; (4) acquaint the public with the potential contributions to mental hygiene which can be made by the physician, social worker, teacher, and other professional persons; (5) outline the essentials of a healthier society, with emphasis on the most needed changes and on the appropriate next steps to be taken by citizens.

Fortunately, the professional groups having most to offer in mental hygiene education recognize more than ever before the need for interpreting their knowledge to the layman and for enlisting the cooperation of the non-professional public in efforts to improve the mental health and stability of our people. For example, the Group for the Advancement of Psychiatry (recently formed within the American Psychiatric Association) and organizations of social workers and clinical psychologists are eager and ready to share with other groups the insights developed by their professions, so that these may be applied more effectively in family relations, education, medicine, industry, religious organizations, governmental services, and other phases of community life. Their interest is a hopeful sign. But as Ridenour points out:

The psychiatric professions are as yet fulfilling only a fraction of their potentialities as interpreters of human behavior. Effectiveness in interpretation requires a public health point of view and continuing development of consultative skills and interpretive techniques. These, in turn, require familiarity with the special problems of related teaching and healing professions and with those of the interpretive professions (press, screen, stage, and radio), and an awareness of the mistakes common to those who, though well trained clinically, are relatively untrained in interpretation.[17]

In-service training in mental hygiene and opportunities for consultation with experts in the field are now available to nurses, teachers, pediatricians, and others who have frequent contacts with young children and their parents. It is also necessary to use mass media for acquainting the public with sound principles of mental health.* In all programs of mental hygiene education the cultural pattern, system of belief, and special needs of the particular group to whom the information is addressed must be carefully considered.

The National Committee for Mental Hygiene, a voluntary organization dating from 1909, has done much to promote awareness of mental hygiene needs and opportunities through community social and health services, schools, and other local groups,

* See also pages 258–261, 352–357.

but its staff and its finances are at present too limited to carry on an adequate over-all educational program. It is significant that the amount of money devoted annually to the dissemination of information regarding tuberculosis and poliomyelitis has been from twenty to forty times as much as the amount spent by all national, state, and local agencies to educate the public regarding mental hygiene needs and opportunities. In per capita terms, $600 has been spent per case of poliomyelitis as against $1.00 per case of mental illness.

Beginners' information, together with some misinformation, has already been given the American public. A really fine job of public education remains to be accomplished. The psychiatric and allied professions are already overburdened, but they have many socially-minded members who will rise to the responsibility. Once the need is seen clearly, sound education will go forward, because it must. Professional persons and enlightened laymen can surely justify their existence in the world of today only by working where and how they can to implement the conviction of Professor Henry deW. Smyth as stated in the War Department's report on the atomic bomb: "If men, working together, can solve the mysteries of the universe, they can also solve the problem of human relations on the planet. Not only in science, but now in all human relations, we must work together with free minds."

REFERENCES

1. Flugel, J. C. Man, morals, and society, chapter XIX. New York, International Universities Press, 1945.

2. Chisholm, G. B. The reestablishment of peacetime society. (*In* The Psychiatry of Enduring Peace and Social Progress, William Alanson White Memorial Lectures.) Psychiatry 9:1–35, February 1946.

3. United States National Commission for UNESCO, Report on the First Meeting, September, 1947, p. 1. United States–United Nations Information Series 14. Department of State Publication 2726. Washington, D. C., Superintendent of Documents, U. S. Government Printing Office.

4. Leighton, A. H. The governing of men, p. 362. Princeton, N. J., Princeton University Press, 1945.

5. Jenkins, R. L., and L. E. Hewitt. Fundamental patterns of maladjustment and dynamics of their origin. (Springfield), State of Illinois, 1946.

    Plant, J. S. Personality and the cultural pattern. New York, Commonwealth Fund, 1937.

6. Malzberg, B. The influence of economic factors on mental health. *In* Mental Health, edited by F. R. Moulton and P. O. Komora. (Lancaster), Am. Assn. for the Advancement of Science, 1939.

7. Falk, I. S., and N. D. M. Hirsch. Social security measures as factors in mental health programs. *In* Mental Health, edited by F. R. Moulton and P. O. Komora. (Lancaster), Am. Assn. for the Advancement of Science, 1939.

8. Annual Wages and Employment Stabilization Techniques. New York, American Management Association, 1945.

9. Schreiber, J. Interdependence of democracy and mental health. Ment. Hyg. 29:606–621, October 1945.

10. Levy, D. M. The toll of intolerance upon the intolerant. *In* The Family in a World at War, edited by S. M. Gruenberg, p. 117–124. New York, Harper, 1942.

11. Chatto, C. I., and A. Halligan. The story of the Springfield plan. New York, Barnes & Noble, 1945.

12. Brown, F. J., and S. Roucek. One America; the history, contribution, and present problems of our racial and national minorities. Revised edition. New York, Prentice Hall, 1945.

    National Council for the Social Studies, National Education Association. Democratic human relations; 16th yearbook. Washington, D. C., the Council, 1945.

    Powdermaker, H. Probing our prejudices. New York, Harper, 1944.

    Vickery, W. E., and S. G. Cole. Intercultural education in American schools. Bureau for Intercultural Education Publication Series. New York, Harper, 1943.

13. National Institute of Social Relations, Inc. Talk it over. Washington, D. C.

14. Watson, G. B. Action for unity. New York, Harper, 1947.

15. MacDonald, E. P. The publisher who made a better world; education for democracy. Reader's Scope 4:83–86, August 1946.

16. James, William. The moral equivalent of war. Association for International Conciliation, Leaflet no. 27, 1910.

17. Ridenour, N. The job ahead; a philosophy of mental hygiene education. To be published in the 25th Anniversary Volume of the Am. Orthopsychiat. Assn.

APPENDIX A

Mental Hospitals

 1 bed per 150 of population. Several states—New York, Massachusetts, Connecticut, do better than this.

 1 psychiatrist per 150 beds. This is a long established standard. It was recently modified, but in neither case included the superintendency. It is exceeded in several places, including veterans' facilities. This ratio applied to the country as a whole would require: 6,000

Institutions for Mental Deficiency

 1 bed per 1000 population. Several states do better than this.

 1 psychiatrist per 500 beds (standard set by the American Association on Mental Deficiency):   260

Community Mental Hygiene Clinics

 1 psychiatrist per 100,000 population. This standard has been used for years by the Division on Community Clinics of the National Committee for Mental Hygiene and has been met or exceeded by several cities—Richmond, Worcester, Dayton, Providence, Hartford.   1,300

Hospital Ex-Patients

 For every 100 admissions there are 40.9 patients discharged as recovered or improved. On this basis, if each patient were to be provided with 6 hours of psychiatric time the first year, 3 hours the second, 1 hour the third and 1 hour thereafter, at 1,750 hours per year per psychiatrist, New York would require 60 psychiatrists, the whole country would need: 600

Mental Defectives in the Community

 1 per cent of the population according to the most conservative figures is mentally defective. (Some go as high as 3 per cent.) On this basis, 1,300,000 cases have to be cared

for. If these were provided with 1 hour of psychiatric
time for 5 years at 1,750 hours per year per psychiatrist,
the total requirement would be: 200

The Mentally Retarded

2 per cent of the population is included in this group, and 2
  per cent of these are new cases each year, or 52,000 cases.
  At the rate of 500 cases per psychiatrist for an initial examination the total requirement would be: 100

Crime and Delinquency

Based on a provision of 2 psychiatrists for Pittsburgh or 1 per
  250,000 population, the need of the whole country would
  be: 425

School Psychiatrists

New York has set for itself a goal of 1 psychiatrist to 40,000
  children. On this basis the need of the United States for
  school psychiatrists would be: 650

University Departments of Psychiatry

At the rate of 3 psychiatrists per medical school, assuming
  that this will provide teaching also to schools of social
  work, education, etc., the need for the whole country
  would be: 250

General Hospital Consultants

The Henry Ford Hospital with admissions of 16,440 patients
  per year employs 7 psychiatrists, or a ratio of 1 psychiatrist per 2,350 patients. The Massachusetts General
  Hospital with an admissions rate of 16,800 has 3 resident
  psychiatrists, or a ratio of 1 psychiatrist per 5,600 patients. If we accept the ratio of 1 psychiatrist per 5,000
  patients and recognize that there are 15,000,000 admissions to general hospitals per year, the minimum number
  of psychiatrists required would be: 3,000

Private Practice

A recent canvass by the Emergency Committee of Neuropsychiatric Societies in New York City has revealed 588
  persons devoted to treating psychiatric problems outside

of institutions. Allowing for neurological cases and other
appropriate reductions, the figure of 300 has been employed. At this rate, for private practice in the country as
a whole we would need: 6,000
                                                             ―――――

As we see it now, but not, however, as vacancies exist,
   the total number of psychiatrists needed is: 18,785

There would be some overlap in the functions described above, and
of the 3,200 psychiatrists already on hand, many would have ceased to
practice before our training processes could anywhere near meet the
figure given above. However, it would seem safe to set as a minimum
goal the number of psychiatrists needed in the United States—10,000.

September 21, 1944.

APPENDIX B

SAMPLE CURRICULUM OF PROFESSIONAL EDUCATION
FOR PSYCHIATRIC SOCIAL WORK*

In order to make clear the professional competence of the psychiatric social worker to assume his professional responsibility, the Committee reviewed the existing standard curriculum established for training in psychiatric social work.

There are today fourteen schools in this country whose curriculum is approved by the American Association of Psychiatric Social Workers for training of psychiatric social workers.

The Committee submits a sample curriculum which illustrates the scope of training of this professional group.

The requirements for admission to a two-year course in a graduate professional school is a college degree.

In order to complete his training and to receive his master's degree, each trainee must complete courses in the following areas:

I. *Courses in Social Treatment*

These include basic case work, advanced case work, child welfare, advanced family and psychiatric social case work, courses in medical information, and a series of at least three courses in psychiatry, which include (1) a course on the development of personality (normal development) from infancy to old age, (2) behavior disorders of children, and (3) psychopathology. Elective courses including the problems of delinquency, clinical psychiatry, etc., are taken.

II. *Courses in Social Research*

These include studies in social statistics, social investigation, and current problems in social research.

III. *Courses in Public Welfare and Social Insurance*

Such courses as The Child and the State, Public Assistance and Public Welfare, Social Insurance are required.

* From the report of the Committee on Psychiatric Social Work of the Group for the Advancement of Psychiatry, Marion E. Kenworthy, M.D., Chairman. *Journal of Psychiatric Social Work*, 16:92–95, Winter Issue 1946–47.

IV. *Courses in Economic and Social Legislation*

Introduction to Industrial Relations, The Law and Social Work and Minimum Standards of Living.

V. *Courses in Community Organization and Related Fields*

The Committee considered the values of these courses in developing a broad base for psychiatric field work practice.

The Committee agreed that the psychiatric social worker must have the ability to make highly selective use of community resources for the individual patient.

He must have also the ability to appraise social economic factors which will affect the use of the services. He must know the individual rights and obligations under the law.

He must have a sound knowledge of social pathology and a knowledge of the implications to be able to effect whatever change is possible in the life of a given individual.

During the first quarter of instruction, the student's program contains:

1. Basic Case Work Course I. This material is presented in the form of Case Discussion (36 hours).
2. The course in the Development of Personality (18 hours—given by a psychiatrist)
3. Medical Information (18 hours—given by a physician, with emphasis on the psychodynamic implications of the subject)
4. Supervised Field Work in a family agency, public or private (20 hours a week for 12 weeks—240 hours)

From the beginning the student is taught to understand the individual, how he feels about his problem, how he feels about asking and accepting assistance.

In the beginning courses, cases are presented dealing with the problems of relatively normal individuals with relatively adequate ego structures.

1. At this point in training, the course in the development of normal personality is taken concurrently.
2. It is necessary for the student to understand the importance of social stresses and their relationship to emotional upsets.
3. It is recognized that the student must become aware of the value of prompt and adequate, therapeutic help as an important preventive measure.

In the process of studying eight to ten cases in his first quarter of instruction, the student becomes aware of the specific services which any given social agency provides and the effective use of community resources when they are available.

He further learns the elementary principles of interviewing, he becomes aware of the confidential nature of the professional relationship, and he begins to develop an awareness of some of the dynamics involved in therapy.

Content of second quarter instruction:

1. Social Case Work II (36 hours)
2. Behavior Disorders in Children (18 hours—given by a psychiatrist)
3. Supervised field work in the same family agency as the first quarter (240 hours)

In this twelve-week period, cases are studied which are selected from a variety of social agencies, designed to present a range of problems, such as illness, physical handicaps, disturbed family relationships, cases of unmarried mothers who need assistance in planning for and deciding about the future of their babies, the problems presented by runaway adolescents, etc.

In this quarter, the major change in case selection is directed toward emphasis upon the more emotionally disturbed issues involved in the individual's social problems.

Much emphasis is placed upon a better understanding of the elements involved in the action-interaction problems of family life. In all of the teaching cases, social problems are present which require specific services, i.e., financial assistance, arrangements for medical care, use of vocational guidance, rehabilitation service, provision for placement of children, special school arrangements, etc.

In the third and fourth quarters, the following courses are required:

1. Psychiatric Social Work I and II (36 hours—given by a psychiatric social worker)
2. Psychopathology (18 hours—given by a psychiatrist)
3. Field work in a mental hospital or a psychiatric clinic setting (child guidance or adult)—480 hours, with intensive case work supervision by a psychiatric social worker and a psychiatrist

Cases selected for treatment in these two quarters are chosen from psychiatric hospital or clinic settings. Broad opportunities are made for a discussion of the work of the clinical team and the place of the psychiatric social worker in this team.

In the fifth quarter, emphasis is placed upon psychiatric field work—240 hours—with more intensive emphasis upon extension of treatment processes and the beginning of a research project in psychiatric social work.

In examining these patterns of progression, the feature of sequence is particularly noteworthy.

By the time the student comes to his specialization in psychiatric social work he (1) has achieved some understanding of psychopathology; (2) has achieved some medical information; (3) has had considerable experience in helping people through his basic understanding of the dynamics involved in the helping process; (4) has acquired a familiarity and understanding of ego strength and weakness, the mechanism of defense and a broader awareness of the psychodynamic factors involved in interpersonal relationships.

In the pursuit of his special field work training in the psychiatric clinical team work, we see him acquiring:

1. A deeper understanding of human behavior
2. Increased knowledge of psychopathology
3. A more adequate understanding of the emotional elements of family life
4. A deeper understanding of the patient-worker relationship, and its management
5. A more effective professional contribution to the psychiatric clinical team work
6. A more adequate selectivity in the use of community resources

A graduate in psychiatric social work must have in addition to his training at least one year of full-time experience in a psychiatric clinical setting, before he becomes eligible for active membership in the American Association of Psychiatric Social Workers.

It is recognized by this Committee that this combination of training and subsequent experience gives the psychiatric social worker a professional basis for his responsible position in the field of psychiatric endeavor and teaching.

INDEX